McDonnell Douglas

Volume II: Francillon

McDonnell Douglas Aircraft

since 1920: Volume II

René J Francillon

PUTNAM

BY THE SAME AUTHOR

Japanese Aircraft of the Pacific War
Lockheed Aircraft since 1913
Grumman Aircraft since 1929
McDonnell Douglas Aircraft since 1920 : Volume I
Tonkin Gulf Yacht Club

First published in one volume in 1979

This edition published in Great Britain 1990 by
Putnam Aeronautical Books, an imprint of
Conway Maritime Press Ltd,
24 Bride Lane, Fleet Street,
London EC4Y 8DR

British Library Cataloguing in Publication Data
Francillon. René J. (René Jacquet) 1937–
McDonnell Douglas aircraft since 1920. -2nd. ed.
Vol. 2
1. McDonnell Douglas aeroplanes, history
1. Title
629.13334

ISBN 0 85177 828 3

Typeset by Saxon Printing Ltd, Derby
Printed and bound in Great Britain by
The Alden Press, Oxford.

CONTENTS

vi

vii

Preface and Acknowledgments

McDonnell Douglas Aircraft since 1920 was originally published in 1979 as a single volume covering the history of the McDonnell Douglas Corporation, its forebears, and their aircraft. However, when it became time to prepare a second edition too many events had occurred, foremost among which was the acquisition of Hughes Helicopters, Inc, during 1984, to keep the work within the confines of a single volume. Accordingly, the history of the firm and its aircraft was split into two volumes, with Volume I covering the history of the Douglas companies and their aircraft from 1920 when Donald Douglas organized the Davis-Douglas Company in Santa Monica, California, to 1967 when the Douglas Aircraft Company was merged into McDonnell Douglas Corporation. Volume I of this second edition was published in 1988.

Volume II began simply as an update of the history of the various McDonnell organizations, beginning with the McDonnell Aircraft Company organized by James McDonnell in 1939, and their aircraft. To this update was to be added the history of the new McDonnell Douglas Helicopter Company, its Hughes forebears, and their aeroplanes and helicopters. However, the work soon gained in magnitude as it was decided to take advantage of this new edition to add considerable detail to chapters dwelling on earlier types (*eg*, the chapter on the XF-88 Voodoo in this edition is twice as long as that in the first edition), to correct an omission which although it went unnoticed by reviewers was nevertheless unfortunate (that concerning the Big Henry programme which had not been included in the first edition), and to include a chapter on the company's manned space projects. The result is virtually a new book.

Work on this edition was greatly facilitated by the assistance provided by personnel from various MDC organizations. In particular, the help provided by Barbara Anderson at MDC, Rich Eichwald at MCAIR, Hal Klopper and Ken Reinstein at MDHC, and Steve Swinney and Teri Walulik at DAC proved invaluable. I also wish to express my sincere appreciation for the considerable assistance provided by numerous individuals and by private and public entities in the United States and elsewhere. Jointly they provided a wealth of historical documents, operational data, and photographs. In this regard, I am most grateful to the following: *Private Individuals*–Christian Boisselon, Alain Crosnier, Jim Dunn, Jerry Edwards, Michel Fournier, Harry S Gann, Maj Gen Wayne C Gatlin, Jerry Geer, Jean-Michel Guhl, Jan Jacobs, Christian Jacquet-Francillon, H L James, Dirk Lamarque, Anthony Leung, Peter B Lewis, William I Lightfoot, Peter J Mancus (Cloud 9 Photography), Toyokazu Matsuzaki, David W Menard, Peter B Mersky, P Miche, Jay Miller, Rick Morgan, Bob Neumeier, Masanori Ogawa, Douglas D Olson, Lionel Paul, George Pennick, Brian Pickering (MAP-Military Aircraft Photographs), Dr Frederick W Roos, Dr Richard K Smith,

Daniel Soulaine, Paul D Stevens, Jim Sullivan, Norman E Taylor, John Wegg, Gordon S Williams, and Dr Masahiro Yamasaki; *Aerospace Companies*—Construcciones Aeronáuticas SA, General Electric Co, Hughes Aircraft Company, Israel Aircraft Industries Ltd, Martin Marietta Corporation, Messerschmitt-Bölkow-Blohm GmbH, Pratt & Whitney/United Technologies, Schweizer Aircraft Corporation, Summa Corporation, and Wrather Corporation; *US Government Agencies*—Department of Defense (Still Media Record Center), Department of the Army (Media Inquiry Branch/OCPA; Army Aviation Museum, Fort Rucker; 82nd Aviation Brigade, Fort Bragg; 1/130th Avn, North Carolina ArNG), Department of the Air Force (Office of History/Air Force Flight Test Center; Air Force Museum; NGB/PA; Military Airlift Command/PAM; Strategic Air Command/PAM; Tactical Air Command/PAM; and Public Affairs Officers at Boise ANGB, Edwards AFB, Fresno ANGB, George AFB, March AFB, Nellis AFB, Reno ANGB, Seymour Johnson AFB, and Travis AFB), Department of the Navy (Media Services Division/CHINFO; Naval Air Systems Command; Naval Aviation History and Archives; Public Affairs Officers aboard the USS *Coral Sea* and USS *Kitty Hawk* and at COMNAVAIRPAC, MCAS El Toro, MCAS Yuma, NAS Fallon, NAS Key West, NAS Miramar, NWC China Lake, PMTC Point Mugu, and at the Naval Air Test Center), Department of Transportation (Federal Aviation Administration/Office of Public Affairs), National Aeronautics and Space Administration (Public Affairs Officers at Headquarters, the Ames Research Center, the Dryden Flight Research Facility, the Johnson Space Center, and the Langley Research Center), and National Archives; *Foreign Government Agencies*—Australia (RAAF Public Relations Office), Canada (Dept of National Defence and Public Archives), Germany (Bundesministerium der Verteidigung, Luftwaffe, and Air Attaché in Washington, DC), Great Britain (MoD and RAF Museum), Israel (Heyl Ha'Avir and Air Attaché in Washington, DC), and Japan (Office of the Defense and Air Attaché in Washington, DC); *Airlines*—Air New Zealand, American Airlines, Balair, CTA, Delta Air Lines, Federal Express, Laker Airways, Lufthansa, Northwest Airlines, Swissair, United Air Lines, and UTA; *Magazines*—Aero Digest, Air Action, Air Classics, Air Fan, Air Force Magazine, Air Forces Monthly, AIR International, Airliners, Air Pictorial, Airpower, Aviation News, Aviation Week & Space Technology, Flight International, Naval Aviation News, The Hook, Warplane, Wide World Photo, Wings, and World Air Power Journal.

In spite of her increasingly busy professional schedule, my wife once again found time to go through the tedious task of editing and proofing the typescript and patiently provided help and guidance. Above all, however, I am grateful to her for helping me realize my long-time ambition and quit the rat race of consulting engineering to spend full-time on aviation writing.

Vallejo, California, February 1990

Origin and History of the Company

Although both were relative newcomers among United States aircraft manufacturers with prototypes for their first production aircraft, the XFD-1 jet fighter and Model 269 light helicopter, first flying in January 1945 and October 1956, McDonnell and Hughes rapidly gained prominent places in the industry. The merger of the McDonnell Company and the Douglas Aircraft Company to form the present McDonnell Douglas Corporation (MDC) in April 1967 and the acquisition by MDC of Hughes Helicopters during 1984 resulted in a giant organization. In 1989, its business turnover kept it as the free world's largest aerospace firm and a major producer of combat aircraft, military jet transports and trainers, airliners, civil and military helicopters, and missiles and space launch vehicles.

The origin of the Douglas Aircraft Company and its history before the 1967 merger having been dealt with in the first volume, the introductory chapters of the present volume provide a brief biography of James Smith McDonnell, who with Donald Wills Douglas was one of the co-founders[1]

Symbolic of the then not yet accomplished merger of the McDonnell Company and the Douglas Aircraft Company, two McDonnell Banshees (an F2H-3 and an F2H-2) of Composite Squadron Three (VC-3) fly in formation with a Douglas F3D-1 Skyknight of the same unit. *(USN/National Archives)*

[1] It is interesting to note that both of these great leaders of the aircraft industry had a Scottish background, were educated at the Massachusetts Institute of Technology, and in turn resigned the position of chief engineer of the Glenn L Martin Company to form their own firms.

1

of the McDonnell Douglas Corporation, and cover the corporate history of McDonnell Aircraft Corporation and McDonnell Company before the merger, of Hughes Aircraft/Hughes Helicopters before its acquisition by MDC, and of McDonnell Douglas Corporation since 1967.

James Smith McDonnell

Fourth child of a cotton grower of Little Rock, Arkansas, James Smith McDonnell was born in Denver, Colorado, on 9 April, 1899. He was rather withdrawn and shy as a child but displayed considerable energy and, being an early riser, every morning before going to school, went on horseback to deliver copies of the *Arkansas Gazette*. After graduating in 1917 from Little Rock High School and serving briefly in the Army, James McDonnell went to Princeton University in New Jersey where, while studying physics, he began to show interest in politics and also obtained his first flying experience. However, James McDonnell Sr, conscious that his son was 'too shy and too serious' to become a politician, cut short his son's political ambition and advised him to pursue a career in aeronautical engineering, a suggestion which subsequent events amply justified.

Following his father's advice, the young McDonnell obtained his Bachelor of Science (Physics) diploma from Princeton in 1921 and immediately enrolled in a graduate programme in aeronautical engineering at the Massachusetts Institute of Technology (MIT). By that time James McDonnell had become an aviation enthusiast and in 1923, after completing his studies but two years before being awarded his Diploma of Master of Science in Aeronautical Engineering, he enrolled in the Commissioned Reserve of the Army Air Service to become a qualified military pilot.

After his release from the Army Air Service at the end of one year of active service, McDonnell went job hunting and in 1924 obtained his first professional job as an aeronautical engineer and pilot for the Huff-Daland Airplane Company in Ogdenburg, NY. For the next 15 years, he went from job to job and accumulated remarkable experience while working for eight companies including his own J. S. McDonnell Jr & Associates. Thus, after a few months with Huff-Daland, he worked in 1924-25 as a stress analyst and draughtsman for the Consolidated Aircraft Company in Buffalo, NY, and then spent a few months as an assistant chief engineer for the Stout Metal Airplane Company of Dearborn, Michigan, where he participated in the design of the 3-AT, the forerunner of the Ford Tri-Motor series. His next move took him to the Hamilton Aero Manufacturing Company in Milwaukee, Wisconsin, where as chief engineer he was responsible between 1926 and 1928 for the design of a series of single-engined metal transport monoplanes culminating in the H-45 and H-47 used by a number of US airlines.

As indicated by his frequent changes in employment, the young engineer was proudly independent and longed to be on his own. Two events led him to make another change and to organize his own firm. On 20 April, 1927, the Daniel Guggenheim Fund for the Promotion of Aeronautics had announced a competition for the design of a light training aircraft offering 'a real advance in the safety of flying' and almost immediately James McDonnell and two fellow engineers, Constantine Zakhartchenko and James Cowling, contemplated the possibility of entering this international competition. For a while, lack of funds prevented the three friends from launching their venture but in 1928, following the absorption of the Hamilton Aero Manufacturing Company by the United Aircraft and Transportation Corporation, McDonnell decided to resign and to organize J. S. McDonnell Jr & Associates in partnership with Cowling and Zakhartchenko.

Still benefiting from the co-operation of the Hamilton Aero Manufacturing Company which provided the necessary manufacturing facilities, the three partners designed the Doodlebug as their entry in the

The Doodlebug, the aircraft entered by J. S. McDonnell Jr & Associates in the competition for the design of a safe light aircraft sponsored between 1927 and 1929 by the Daniel Guggenheim Fund for the Promotion of Aeronautics. *(Aero Digest)*

Guggenheim competition. However, in spite of its intrinsic qualities, the aircraft failed to win the competition because lack of funds and bad luck combined to slow its construction and development and the Great Depression robbed it of its chance to enter production for the private market. Fortunately, while attempting to find a market for the Doodlebug, McDonnell had joined, on a part-time basis, the consulting firm of Airtransport Engineering Corporation of Chicago, and until 1931 he was able to survive the economic chaos which had engulfed the country after the stock market crash of October 1929.

In 1931 a chance to return to aircraft engineering and test flying presented itself, and James McDonnell joined the Great Lakes Aircraft Corporation in Cleveland, Ohio, where he worked for a few months before joining the Glenn L Martin Company in Baltimore, Maryland, in early 1933. At last he had found a challenging position and, as Chief Engineer for Landplanes, was responsible over a period of six years for several major Martin projects including development work on the B-10/B-12 series for the Air Corps, on the Martin 139W, 146, and 166 series of bombers for the export market, and design of the Martin 167, the Baltimore bomber.

The civil-registered (NX22076) prototype of the Martin 167 bomber, the last aircraft designed by James McDonnell for the Glenn L Martin Company. *(Air Force Museum)*

James Smith McDonnell (1899-1980) in 1967, shortly after the McDonnell Douglas Corporation had come into being as the result of the merger of the McDonnell Company and the Douglas Aircraft Company. *(MDC)*

4

The astute and talented Scot, however, still wished to establish himself independently and, as worsening world affairs created a sharply increased demand for aircraft production, he decided to take a chance and resigned from the Martin Company in late 1938. As Donald Douglas had had to do over a quarter of a century earlier, James McDonnell first had to hunt for the necessary financial backing with which to launch his proposed aircraft manufacturing company. Eventually, his search was rewarded and on 6 July, 1939, the McDonnell Aircraft Corporation was incorporated in the State of Maryland. At last he was master of his own destiny and in 28 years the fledgling McDonnell Aircraft Corporation grew into the extremely healthy McDonnell Company which on 28 April, 1967, absorbed the Douglas Aircraft Company to become the McDonnell Douglas Corporation.

Following the organization of the McDonnell Douglas Corporation, James McDonnell first served as Chairman of the Board and Chief Executive Officer. In 1970, when David S Lewis resigned to become Chairman of the General Dynamics Corporation, McDonnell temporarily took over the responsibilities of President and Chief Operating Officer. In 1971, following the appointment of his brother, Sanford N McDonnell, as President, he again served as Chairman of the Board and Chief Executive Officer before relinquishing the CEO duty to his brother in 1972. From then until his death on 22 August, 1980, James Smith McDonnell remained as Chairman of the Board of Directors of the McDonnell Douglas Corporation.

As a result of the success of his venture, James McDonnell added to his academic credentials and professional success an impressive list of awards and honours, including four Honorary Doctor Degrees—Engineering from the University of Missouri in 1957, Engineering from Washington University in 1958, Law from Princeton University in 1960, and Law from the University of Arkansas in 1965, the 1966 Robert J Collier Trophy, the Guggenheim Medal in 1963, the Founders Medal of the National Academy of Engineering in 1967, and the NASA Public Service Award in 1966 and 1968. James McDonnell was an honorary Fellow of the Royal Aeronautical Society and was enshrined in the Aviation Hall of Fame in Dayton, Ohio. Respected and admired by his competitors and his staff, by whom he was affectionately known as 'Old Mac', he is also remembered for his many civic activities and particularly for his chairmanship of the United Nations Association of the United States of America (it is a measure of his commitment to the United Nations, which he began to support publicly in 1955 at the request of Secretary of State John Foster Dulles, that in 1958 the McDonnell Aircraft Corporation became the first organization in the world to celebrate United Nations Day as a paid holiday).

McDonnell Aircraft Corporation,
1939 to 1966

Modest as it was, the first year of operations of the Davis-Douglas Company—the first of the forebears of the McDonnell Douglas Corporation—had been grandiose when compared to the first 12 months of operations of the McDonnell Aircraft Corporation. Following incorporation of the firm in the State of Maryland on 6 July, 1939, with a paid-up capital of $165,000, McDonnell rented office space first in the Park Plaza Hotel in St Louis, Missouri, and then from American Airlines in the second storey of a small building adjacent to Lambert Field in St Louis. Operations got under way on 25 September and during the following 12 months the company struggled for survival while its small engineering

The American Airlines building at Lambert Field in which McDonnell rented space in 1939. *(MDC)*

team submitted 12 proposals to the Air Corps and four proposals to the Navy. The return was dismal and James McDonnell had to report to the stockholders a first year loss of $3,892.17.

Prospects, however, were brighter. On one hand, as a result of the rapid build-up of the American aircraft industry following the start of the war in Europe, the company obtained its first sub-contract business from larger manufacturers and, on the other hand, the McDonnell Aircraft Corporation made its first sale to the Air Corps when in June 1940 the Materiel Division acquired design data for the Model I fighter for $3,000. From these early activities stemmed the bulk of McDonnell's wartime business which consisted of the manufacture in various factories in and around Lambert Field of parts and subassemblies for Douglas (A-20 cowling assemblies and C-47 empennages), Boeing (B-29 fuselage

6

sections), and others, as well as in the complete manufacture of twin-engined trainers. Initially, following award in January 1942 of its first production contract, McDonnell was selected to build 360 Boeing-designed AT-15s. However, this contract, as well as contracts for the production of 325 additional AT-15s to be built by Bellanca and for 360 Boeing-built AT-15s, was cancelled. This loss was later partially offset by the award of a production contract for 30 Fairchild-designed AT-21-MM twin-engined trainers which McDonnell built during 1943-44 in government-furnished facilities in Memphis, Tennessee.

More significant for McDonnell's long-term future was the AAF approval on 14 August, 1941, of Authority to Purchase No.182428 issued by the Chief, Experimental Engineering Division, Materiel Command, for the design and construction of two prototypes of a novel twin-engined

The novel McDonnell XP-67 powered by two Continental XI-1430 liquid-cooled engines.*(USAF)*

fighter[2]. Designated XP-67, the aircraft was of unconventional design with the engineering team attempting to maintain true aerofoil section throughout the airframe and to maximize the use of exhaust to augment thrust. Completed in St Louis in December 1943, the first XP-67 was trucked across the Mississippi to Scott Field, Illinois, where it was flown on 6 January, 1944. Unfortunately, its experimental Continental XI-1430 engines and their installation were the source of protracted teething troubles and performance fell below guarantee (in particular, top speed was 405 mph—652 km/h versus the predicted 472 mph—759 km/h). Hence, following the loss of this aircraft eight months after its first flight, the USAAF decided to terminate the contract and the second XP-67 was never completed.

Early in the existence of the company, McDonnell engineers began studying the application of jet propulsion for combat aircraft design. This early interest in the novel powerplant, coupled with the fact that the

[2]   This Authority to Purchase was confirmed by the issuance of Contract W535-AC-21218 on 29 October, 1941.

7

engineering teams of established Navy contractors were already fully occupied with the design and production of urgently needed conventional aircraft, led the Bureau of Aeronautics to select the St Louis firm to develop a jet-powered, carrier-borne fighter. Design of the new aircraft, which on 21 July, 1946, became the first jet fighter to take-off from and land on the deck of a United States aircraft carrier, began in answer to a Letter of Intent dated 7 January, 1943, and the aircraft pushed the small McDonnell Aircraft Corporation into the major aerospace league. At that time, McDonnell was assigned the manufacturer's designation letter D, the new aircraft being designated XFD-1, as Douglas, to which the designation letter had been assigned since 1921, was no longer supplying Navy fighters. The letter D was retained by McDonnell until Douglas's return as a manufacturer of Navy fighters in 1946. The St Louis firm was then assigned the letter H.

In mid-1942 James McDonnell's endeavours to find work for his firm also led him to make a modest investment in the Platt-LePage Aircraft Company, a small company in Eddystone, Pennsylvania, which in July 1940 had received a contract from the Army Air Corps to build the XR-1,

The Platt-LePage XR-1, the first helicopter ordered by the Army Air Corps. *(Air Force Museum)*

the first helicopter ordered for the USAAC. One year after investing in Platt-LePage, McDonnell took another step in what was to be his long quest to break into the helicopter field when he authorized Constantine Zakhartchenko, one of his two partners from the old J S McDonnell Jr & Associates, and a few engineers to undertake research on design and construction of rotors. Actual helicopter design work began with the award on 15 May, 1944, of a Navy Letter of Intent for the construction of the world's first twin-engined/twin-rotor helicopter, the McDonnell

XHJD-1. Furthermore, in June 1944, McDonnell acquired control of the Platt-LePage Aircraft Company by purchasing 2,650 shares (38.74 per cent of the outstanding shares) and $149,500 (73.6 per cent) of notes from this firm. Unfortunately for James McDonnell, his enthusiasm for helicopters proved disappointing during his lifetime as Platt-LePage ceased operation and was liquidated in 1946 and none of the numerous and highly-advanced types of rotary wing machines produced by the McDonnell Aircraft Corporation between 1946 and 1957 was the recipient of a quantity production contract. However, the McDonnell Douglas Corporation became a major force in this segment of the aerospace industry in January 1984, over three years after James McDonnell's death, when it acquired Hughes Helicopters, Inc.

Better luck rewarded the company's initial jet fighter programme and, six weeks after the maiden flight of the XFD-1 prototype, McDonnell received its first major production contract when the Navy Department issued a Letter of Intent on 7 March, 1945, for 100 FD-1 Phantoms. Fifteen days later, three prototypes of a more advanced carrier-borne,

The second McDonnell XF2D-1 Banshee (BuNo 99859) in front of its smaller predecessor, XFD-1 Phantom (BuNo 48235). *(NA&SM)*

jet-powered fighter, the XF2D-1, were ordered by the Navy. The advanced nature of these two projects saved the McDonnell Aircraft Corporation from sharing the fate which befell most other manufacturers at the end of the Second World War: the mass cancellation of wartime contracts. McDonnell, however, did lose its profitable sub-contracting business and 40 of the 100 FD-1s ordered in March 1945 were also

9

cancelled following VJ-Day. On the other hand, the war's end benefitted McDonnell in that the company was able to lease the better facilities previously occupied by the Curtiss-Wright Corporation at Lambert Field, St Louis.

The termination of the sub-contracting work which had sustained McDonnell during the early years of its existence and the depletion taken when the Platt-LePage Aircraft Company went out of business resulted in a net loss of $226,134 in 1946. A year later, however, the profitability of the company was restored and thereafter the McDonnell Aircraft Corporation, until 1965, and the McDonnell Company, in 1966, reported a steadily growing annual income. During the remainder of the 1940s sales and profits were sustained by the quantity manufacture of F2H Banshees, the production version of the XF2D-1. Significant development work centred on the design of two radically different escort jet fighters, the XF-85 Goblin and the XF-88 Voodoo for the USAAF/ USAF, and on the continuation of helicopter engineering, including the development of the diminutive XH-20 Little Henry, and of high-speed rotary/fixed-wing aircraft.

The beginning of the Korean War found the McDonnell Aircraft Corporation in the midst of delivering Banshees, the last contract for the type being placed two and a half weeks after the start of hostilities. On 23 August, 1951, F2H-2s of VF-172 became the first McDonnell aircraft to

An F2H-2 from VF-172, CVG-5, landing aboard the USS *Essex* (CV-9) in August 1951 when the Banshee became the first McDonnell aircraft to be used in combat. *(USN: National Archives)*

go into action. To house its expanded wartime activities McDonnell purchased on 31 July, 1951, the facilities it had previously leased at Lambert Field: this plant, since expanded and modernized, still houses part of the present McDonnell Aircraft Company, one of the major components of the McDonnell Douglas Corporation. This period also saw the first flight of the XF3H-1, the prototype of one of the most frustrating, albeit eventually successful, aircraft development programmes ever undertaken by McDonnell, and the ordering of the first McDonnell type to be built in quantity for the USAF, the F-101 series. Concurrently with these aircraft, McDonnell continued working on helicopter designs.

By 1954, when net income reached the $3 million level, the company had received production contracts for only four aircraft of its own design and for one designed by Fairchild. In terms of numbers of aircraft produced, the F2H Banshee had been its most successful line (895 aircraft were built between January 1947 and October 1953). It was in that year, however, that the McDonnell Aircraft Corporation reached a significant milestone with the delivery on 29 December of its 1,000th aircraft—a US Navy F3H-1N—and obtained the initial contract leading to the subsequent production of 5,195 F-4 Phantom IIs (including 127 built under licence by Mitsubishi). The design of this aircraft, then known as the AH-1, was undertaken in October 1954 and its success made McDonnell one of the world's leading aerospace companies.

McDonnell F3H Demons and F-101 Voodoos in production at St Louis.
(MCAIR)

11

During the second half of the 1950s, aircraft-related activities of the McDonnell Aircraft Corporation were dominated by the production of F3H Demons and F-101 Voodoos and by stepped-up work on the XF4H-1 programme which culminated in the first flight of the Phantom II prototype on 27 May, 1958. This period was also marked by the receipt in 1955 of the first export contract for McDonnell aircraft, 39 ex-US Navy F2H-3s for the Royal Canadian Navy, and by the development and testing of the Model 119/220, a small four-engined jet transport designed jointly to fulfill the needs of the USAF for a utility transport and for an executive jet for the private market. Meanwhile, McDonnell made a final attempt to break into the helicopter market with the design of the Model 120, a 'flying-crane' of diminutive size but unusual lift capabilities. In spite of the lack of success of the Model 119/220 and Model 120 programmes, net sales and net income continued to grow and reached $436 million and $10 million respectively by the end of the Fiscal Year 1959.

While jet aircraft and helicopter designs dominated McDonnell's range of products during most of its first two decades, the company's interest in novel developments had led it early to devote efforts to the missile field. Contract-supported missile programmes had begun at McDonnell in 1944 with a Navy contract for a radio-controlled dive bomb, the KUD-1 Gargoyle. This early activity was followed by a number of research and production programmes including the SAM-N-6 Talos surface-to-air missile for the Navy, the GAM-72 Quail decoy for the USAF and the MAW anti-tank missile for the Army, as well as by research in the field of hypersonic flight and re-entry vehicles. However, the McDonnell Aircraft Corporation achieved fame in the missile and space domain mainly as the result of its selection by NASA on 12 January, 1959, as the prime contractor for Mercury, the first American manned orbital capsule.

The Mercury programme, which became operational on 5 May, 1961, with Alan Shepard's suborbital flight aboard *Freedom 7*, included two manned suborbital missions and four manned orbital flights. It was followed by the Gemini programme which was announced on 7 December, 1961. Also produced by McDonnell under a contract awarded in April 1963, the Gemini capsule was 50 per cent larger in volume and was a two-man spacecraft. Ten successful manned missions were flown by Gemini capsules and included the world's first space rendezvous (*Gemini VIA* and *Gemini VII* on 15 December, 1965) and the first space docking (*Gemini VIII* and Gemini Agena Target Vehicle on 16 March, 1966). The Gemini programme also led to the first joint award to the McDonnell Aircraft Corporation and the Douglas Aircraft Company which were selected in 1965 by the USAF to develop the Manned Orbiting Laboratory (MOL). Before this award, later cancelled for budgetary reasons, the two components of the present McDonnell Douglas Corporation had been co-operating in research for the supersonic transport programme and in manufacturing the Phantom II for which

Gemini VII, with Frank Borman and James Lovell on board, at an altitude of about 160 miles (260 km) on 15 December, 1965, during rendezvous and station-keeping manoeuvres with Gemini VIA crewed by Walter Schirra and Thomas Stafford. *(NASA)*

Douglas produced outer wing panels in its Long Beach plant.

The McDonnell Aircraft Corporation's activities in aeronautics and astronautics had also been further diversified in March 1960 when the McDonnell Automation Center had been organized to handle not only the company's own usage of automation and data processing but also to sell computer services to business, science and industry throughout the nation. Further diversification efforts were expanded by McDonnell and, in recognition of the wider product base of the corporation, the shareholders voted at their 1966 annual meeting to change the name of the McDonnell Aircraft Corporation to that of McDonnell Company.

McDonnell Company,
1966 to 1967

At the time of the corporate name change, McDonnell was experiencing a boom as its Phantom II had become the mainstay of the fighter force of the Navy, the Marine Corps, and the Air Force, and as it was also in production for the Fleet Air Arm and the Royal Air Force. Benefitting from the fact that increased production orders resulting from the large-scale US intervention in Southeast Asia came when the production of the F-4 had arrived at a favourable level on its learning curve, the McDonnell

A McDonnell F-4M Phantom FGR 2 of No. 41 Squadron, Royal Air Force, with massive load including Sparrow air-to-air radar-guided missiles, Sidewinder air-to-air infra-red missiles, and BL. 755 cluster bombs. *(MOD)*

Company was able to achieve very good earnings and an excellent cash position. However, whereas the financial situation of the corporation was most rewarding, the future appeared less promising due to the failure to balance military aircraft production with the manufacture of either helicopters or commercial aircraft.

Being aware of the need to reduce the reliance of the company which bore his name on military aircraft contracts and having long desired to branch off into the design and production of commercial aircraft, James McDonnell had attempted in 1963 to acquire control of the Douglas Aircraft Company. This attempt, however, had been frustrated by the recovery of the commercial aircraft market which had enabled Douglas to bolster its financial position and thus had temporarily eliminated Douglas's need to resort to a merger.

When in 1966 it became obvious that the Douglas Aircraft Company was facing a much more serious crisis, James McDonnell and his McDonnell Company were ready. Not only did the McDonnell Company have what the Douglas Aircraft Company needed urgently, cash and well-qualified management personnel, but James McDonnell and several of the top officers of his company had substantial holdings of Douglas stock. Although insufficient to obtain outright control of the Santa Monica firm, these holdings none the less gave a strong position at the bargaining table to James McDonnell and his associates. However, it was not this privileged position but rather the intrinsic value of his offer which

14

The parallel final assembly line for the Douglas DC-8 and DC-9 at the Long Beach plant. *(DAC)*

won for James McDonnell the favour of the team evaluating for Douglas the merger offers received from Sherman Fairchild (a dominant figure in both Fairchild Hiller and Fairchild Camera), General Dynamics, Martin Marietta, McDonnell Company, North American Aviation, and Signal Oil & Gas.

Astutely, McDonnell avoided making an initial offer contingent on prior approval of the proposed merger and offered to purchase immediately 1.5 million of new Douglas common shares for $68,700,000, thus enabling Douglas to obtain at once the critically needed cash to continue operations while legal procedures were taking place. McDonnell's offer further provided that, should the proposed merger be approved by the Justice Department, all shares of Douglas stock would be exchanged for 1³/₄ shares of McDonnell common stock. It also preserved temporarily the position of the officers of the Douglas Aircraft Company—in particular Donald Douglas Sr was offered the position of Honorary Chairman of the board whilst his son, Donald Douglas Jr, was to remain briefly as President of the new Douglas Aircraft subsidiary before becoming Corporate Vice President-Administration for the parent McDonnell Douglas Corporation. Furthermore, the offer gave satisfactory assurances regarding Douglas's employees and assured the continued existence, albeit only as a divisional company of the McDonnell Douglas Corporation, of the Douglas Aircraft Company.

Among factors which eventually forced Douglas to seek a merger partner were the unexpectedly strong demand for DC-9s and resulting need for capital to increase production rate. The aircraft in the foreground, the 118th DC-9 (s/n 47050, N970VJ), was delivered to Allegheny Airlines on 2 June, 1967, less than two months after the merger. *(DAC)*

Approval of the McDonnell offer was unanimously recommended on 13 January, 1967, by the joint negotiating committee set up by Douglas and its financial consultants, Lazard Frères, to advise the Board of Directors of the ailing Santa Monica firm. McDonnell and Douglas stockholders went along with this recommendation, government approval followed swiftly as continuation of operations by Douglas was important to sustain the US war effort in Vietnam, and the merger became effective on 28 April, 1967.

Hughes Aircraft and Hughes Helicopters, 1934 to 1984

Stemming from a small organization initially set up in 1934 to undertake the design and manufacture of a high-speed aircraft for its eccentric and wealthy owner, Hughes Helicopters, Inc had become a major manufacturer of rotary wing aircraft by the time it was taken over by McDonnell Douglas Corporation on 6 January, 1984.

The only son of a Texas industrialist, Howard Robard Hughes, Jr, was born in Houston, Texas, on 24 December, 1905. Already displaying a moody personality during his teens, he attended several secondary schools but, unlike the well-educated Donald Douglas and James McDonnell, never went to college and lacked a formal education in either engineering or business. Nevertheless, when he inherited three-quarters

16

of the stock of the Hughes Tool Company before the age of 19, he quickly proved to be an adept if unconventional businessman. The firm, which specialized in the development and manufacture of mining and oil drilling equipment, had been co-founded by his father and Walter B Sharp as the Sharp-Hughes Tool Company in 1908 and had become the Hughes Tool Company following the death of Walter Sharp in 1917.

Although lacking education and experience and being a minor under Texas law, Howard Hughes quickly succeeded in proving to the court's satisfaction that he was mature and responsible enough to be allowed to run the Hughes Tool Company before reaching the legal age of 21. Promptly paying $350,000 to acquire the remaining 25 per cent of the stock from various family members and to become the sole owner of the firm, the young millionaire initiated the unique style of management *in absentia* which was to characterize much of his business dealings. Becoming increasingly aloof and remote from the day-to-day operation of his diversified business empire as years went by, Howard Hughes lived his last 25 years as a recluse and died on 5 April, 1976, while being flown from Mexico for medical treatment in the United States.

Howard Hughes took his first aeroplane ride with his father when he was 14 but, apparently, this initial flying experience did not overly impress him as he did not learn to fly until eight years later when he felt that first-hand knowledge of aircraft piloting would be an asset in one of

Howard Hughes in the cockpit of his Racer at Mines Field, Los Angeles-Inglewood, in August 1935. *(Summa Corporation)*

his new business ventures. In 1927, after producing several motion pictures of unequal quality, Hughes realized that an aviation movie could be a successful venture as Charles Lindbergh's New York–Paris flight had generated much public interest and enthusiasm. In support of his new Hollywood venture, the soon to be acclaimed *Hell's Angels*, he assembled a fleet of some 80 aircraft, hired professional stunt pilots, and, after flying a few times as a passenger to gain a better understanding of flying, he decided to learn to fly before proceeding with his new film.

On 10 November, 1927, Hughes obtained his private pilot's licence and immediately purchased his first aeroplane, a Waco 10 two-seat biplane. Thereafter, his enthusiasm for flying quickly increased. Even though he was slightly injured when he crashed in a Thomas-Morse scout while trying to demonstrate to stunt pilots a manoeuvre he wanted them to fly for the benefit of the cameramen filming *Hell's Angels*, he purchased the Boeing 100A, a two-seat demonstrator derived from the F4B-1 naval fighter, in June 1929 and four months later obtained a transport licence. Wishing to extract the maximum performance from the Boeing biplane, Hughes had it modified and streamlined first by Douglas and then by Lockheed. Following the final set of modifications, he flew that aircraft to a new national speed record of 212.39 mph (341.74 km/h) on 5 March, 1933, and with it won the 5-mile triangular race at the All-American Air Maneuvers held in Miami, Florida, on 14 January, 1934. However, not unduly impressed with his win as he felt that none of the competing aircraft had satisfactory performance, Howard Hughes decided there and then to have a special high-speed aircraft built to break the world speed record.

Hiring Richard W Palmer, the brillant engineer who had modified the Model 100A while working for Lockheed, to undertake the design of the high-speed aircraft, Howard Hughes set up an aircraft development group within his Hughes Tool Company on 14 February, 1934, and leased space in a small garage in Glendale, California, in which to have his 1B Racer built. As detailed in the main body of this book, that aeroplane first flew on 17 August, 1935, and was subsequently flown by Howard Hughes to a new world land speed record of 352.388 mph (567.115 km/h) on 13 September. During the following year, the aircraft development group of the Hughes Tool Company became the Hughes Aircraft Company, and on 19 January, 1937, Howard Hughes flew the extensively modified 1B from Burbank, California, to Newark, New Jersey, to set a new transcontinental record.

In addition to work on the 1B Racer, activities undertaken by the aircraft development group of the Hughes Tool Company and the Hughes Aircraft Company before the war included the modification of three famous aircraft. The first was the Northrop Gamma 2G which Howard Hughes leased from noted aviatrix Jacqueline Cochran and in which he set his first US transcontinental record on 13 January, 1936, as well as point-to-point records between Miami and Floyd Bennett Field,

The Lockheed 14-N2 (NX18973) in which Howard Hughes and a crew of four flew around the world on 10/14 July, 1938. *(Gordon S Williams)*

New York, and from Chicago to Burbank, respectively on 21 April and 13 May, 1936. Next came the Douglas DC-1 which Howard Hughes acquired in 1936 through Western Aero & Radio Co of Burbank with the intent of setting a new round-the-world record but which he resold in early 1937 without attempting the world flight. Finally, the Hughes Aircraft Company prepared the Lockheed 14-N2 in which Howard Hughes and a crew of four flew around the world in the record time of 71 hr 11 min 10 sec on 10/14 July, 1938.

While not losing interest in record flights and, in fact, having the development of the twin-engined D-2 initiated in great secrecy in preparation for a planned attempt at bettering his own round-the-world record, Howard Hughes prepared his organization to contribute to the

A Douglas A4D-2 at NOTS Chincoteague, Virginia, on 14 April, 1958, during evaluation of the twin barrel MK-11 20-mm cannon in a centreline Hughes MK-4 gun pod. Full details of the A4D (A-4) are included in Volume I. *(USN)*

war's effort. During 1940, ground was broken for a new Hughes facility in Culver City, California, and aircraft activities were moved into this new plant during that spring. Hughes hired additional engineering and manufacturing personnel to begin the manufacture of the first flexible ammunition feed chutes for military aircraft. Significantly, this last activity marked the starting point for the weapons business which has led Hughes Aircraft, then Hughes Helicopters, and now McDonnell Douglas Helicopter to play increasingly important roles as producers of ordnance and guns. The first significant gun developed by the company was the twin barrel MK-11 20-mm cannon which was test fired in 1951 and placed in production in 1965 as the MK-4 pod for naval fighter and attack aircraft. Other significant weapons developed by Hughes teams include the Chain Gun family (the 7.62-mm EX-34 machine gun for light vehicle and helicopter applications, the 25-mm M242 Bushmaster automatic cannon for use in armoured fighting vehicles, and the 30-mm M230 cannon for the AH-64 Apache attack helicopter), the 40-mm M129 grenade launcher, and several pods (eg the M27E1 with the General Electric M134 Minigun, the HGS-55 with the Hughes EX-34 machine gun, and the XM8 with the Hughes M129 grenade launcher).

During the Second World War and in the immediate postwar period, aviation activities of the Hughes Aircraft Company were shrouded in mystery and surrounded by much political manoeuvring on the part of its sole owner. The most mysterious project of the time was the private venture twin-engined D-2, which first flew in total secrecy at Harper's Dry Lake, California, on 20 June, 1943. The most notorious was the giant Hughes-Kaiser HK-1 flying-boat (later becoming the Hughes HFB-1 or H-4), which was the recipient of an $18 million contract awarded by the Defense Plant Corporation on 16 November, 1942.

Repeatedly Howard Hughes attempted to obtain government contracts for military derivatives of his high-speed, long-range D-2. He first succeeded in 1940 when the Army Air Corps authorized the development of the XA-37 five-seat attack bomber. Subsequently, work on the XA-37 was terminated and efforts were diverted to developing the D-2 into either a long-range fighter, for which the XP-73 designation appears to have been set aside, or a long-range, high-altitude reconnaissance aircraft. By then, the design had grown considerably both in size and weight but, on the power of two turbosupercharged Pratt & Whitney R-4360 engines, performance was sufficiently promising for the Army Air Forces to order two XF-11 reconnaissance prototypes and 100 production F-11As before the war's end. Howard Hughes was seriously injured when the first XF-11 crashed during its maiden flight on 7 July, 1946. Not yet fully recovered, Hughes determinedly and courageously made the first flight of the second XF-11 on 5 April, 1947, before being called to testify in front of a Senate subcommittee investigating alleged impropriety by government officials in respect to contracts awarded during the war to the Hughes Aircraft Company. Subjected to sharp criticism for the failure of

Howard Hughes in the cockpit of the first XF-11 at Culver City on 5 July, 1946.
(Summa Corporation)

his company to complete even one of the three flying-boats ordered in 1942, Howard Hughes felt compelled to expedite the completion of the HFB-1 and to demonstrate that it was flyable by taking it up for a short hop on 2 November, 1947. The popularly called 'Spruce Goose' never flew again and the second XF-11 was dropped from the Air Force inventory in November 1949, thus ending pitifully the wartime activities of the Hughes Aircraft Company. By then, however, Howard Hughes had redirected the company's operations into fields in which it was to gain

The Hughes HFB-1 (H-4) being assembled at Terminal Island, Long Beach, California, on 1 July, 1946. *(Summa Corporation)*

much acclaim, the development of guided missiles and airborne electronic systems and that of helicopters.

The first achievement of the Hughes electronic engineering team was the development of a radar-based ground proximity warning system for transport aircraft which was demonstrated in prototype form in late 1947. While that system failed to attract sufficient interest to be placed in production, initial efforts to develop fire control systems were soon rewarded as the threat of Soviet long-range bombers lent a new urgency to the development of night and all-weather fighters. Development of the E-1 fire control system, which was initiated in March 1948 and was eventually comprised of the AN/APG-33 radar and A-1C gunsight, led to the installation of a first production model in a Lockheed F-94A in October 1949. Subsequently, Hughes fire control systems equipped virtually all types of USAF and RCAF interceptors in service during the fifties and sixties.

The greatest achievement of the Hughes Aircraft Company in the field of fire control systems was the development of the MA-1 which began in May 1949 when the Air Force called the leaders of the aircraft and electronics industry together to discuss the proposed '1954 interceptor' and a new approach to the development of this aircraft, its armament, and its fire control system. Dissatisfied with industry responses, the USAF decided in November 1949 to request first the development of a suitable electronic fire control system and then that of an airframe compatible with the electronic equipment. Accordingly, 50 firms, including Hughes, were invited in January 1950 to submit bids for developing the fire control system. Eighteen firms responded and, after protracted proposal evaluation during which various Air Force organizations reached conflicting decisions, Hughes was declared the winner in July 1950 and a contract for the development of Project MX-1179 (later to be designated MA-1) was awarded on 2 October, 1950. Competition for the airframe was then organized and, following the submission of proposals at the end of January 1951, Convair was awarded a development contract for Project MX-1554, the F-102A interceptor, in September 1951.

While the '1954 interceptor' competion was going on, the Air Force initiated the development of interim interceptors and Hughes went on to develop the E-3 and E-4 fire control systems for the North American F-86D, the E-5 for the Lockheed F-94C, the E-6 for the Northrop F-89D, and the E-9 for the Northrop F-89H. The last of these, which was the first

The Hughes plant and airfield facilities in Culver City, California, in 1976. *(Summa Corporation)*

fire control system to be used in conjunction with air-to-air guided missiles, was also selected in November 1952 for the F-102A due to delays in the development of the highly complex MA-1. The MA-1 fire control system was eventually fitted to the Convair F-106, the ultimate development of the '1954 interceptor.'

Work on missiles, which had also been initiated by Hughes Aircraft in 1947 as part of the Air Force sponsored Project *Dragonfly*, led to the development and production of the long-lived series of semi-active radar homing and infrared homing Falcon missiles. In its initial semi-active radar homing version (successively designated XF-98, GAR-1, and AIM-4 by the Air Force), the Falcon was selected in preference to the Ryan Firebird as the primary weapon for USAF interceptors in April 1949 and was first fired from an airborne platform, a Northrop F-89D, on 21 October, 1953.

Subsequent development of Falcon missiles and fire control systems was undertaken by a new Hughes Aircraft Company which came into being in 1953 when the original Hughes Aircraft Company was separated from the Hughes Tool Company to become the property of Howard Hughes Medical Institute. As thereafter the Hughes Aircraft Company remained legally separated from other Hughes organizations, including Hughes Helicopters, Inc, the predecessor of the present McDonnell Douglas Helicopter Company, its post-1953 activities are not dealt with in this corporate history of the McDonnell Douglas Corporation. Suffice to say, that the Hughes Aircraft Company continued to flourish (*viz* the development of the AIM-54 Phoenix missile system for the Grumman F-14 and of the AN/APG-63, AN/APG-65, and AN/APG-70 for the F-15A/D, F/A-18, and F-15E) and that in December 1985 it was acquired by General Motors Corporation, the automotive giant.

The third prong of the aerospace diversification programme initiated

The Hughes XH-17 during initial trials at Culver City in 1952. *(MDHC)*

by Howard Hughes in the late forties began in 1948 with the acquisition of the rights and Air Force contract for the XH-17 helicopter from the Kellett Aircraft Company of Philadelphia, Pennsylvania, for $250,000. The XH-17 ground rig was first tested in December 1949 and, as results were promising, the rig was modified into an airborne test stand for use in the development of a tactical heavy lift helicopter. Following these modifications, the XH-17, Hughes' first helicopter, was flown on 16 September, 1952. During the next year, after the Hughes Aircraft Company and its missile and fire control system activities had been transferred to the Howard Hughes Medical Institute, work on helicopters was continued by the Hughes Tool Company's Aircraft Division. Interestingly, both this division and the Hughes Aircraft Company continued to share the Culver City facility managed by Hughes Aircraft after these two units were legally separated.

A Hughes 530F during an external load carrying demonstration at Culver City in December, 1984. *(Hughes Helicopters)*

On the strength of its work on the XH-17, Hughes had been awarded a contract for a larger XH-28 crane helicopter. However, this promising project did not advance past the mock-up stage due to cutbacks toward the end of the Korean War and once again Hughes had to go outside to obtain the technology with which to continue helicopter development. This time, the gamble paid off and the Model 269, which made use of the rotor design conceived by D K Jovanovich for his tandem rotor JOV-3 helicopter, was first flown in October 1956. As Models 269A, 200, and 300, this series of small helicopters went into large scale production for civil and military customers in the United States and abroad. More than 2,900 of these light helicopters had been built when McDonnell Douglas announced the sale of this helicopter line to Schweizer Aircraft Co in November 1986.

Whereas the XV-9A, which first flew in November 1964, remained experimental, the first flight of the YOH-6 in February 1963 marked the start of another major helicopter line which more than a quarter of a century later continued to contribute significantly to the overall success of the McDonnell Douglas Corporation[3]. The next major Hughes helicopter development programme was inititated in answer to a Request for Proposals issued in November 1972 and calling for the design of an Advanced Attack Helicopter. The Hughes Model 409 (YAH-64A) was first flown in September 1975 and won the competition in December 1976. The resulting Apache programme became important, first for Hughes Helicopters and then for McDonnell Douglas Helicopter, and was expected to remain in production until the mid-nineties. However, in 1989 the need to reduce the military budget prompted the Bush Administration to recommend terminating production after completion of AH-64As ordered under the Fiscal Year 1991 budget.

Before and immediately after the acquisition of Hughes Helicopters, Inc by McDonnell Douglas Corporation, six changes were made in the corporate structure of the organization controlling the development and production of Hughes helicopters. First, in 1972 Howard Hughes sold the Oil Tool Division of Hughes Tool Company while retaining the helicopter unit and his other holdings which were consolidated under a new company, Summa Corporation. With this change, Hughes Helicopters became a division of Summa Corp and remained as such for five years after the death of Howard Hughes on 5 April, 1976. Next, in 1981, Hughes Helicopters was separated from Summa and was incorporated to become, along with Summa Corporation, one of the principal subsidiaries of a new holding company, The Hughes Corporation. Further changes occurred in early 1983, when ownership of Hughes Helicopters, Inc was transferred to the estate, in December 1983, when McDonnell Douglas Corporation announced that it was purchasing Hughes Helicop-

---

[3] *eg* in 1988 McDonnell Douglas Helicopter sold 109 MD 500Es and MD 530Fs and early in 1989 the company announced that the MD 520N and MD 530N variants would be put into production.

A McDonnell Douglas AH-64A at Fort Hood, Texas. *(MDHC)*

ters, Inc from the Howard Hughes estate, and on 6 January, 1984, when this sale became final. On 27 August, 1985, the firm's identity was changed to the present McDonnell Douglas Helicopter Company (MDHC).

Throughout this series of corporate reorganizations, changes were also made in the physical make-up of the company. In 1982, plant facilities in Culver City, which had been previously leased from the Hughes Aircraft Company, were purchased and construction of a new plant at Falcon Field in Mesa, Arizona, was begun. Apache production moved to that plant in December 1982, and the MDHC headquarters was moved from Culver City to Mesa in September 1986. Finally, in 1987, light helicopter assembly operations were transferred from California to Arizona and flight test, maintenance training, and delivery operations were moved from Palomar, California, to Mesa. After these moves, however, MDHC still retained component manufacturing facilities in California.

McDonnell Douglas Corporation
since 1967

When the McDonnell Douglas Corporation began operating on 28 April, 1967, 47 years after the foundation of the Davis-Douglas Company and 28 years after the debut of the McDonnell Aircraft Corporation, it had a solid and well diversified product line which included military aircraft (with F-4s, A-4s, and TA-4s in production), commercial aircraft (DC-8 and DC-9), spacecraft and boosters (MOL, S-IVB stage for Saturn V, Thor, and Delta), missiles (Nike Hercules, Spartan, and Dragon), data processing services, and electronic products, and the company employed

27

PH-DNN, s/n 47192, in front of the Douglas Aircraft Company's administration building in Long Beach. This DC-9-33-RC was delivered to KLM on 17 April, 1968. *(DAC)*

more than 140,000 people. These assets, however, were partially offset by the problems inherited from the Douglas Aircraft Company, chiefly production problems which resulted in late deliveries of DC-8s and DC-9s and uncontrolled costs.

Settling down to correct these problems which were leading to poor customer relations and financial troubles, the McDonnell Douglas management team succeeded in reversing the trend with minimum personnel upheaval. None the less, and in spite of the profitable operations of the McDonnell Aircraft Company, the McDonnell Douglas Corporation closed its first fiscal year on 31 December, 1967, with an operating loss before income taxes. After accounting for a large tax credit, this operating loss resulted in a consolidated net income of only $7,515,503. The success of the corrective measures, however, soon brought deliveries back on schedule and the temporary drop in earnings

N1801U, the first DC-10-10 for United Air Lines. *(DAC)*

experienced in 1967 gave place in 1968 to a consolidated net income after taxes of $98,475,302—a more than thirteen fold increase in one year!

Besides witnessing the financial recovery of the McDonnell Douglas Corporation, the year 1968 saw the go-ahead for the DC-10 programme. A first order for this wide-body trijet, design of which had been started by Douglas in late 1965, was received from American Airlines on 19 February, 1968, and resulted in a production commitment contingent on sufficient additional orders being obtained within the following three months. In the face of intense competition from Lockheed (in late March 1968 the selection of the L-1011 TriStar by Air Holdings, Delta, Eastern, Northeast, and TWA almost resulted in the cancellation of the DC-10 programme), McDonnell Douglas was able to secure a record order from United Air Lines on 25 April, 1968, which put the DC-10 firmly in production. Later in the year, following the approval by the company's Board of Directors of funding for the design of long-range versions of the DC-10, McDonnell Douglas received an order from Northwest Airlines for the first intercontinental model of the aircraft, the Pratt & Whitney JT9D-powered DC-10-20. Early in 1969, the gamble taken by management paid off further with the ordering by the European KSSU group of long-range DC-10-30s powered by General Electric CF6-50 turbofans. The DC-10's future appeared promising and high hopes existed for sales of the trijet eventually to surpass those of the DC-8. Unfortunately, these hopes failed to materialize.

Problems with the locking mechanism of an aft cargo door and unapproved maintenance practices resulted in two major accidents and, due in part to endemically poor press relations, the DC-10 received much adverse publicity. Moreover, a coincidental downturn in airline business prevented McDonnell Douglas from going ahead in the late 1970s with the planned development and manufacture of stretched and longer-ranged versions. Although the DC-10 programme had received a boost in 1977 when the Air Force selected a version of the Douglas trijet as the winner of its Advanced Tanker/Cargo Aircraft (ATCA) competition, it never recovered and production ended at the beginning of 1989 with the completion of the 446th aircraft in the joint DC-10/KC-10 line. The programme, however, had been resurrected two years earlier when management had given the go-ahead for the MD-11 derivative in December 1986.

After the excitement of 1968[4], the third year of operations gave every appearance of being a comparatively quiet year marked by efforts to consolidate the company's leadership position. Then one day after the

---

[4] In December 1968, when the author resigned from the McDonnell Douglas Corporation, employment stood at nearly 125,000 and a share of common stock was quoted at $51 on Wall Street. Over the next 20 years, neither employment nor stock value (after taking inflation into account) again reached such lofty levels. However, one would be ill-advised to reach too quick a conclusion...

The AV-8C prototype (BuNo 158384) during trials aboard the USS *Saipan* (LHA-2) in October 1979. *(MCAIR)*

announcement on 22 December, 1969, by McDonnell Douglas and Hawker Siddeley Aviation Ltd that the AV-8A Harrier V/STOL attack fighter could be built under licence by McDonnell Douglas in the event that sufficient orders were received from the Marine Corps, further elation marked the announcement that the McDonnell Aircraft Company had won the competition to design and build the new USAF air superiority fighter, the F-15.

The company's Golden Anniversary was highlighted by the roll-out of the first DC-10 on 23 July, 1970, 50 years and one day after the founding of the Davis-Douglas Company. Reaching this significant step in its corporate history, the McDonnell Douglas Corporation could proudly and confidently proclaim on the cover of its Annual Report that:

'The progress of McDonnell Douglas spans and epitomizes a half century that brought greater aerospace advance than in all previous history. But we have only come to the end of the beginning. Each fresh tomorrow offers undiminished opportunities—in air commerce, in the exploration of space and in providing the sinews of strength that are the only sure foundation for peace. The historic accomplishments of McDonnell Douglas, 1920-1970, are a stimulating prologue for tomorrow's new achievements in service of the community, the nation and the world.'

That year, however, saw net sales drop from $3,023.8 million to $2,088.2 million while net income plummeted from $79.7 to $5.5 million. Employment, which had already gone done from its zenith in 1967, went down from 107,503 employees at the end of 1969 to 92,552 employees a year later.

During the first half of the 'seventies, a period during which miltary contracts decreased significantly following the US disengagement from Southeast Asia and airline earnings and equipment procurement were down, annual sales and income averaged respectively $2,592 million and $73 million. Significant events in the history of the McDonnell Douglas Corporation during that period included the delivery of the last DC-8 on

McDonnell Douglas F-15A-7-MC of the 58th Tactical Fighter Training Wing at Luke AFB, Arizona. *(Courtesy of Cloud 9 Photography)*

12 May, 1972; the first flight of the F-15 on 27 July, 1973; and the successful completion of the three-mission Skylab programme on 8 February, 1974.

Employment continued to drop during the next three years and reached a year-end low of 57,867 at the end of the nation's bicentennial year. Thereafter, the number of employees slowly went back up to reach the 82,736 level at the end of 1979 while the five-year sales and income average stood at $3,974 million and $136 million. Much of this apparent improvement in the company's financial health, however, was due to rapid inflation, as commercial aircraft orders remained at an unsatisfactory level. Nevertheless, on 19 October, 1977, McDonnell Douglas announced the go-ahead for a new DC-9 version, the Super 80, which was to be powered by refanned engines and which after a slow start led to the most successful MD-80 programme. The company's commercial activities, however, remained the source of disappointment as the planned development of a wide-body twin-jet, which had been temporarily designated DC-X-200 and was to have become the DC-11 when built, had to be cancelled in 1978. Even more serious were the after shocks of the crash of an American Airlines DC-10 on 25 May, 1979, and the subsequent grounding until 13 July of US-registered DC-10s. The expected launch of stretched versions of the DC-10 had to be abandoned due to an unwarranted, yet most damaging, loss of confidence on the part of the travelling public.

In the military aircraft segment, which during the five-year period ending in December 1979 accounted for 51 per cent of the company's revenues (versus 29.9 per cent from commercial aircraft), major events included the selection of the McDonnell Douglas/Northrop design as the F/A-18 winner of the Naval Air Combat Fighter competition on 2 May, 1975; the first flight of the YC-15 military transport aircraft on that same date; the announcement of the selection of the KC-10 as the winner of the

A McDonnell Douglas KC-10A of the 22nd Air Refueling Wing landing at March AFB, California, in January 1984. *(René J. Francillon)*

ATCA competion on 19 December, 1977; the maiden flight of the YAV-8B on 9 November, 1978, and that of the F/A-18 prototype nine days later; and the delivery of the 2,960th and last Skyhawk on 27 February, 1979, and that of the 5,068th and last McDonnell-built Phantom II on 25 October, 1979.

An era ended for the McDonnell Douglas Corporation with the passing of its founders. James S. McDonnell died on 22 August, 1980, and Donald W. Douglas on 1 February, 1981. Their deaths came at a time when the company was experiencing sustained growth in all major lines of business but was nevertheless starting to register reduced earnings. New military business obtained during the first two years of the 'eighties included the winning in August 1981 of a competitive source selection for development and production of the C-X (C-17) and the selection during the fourth quarter of 1981 of an international team led by McDonnell Douglas as the winner of the Navy VTXTS training aircraft (T-45) and pilot training system competition.

For McDonnell Douglas commercial operations, however, the early 'eighties were a most difficult period as airlines continued to suffer from a worldwide business recession and as competition among manufacturers had become fierce. Compounding these problems was the announcement in January 1982 that the Air Force did not plan to proceed with the full-scale development of the C-17. Without the expected work on this advanced cargo aircraft and as the result of the disappointing number of jetliners sold in 1981 and early 1982, it appeared that overhead costs at the Long Beach plant would have to be absorbed by an insufficient number of Super 80s and DC-10s/KC-10s. Thus, when on 20 September, 1982, the 2,000th Douglas jetliner (a DC-10-10CF) was delivered to United Airlines, it seemed likely that the proud line of Douglas commercial transports would soon come to an end.

In an attempt to forestall this unsatisfactory turn of events, McDonnell Douglas developed a new marketing strategy and implemented an innovative package of short-term jetliner leases. American Airlines and Trans World Airlines found merit to this attractive offer and, in September and October 1982 respectively, reached agreements to lease 20 and 15 Super 80s, thus enabling the manufacturer to keep open its DC-9 production line. Moreover, congressional support for the KC-10

A McDonnell Douglas DC-9-82 (MD-82) of Adria Airways landing at Paris-Orly in the summer of 1989. *(Christian Jacquet-Francillon)*

and C-17 programmes resulted in the award of a multi-year contract for 44 additional tankers and lent a new lease to the military airlifter.

As the long awaited improvement in the financial condition of the world's airlines once again failed to materialize in 1983, a year during which the historical DC designation system was replaced by the MD nomenclature and during which the number of MD-80s and DC-10s delivered exceeded that of jetliner orders received by the company, McDonnell Douglas announced a reduction in its commercial aircraft activities in November. The manufacture of MD-80s and minimum-change derivatives was to continue but development of the MD-90, a more drastic development of the MD-80, and of the MD-100, a DC-10 derivative, would be terminated. Continued disappointment in the commercial aircraft market was, however, more than offset by sustained

An AF/A-18A Hornet of No.2 OCU, Royal Australian Air Force, over the harbour area in Sydney. *(RAAF)*

strength of the company's combat aircraft lines. Furthermore, prospects for the corporation were greatly improved through the acquisitions of Computer Sharing Services, Inc, and Hughes Helicopters, Inc, which were both announced in 1983 and completed in January 1984. In particular, the purchase of Hughes Helicopters added two important product lines, the state-of-the-art AH-64 Apache attack helicopter and the steadily selling 500 and 530 light helicopter series for military and civil customers in the United States and abroad. Prospects also appeared bright for the light helicopter being designed for the US Army LHX competition.

MD-80 orders received in 1984 were sufficient to assure continued production at efficient rates through 1986 and demand for new wide-cabin trijets also appeared to be picking up. These events convinced the Board of Directors not to terminate production of jetliners in Long Beach, as had been predicted by unduly pessimistic soothsayers, and prompted it to authorize the Douglas Aircraft Company to pursue jetliner programmes with renewed determination.

Combat aircraft and MD-80s continued to provide satisfactory revenues and earnings in 1985 and 1986 but computer services, which earlier had been reorganized into the Information Systems Group, operated at a

S/n 49254, N241AA, a McDonnell Douglas DC-9-82 (MD-82) of American Airlines. *(John Wegg)*

substantial loss. Moreover, in 1986 the McDonnell Aircraft's ATF (Advanced Tactical Fighter) proposal failed to be selected by the Air Force. However, as prime sub-contractor to Northrop Corporation, the designer of one the two ATF finalists, McDonnell Douglas hoped to retain a major force in the combat aircraft field.

Notwithstanding the drain on the company's finances resulting from the poor showing of its Information Systems Group and the fact that the McDonnell design failed to qualify in the ATF competition, the Board of Directors felt confident enough to authorize the Douglas Aircraft Company to go ahead with the development of the MD-11 jetliner, an advanced version of the DC-10/KC-10 trijet, for which contingent orders for 52 aircraft had been received by the end of 1986. Moreover, the diversified future of the company was further improved when a year later the US Navy selected the team of McDonnell Douglas Corporation and General Dynamics Corporation to develop an advanced tactical aircraft, the A-12. With the start of these new commercial and military product lines, the activities of the McDonnell Douglas Corporation were set for the coming decade, the eighth since the founding of its Davis-Douglas forebear in 1920.

At the end of the 'eighties, the corporate structure of the McDonnell Douglas Corporation (MDC) was as follows:

• The McDonnell Aircraft Company (MCAIR), which has consistently been the corporation's major earning centre, continued in the late 'eighties to manufacture AV-8Bs and Harrier G.R.5s for the Marine Corps and the Royal Air Force, F-15s for the Air Force, and F/A-18s for the Navy, the Marines and export customers in its St Louis plant. It also was working with Northrop Corporation on the design of the YF-23 and with General Dynamics Corporation on that of the A-12. Along with the AH-64 and other military helicopter programmes from McDonnell Douglas Helicopter, these combat aircraft activities contributed 40.6 per cent of the revenues and 107.2 per cent of the earnings reported by the McDonnell Douglas Corporation in 1989. MCAIR began the new decade by being selected by the Air Force to manage the Tanker Transport Training System (TTTS), through which Beech Aircraft will deliver up to 211 Beechjet 400A trainers and Quintron Corp will provide flight simulators.

• The Douglas Aircraft Company (DAC), with its principal facilities in Long Beach, California, provided 32.5 per cent of corporate revenues in 1989, but lost almost as much as MCAIR earned ($222 million loss versus $268 million profit). At the end of the decade, its four major programmes were the MD-80 and MD-11 jetliners, the T-45 jet trainer (responsibility for this programme has since been transferred to MCAIR), and the C-17 airlifter. In late 1988 and early 1989, much as had been the case before the merger when Douglas ran into trouble when the demand for DC-8s and

BuNo 162787, the first prototype of the McDonnell Douglas T-45A Goshawk developed from the British Aerospace Hawk trainer, taking off on its first flight from Long Beach on 16 April, 1988. *(DAC)*

DC-9s had grown more rapidly than anticipated, rapid and simultaneous build-up of these four programmes and problems related to training and integrating thousands of new workers resulted in increased costs, taxed management systems and processes, and were accompanied by difficulties in obtaining adequate parts and components from suppliers and sub-contractors. In 1988, to provide relief from capacity and staffing problems, MDC leased a plant owned by the Air Force in Columbus, Ohio, purchased its equipment from the previous leasor (Rockwell International), and gained its trained workforce. In addition, previously undertaken plant expansions in Long Beach, Salt Lake City, and Macon were stepped up. Nevertheless, difficulties continued to mount, their most obvious impacts being late delivery of jetliners and the much delayed first flight of the MD-11, with that event taking place on 10 January, 1990, ten months behind schedule.

• The McDonnell Douglas Helicopter Company (MDHC) came into existence on 27 August, 1985, when MDC renamed Hughes Helicopters, Inc. which it had acquired 19 months earlier. With headquarters in Mesa, Arizona, since November 1986, MDHC still retains some plant facilities in California. In 1989, MDHC was producing AH-64 attack helicopters for the Army and MD 500 and 530 light helicopters for civil customers in

The McDonnell Douglas Helicopter Company's headquarters and production facility in Mesa, Arizona, was officially opened on 1 November, 1986. *(MDHC)*

the United States and civil and military customers abroad. Projects then under development included the LHX, a light helicopter for the Army which is being developed jointly with Bell Textron, and the MDX, a twin-engined light helicopter for the commercial market. At that time, MDHC remained a major designer and producer of a broad range of guns for ground and air use (including the 7.62 mm EX-34 machine gun built under licence by the Royal Small Arms Factory-Enfield in England).

• The McDonnell Douglas Missile Systems Company and the McDonnell Douglas Space Systems Company, which in 1989 provided 13.3 per cent of corporate revenues and 44.0 per cent of earnings, are responsible for MDC's missile and space activities. Major activities in the late 'eighties included production of AGM-84 anti-ship missiles (the 5,000th Harpoon was delivered in 1988 as were the first test models of its SLAM—Stand-off Land Attack Missile—derivative), AGM-129 advanced cruise missiles, and BGM-109 Tomahawk naval cruise missiles. In the same period, the Space Systems unit was continuing development work of the Space Station *Freedom* and was producing the reliable Delta II booster.

• The Information Systems Group, which in 1988 accounted for 8.6 per cent of corporate revenues but sustained a $76 million loss, operated in three related business areas: network systems, systems integration, and computer applications. In 1988, the McDonnell Douglas Network Systems was the second largest data transmission network in the United States and one of the largest in the international market. The Health Systems Company, a provider of automated systems for the health care delivery industry, was sold during the first quarter of 1989.

• The McDonnell Douglas Finance Corporation (MDFC), a diversified financial services organization, pursued in 1989 its original activity, financing MDC-built commercial aircraft. This activity, however, accounted for only about one-tenth of its operations as MDFC has branched into leasing of smaller (non-MDC built) aircraft to regional airlines, automobile leasing, commercial real estate lending, and capital equipment leasing. In 1989, MDFC contributed only 3.4 per cent of the corporation's revenues but profitability was high and this subsidiary contributed 30.8 per cent to MDC earnings.

Annual Net Sales and Net Income
McDonnell, 1940 to 1966

Year	Net Sales US $	Net Income US $
1940	Fiscal Year ended 30 June, 1942	
1941	represented first year of operations	
1942	194,391	80,412
1943	10,585,979	63,757
1944	21,704,255	144,909
1945	20,667,848	187,407
1946	6,562,001	(226,134)
1947	11,172,427	540,870

1948	20,704,996	1,675,327
1949	32,659,384	1,731,832
1950	38,688,383	2,815,219
1951	65,123,014	2,488,746
1952	81,743,306	2,910,370
1953	133,531,447	3,308,850
1954	123,091,691	3,621,417
1955	154,588,816	4,555,795
1956	186,204,381	6,751,569
1957	335,287,764	9,671,654
1958	442,408,483	10,028,577
1959	435,878,979	10,037,995
1960	436,981,100	12,087,025
1961	344,413,501	12,109,357
1962	390,718,187	13,879,691
1963	565,339,262	17,036,020
1964	865,376,700	24,499,585
1965	1,007,829,337	32,013,544
1966	1,060,039,414	43,217,072

Annual Employment, Net Sales, and Net Income
McDonnell Douglas, 1967 to 1989

Year	Number of employees	Net Sales	Net Income
		(US Dollars in Millions)	
1967	140,050	2,933.8	7.5
1968	124,740	3,609.3	98.5
1969	107,503	3,023.8	79.7
1970	92,552	2,088.2	5.5
1971	92,105	2,069.1	20.4
1972	86,713	2,725.7	97.6
1973	78,799	3,002.6	133.3
1974	70,739	3,075.0	106.7
1975	62,830	3,255.7	85.6
1976	57,867	3,543.7	108.9
1977	61,577	3,544.8	123.0
1978	70,547	4,192.0	161.1
1979	82,736	5,331.7	199.1
1980	82,550	6,124.8	144.6
1981	74,264	7,453.8	176.6
1982	72,451	7,412.3	214.7
1983	74,466	8,242.4	274.9
1984	88,391	9,819.3	325.3
1985	97,067	11,617.7	345.7
1986	105,696	12,771.9	277.5
1987	112,400	13,289.4	313.0
1988	121,421	15,069.0	350.0
1989	127,926	14,589.0	219.0

McDonnell Doodlebug

On 20 April, 1927, the Daniel Guggenheim Fund for the Promotion of Aeronautics announced that it would sponsor an International Safe Aircraft Competition and would award $100,000 to the winning design demonstrating a 'real advance in safety of flying . . . without sacrificing the good, practical qualities of the present day aircraft.'

To design and build an aeroplane meeting these requirements, James McDonnell, James Cowling and Constantine Zakhartchenko joined forces and in early 1928 established J. S. McDonnell Jr & Associates for this specific purpose. Working part-time on the project, under the leadership

The Doodlebug on 19 November, 1929. *(Aero Digest)*

of James McDonnell, the partners designed a two-seat low-wing monoplane which, to ease construction, had a tapered rectangular cross-section fuselage and externally braced wings and horizontal tail surfaces of rectangular planform. The structure was of metal with fabric and light alloy covering. Power was supplied by a 110 hp Warner Scarab seven-cylinder radial with two-blade metal propeller and, to obtain good low-speed performance, the aircraft was fitted with full-span automatic slots on the wing leading edge and large slotted flaps on two-thirds of the trailing edge. Good taxi-ing and landing characteristics were assured by the use of a wide-track undercarriage with large oleo-pneumatic shock struts.

Built in a hangar belonging to the Hamilton Aero Manufacturing Company in Milwaukee, Wisconsin, and known as the Doodlebug, the aircraft was completed in October 1929 but was too late to meet the 31 October deadline for entering the competition; however, an extension was granted and on 15 November, 1929, James McDonnell took the aircraft on its first flight in Milwaukee before ferrying it to Mitchel Field, New York, where the competition was held. While at Mitchel Field the aircraft's tailplane collapsed and further damage was incurred when James McDonnell force landed the Doodlebug. Nevertheless, the aircraft had already shown sufficient promise for Guggenheim officials to grant a new extension and the aircraft was shipped back to Milwaukee for repairs. Finally, the

Doodlebug was ready to resume flying. However, while being ferried back to New York, it suffered engine failure and was again damaged, thus losing its chance to compete for the coveted Guggenheim purse.

Undaunted, McDonnell had his aircraft repaired and, taking part in numerous air shows, demonstrated the pleasant flying characteristics and

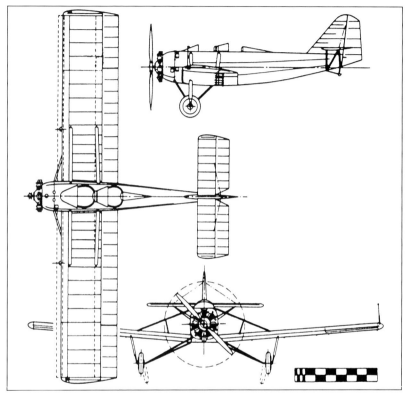

McDonnell Doodlebug.

spectacular short take-off and landing performance of the Doodlebug. In spite of this, no one came forth to sponsor quantity production. Finally, early in 1931, the Doodlebug was sold to the National Advisory Committee for Aeronautics (NACA) which used it to test the efficiency of full-span slots during flying and wind-tunnel tests.

With the demise of the Doodlebug, J. S. McDonnell Jr & Associates was wound up and James McDonnell had to wait until March 1945 to have one of his own aircraft, the FH-1 Phantom, ordered into quantity production.

Span 35 ft (10.67 m); length 21 ft 4 in (6.50 m); wing area 196.5 sq ft (18.26 sq m).
Empty weight 1,250 lb (567 kg); loaded weight 1,800 lb (816 kg); wing loading 9.2 lb/sq ft (44.7 kg/sq m); power loading 16.4 lb/hp (7.4 kg/hp).
Maximum speed 110 mph (177 km/h); endurance 5 hours.

41

Howard Hughes in the cockpit of the Racer during an engine run-up at Mines Field, Los Angeles, in August 1935. *(Summa Corporation)*

Hughes 1B Racer

Shortly after taking part in the All-American Air Maneuvers, an aviation meet held in Miami in January 1934, and during which he won the 5-mile triangular race in his much modified Boeing 100A biplane, Howard Hughes concluded that an aircraft substantially faster than existing American racers could be build and he set about to have such an aircraft built. As he liked the way in which Richard W Palmer had modified his Boeing 100A in 1931-32 while working for Lockheed, Hughes asked this talented engineer if he would be interested in designing the 'fastest plane in the world.' Dick Palmer readily accepted the challenge and quit his engineering work at the Airplane Development Corporation to head the design and construction team which Howard Hughes was ready to hire.

Work on the 'Palmer Racing Plane' was initiated at the end of February 1934, under the aegis of the Hughes Development Company in a two-car garage which Palmer had rented earlier to work on a project of his own. Preliminary design was completed in less than two months, and a $^{7}/_{25}$th scale model with alternate wings, fuselage sections, and cowlings was tested in the wind tunnel at the California Institute of Technology from 21 April until the end of July before the final low-wing configuration was selected. Of mixed construction, with ply-covered wings, metal fuselage, and fabric-covered tail surfaces, the aircraft was to be fitted with a fully retractable undercarriage and enclosed cockpit. It was to be powered by a Pratt & Whitney Twin Wasp Jr S5A-G which, by substituting 100-octane petrol for the usual 87-octane fuel and changing carburettor settings, was to have its normal rating of 700 hp on take-off and at 9,000 ft (2,745 m) boosted to around 1,000 hp.

While the manufacture of the racing aeroplane was proceeding under the direction of its designer in a leased warehouse at the Grand Central Airport in Glendale, without Palmer's knowledge, Howard Hughes had another team work on a fighter variant to be entered in the Pursuit Competion which the Army Air Corps had announced would be held at Wright Field, Ohio, in August 1935. Nothing came out of this endeavour as the fighter, which was given the military sounding designation XP-2 by the Hughes team, could not be built in time for entry in the competition. Its proposed development, however, was to have a long-term effect on the relationship between Howard Hughes and the AAC following an attempt by the abrasive industrialist to misrepresent a statement made by the Air Corps project officer[1].

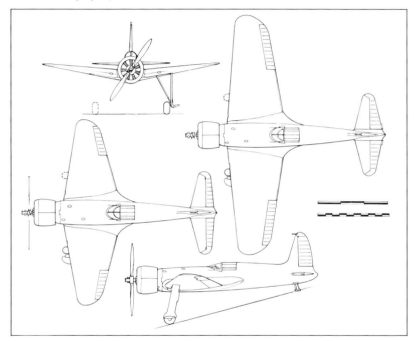

Hughes 1B Racer.

Fortunately for Howard Hughes, better luck attended the development of the racing aircraft which, designated 1B or Special 1B and registered NR258Y, was completed on 10 August, 1935. Following ground testing at Grand Central Airport, the aircraft was trucked from Glendale to Los Angeles and on 17 August Howard Hughes flew it at Mines Field. This first flight was limited to 15 minutes due to a malfunction in the propeller pitch changing mechanism. Replacement

[1]   Then a captain, O P Echols rose to general rank and commanded the Materiel Command during the Second World War when Howard Hughes repeatedly attempted to obtain from the AAF a contract for the development of a military version of his D-2. It was only after some high level intervention that a derivative of this twin-engined aircraft, the F-11, was ordered in October 1943.

The short-span Hughes 1B Racer at Mines Field in August 1935. *(Courtesy Robert Hirsch)*

parts were installed but on 28 August Hughes came close to baling out as the undercarriage refused to come down until a final attempt at using the emergency system succeeded in dislodging the main wheels from their wells. A safe landing was made at the Union Terminal in Burbank where a new hydraulic pump was installed before two uneventful flights could be made on 9 and 11 September. With airborne time totaling 3 hr 20 min at

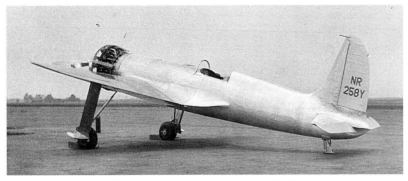

Hughes 1B (NR258Y) at Mines Field in August 1935. *(Summa Corporation)*

the end of the fourth flight, Hughes declared himself and the 1B ready for an attempt at breaking the Class C (landplane) speed record of 505.848 km/h (314.319 mph) set eight-and-a-half months earlier by R Delmotte in a Caudron C.460.

A first attempt was made at Santa Ana, California, on 12 September but the late afternoon light was insufficient for official cameras to record whether the flight had been made properly over the designated course. A second attempt in the morning of 13 September, 1935, almost did not succeed. After flying the required four passes over the 3-km course, the

1B Racer ran out of fuel when Howard Hughes decided to make two more passes as insurance for the possible failure of recording equipment during previous passes. Skillfully, Hughes made a wheels-up landing short of the airfield. Officials, however, agreed that the emergency landing had been a controlled landing as required when submitting a record for homologation, and on 5 November the Fédération Aéronautique Internationale confirmed the new Class C speed record of 567.115 km/h (352.388 mph). This record[2] held for for 42 months until Hans Dieterle flew at 746.606 km/h (463.919 mph) in the Heinkel He 100 V8 on 30 March, 1939.

Having broken the landplane speed record, Howard Hughes set

The Hughes 1B after fitting of long-span wings. The registration number has been changed from NR258Y to NX258Y. *(Courtesy of Robert Hirsch)*

[2] Remarkable as it was, the world landplane speed record set by Howard Hughes paled when compared with the absolute speed record of 709.209 km/h (440.681 mph) which had been set by F Agello in a Macchi-Castoldi 72 floatplane on 24 October, 1934. Ever since, however, the Hughes 1B Racer has generated an apparently disproportionate amount of enthusiasm, particularly in the United States. Hence, it is appropriate to note that the speed achieved by the 1B Racer was indeed quite an achievement as, for example, it substantially exceeded the top speed of 270 mph (434 km/h) achieved at *sea level* by the prototype of the Hawker Hurricane which first flew less than six weeks after Hughes set his record. Furthermore, one must remember that the first US operational fighter to reach a speed of 350 mph (563 km/h) at *low level*, the Republic P-47C, did not do so until September 1942, seven years after the 1B had been flown at over 352 mph (567 km/h). Of course, by the end of the thirties, other types of fighter aircraft were flying at speeds of over 350 mph at *higher altitudes*.

breaking the US transcontinental record as his next goal. To do so, he followed a dual approach and had Dick Palmer design the modifications needed to extend the range of the 1B Racer while another team modified the Northrop Gamma 2G leased from Jacqueline Cochran (as described in Volume I). With that last aircraft, Hughes flew from Burbank to Newark, New Jersey, in 9 hr 26 min 10 sec on 13/14 January, 1936.

To improve upon this time, the 1B Racer was extensively modified and received new wings of greater span (32 ft versus 24 ft 11 in, 9.75 m vs 7.59 m) and area (191 sq ft vs 138 sq ft, 17.74 sq m vs 12.82 sq m), revised horizontal tail surfaces, and a new Twin Wasp Jr SB-G radial with maximum rating boosted from 825 hp to around 1,000 hp. In addition, fuel tankage was increased from 250 to 280 US gallons (946 to 1,060 litres) and a radio and additional navigation equipment were installed. The modified aircraft was first tested on 28 December, 1936, and on 19 January, 1937, Howard Hughes flew it from Burbank to Newark in 7 hr 28 min 25 sec, shattering his own year-old transcontinental record. Nine years were to go by before Col William H Council broke this record by flying from Long Beach to LaGuardia in a Lockheed P-80A in 4 hr 13 min 26 sec on 26 January, 1946.

Hughes 1B Racer photographed at Culver City in 1945. The fuselage and tail surfaces are natural metal or silver dope whereas the wings are dark royal blue. The wing registration is deep yellow. *(Dusty Carter, courtesy of Robert Hirsch)*

After the transcontinental flight, Hughes ignored an informal request from the Army Air Corps to take the 1B Racer to Wright Field and discuss the possible development of a pursuit aircraft. Instead, he had the record-breaking aircraft flown back to California by a contract pilot and put into storage. After less than three years in storage, title to the 1B Racer was apparently transferred to Timm Aircraft Co in a $100,000 paper transaction which preceded desultory efforts made in 1940 to have the basic design modified into that of an all-metal fighter. However, Howard Hughes had other interests and, in any event, was not yet prepared to work within the guidelines of Army procurement procedures. Once again nothing materialized and the record-breaking aircraft remained in storage in California until 1975 when negotiations between the Hughes organization and the National Air and Space Museum were concluded. Howard Hughes paid to have the 1B Racer restored to pristine condition and shipped to Washington, DC, and the National Air and Space Museum put the aircraft on permanent display.

	Racer (speed record)	**Racer** (transcontinental flight)
Span, ft in	24 11	32 0
(m)	(7.59)	(9.75)
Length, ft in	27 0	27 8
(m)	(8.23)	(8.43)
Height, ft in	10 10	10 10
(m)	(3.30)	(3.30)
Wing area, sq ft	138	191
(sq m)	(12.82)	(17.74)
Empty weight, lb	3,565	4,097
(kg)	(1,617)	(1,858)
Loaded weight, lb	5,492	6,200
(kg)	(2,491)	(2,812)
Wing loading*, lb/sq ft	39.8	32.5
(kg/sq m)	(194.3)	(158.5)
Power loading*, lb/hp	5.5	6.2
(kg/hp)	(2.5)	(2.8)
Maximum speed, mph	352	330
(km/h)	(567)	(531)

* wing and power loadings are calculated at normal loaded weight and maximum take-off power.

Platt-LePage XR-1

Even though the XR-1 helicopter was not a product of McDonnell or Douglas or one of their subsidiaries, its history is included because it was designed and built by a short-lived company, the Platt-LePage Aircraft Company of Eddystone, Pennsylvania, in which McDonnell Aircraft had acquired a significant interest by purchasing in June 1944—38.74 per cent of the outstanding shares and 73.6 per cent of the notes issued by the company—when the XR-1 and XR-1A were still being tested. Furthermore, its investment in Platt-LePage contributed markedly to McDonnell's long and unsuccessful, until the acquisition of Hughes Helicopters, venture in the field of helicopters.

The XR-1 during hover trials at Eddystone, Pennsylvania. *(WADC/National Archives)*

Impressed by the five world's records set with the Focke Achgelis Fa 61 helicopter[1] (including a 109-km/68-mile, distance record set by the noted aviatrix Hanna Reitsch when she flew from Bremen to Berlin on 25 October, 1937), a Pennsylvania industrialist, W Laurence LePage, acquired the manufacturing rights for this experimental German helicopter in early 1938. Upon his return to the United States, LePage immediately attempted to gain the attention of the Army. After showing a film of a demonstration by Hanna Reisch in the Deutschlandhalle in Berlin to Maj Gen Oscar Westover, LePage was advised by the Chief of the Air Corps to secure the aid of the Materiel Division in the development of this machine. To that end, LePage made a presentation to the Engineering Section at Wright Field, Ohio, on 27 April. His timing

[1] Designed by Professor Heinrich Karl Johann Focke and powered by a 160 hp Bramo Sh 14A radial engine mounted in the nose, the Fa 61 had three-bladed rotors mounted on each side of the fuselage at the end of tubular fittings. Two prototypes were built and the first free flight was made on 26 June, 1936.

proved fortunate as on 30 June, 1938, Congress passed the Dorsey Bill[2] which appropriated the sum of $2,000,000 to enable the Air Corps to initiate a development programme for rotary wing aircraft.

Encouraged by the initial response from the Air Corps, LePage formed the Platt-LePage Aircraft Co, with Haviland H Platt as the principal stockholder, and proceeded to design the PL-3 helicopter inspired by the Fa 61. Preliminary specifications were prepared by February 1939 and in September of that year, when design work was at the threequarters mark and construction of a PL-3 prototype was at the one-fifth stage, Platt-LePage offered to complete the prototype for the Air Corps at a cost of $150,000. However, the Air Corps could not consider procuring the PL-3 on a single-source basis as it was already preparing to issue characteristics and specifications for experimental rotary wing aircraft. Draft Specification XC-147, which was issued on 10 June, 1939, and approved in final form on 25 August, called for aircraft designed to meet no specific requirement but susceptible to be modified to meet military and other federal requirements. A design useful load of 1,200 lb (544 kg) and a rate of climb of at least 1,000 ft/min (5 m/sec) were listed. Circular Proposal No 40-620 incorporating this specification was published in the autumn of 1939 and a design competition was opened on 15 April, 1940.

Several companies submitted bids but only four were considered appropriate, Vought-Sikorsky and Platt-LePage proposing helicopters and Kellett and Pitcairn submitting autogiros, and were evaluated by a special Engineering Evaluation Board which submitted its report on 28 May, 1940. Three weeks later, the Assistant Secretary of War granted authority to the Materiel division to negotiate a contract with Platt-LePage as recommended by the Board. Contract AC15375, which initiated the development of the Army's first helicopter, was signed on 19 July, 1940. It called for Platt-LePage to design, build, and test one XR-1 helicopter and one static test airframe for $199,075. The company immediately started the redesign of the PL-3 to meet military requirements. Delivery of the flying prototype was scheduled for January 1941.

Assigned the serial 41-1, the XR-1 was completed three months behind schedule. It was powered by a fuselage-mounted 440 hp Pratt & Whitney R-985-21 radial engine which drove two contra-rotating, three-blade rotors of 38 ft 5 in (11.71 m) diameter mounted at the tips of faired pylons extending from each side of the fuselage. Of mixed construction with fabric covering, this helicopter had conventional tail surfaces with braced tailplane mounted high on the fin and a non-retractable undercarriage. The crew of two sat in tandem under a long canopy and was provided with good visibility forward and immediately below through an extended

2 Not so coincidentally, Frank J G Dorsey was a Representative from Pennsylvania, a state in which were located four of the leading US manufacturers of rotary wing aircraft, Convertoplane Development Corp, Kellett Autogiro Corp, Pennsylvania Syndicate Inc, and Pitcairn Autogiro Co.

lower fuselage glazed area. All control as well as translational flight was obtained through a combination of collective and cyclic rotor blade pitch.

The XR-1 made its first restrained flight on 12 May, 1941, at Eddystone and its first free flight on 23 June when it reached a height of not more than three feet and remained airborne not more than 30 seconds. During the next six weeks flights of 15-minute duration at an altitude of 15 feet (4.6 m) were made regularly in spite of numerous teething problems, the worst of which was inadequate control. Improved control was obtained by changing leverage ratio and later by differential collective pitch change, but resonant oscillations caused objectionable reactions in control. More changes followed, but by June 1942 Materiel Command still reported considerable difficulty in overcoming vibration and poor overall control. Additional modifications were made but progress was impaired by inadequate Platt-LePage financing (notwithstanding Contract Change Orders providing for additional funding by the AAF), lack of skilled personnel, and an unscientific approach to solving the troubles in the XR-1.

The XR-1 was tested at Wright Field by the Rotary Branch of the Air Technical Service Command beginning in May 1943 but was damaged on 4 July due to the failure of a rotor blade spinner. More problems were revealed during static tests as tail surfaces failed when up load reached between 140 and 150 per cent of the design figure. Damage was repaired and the tail surfaces were strengthened before trials resumed in the summer of 1944, but lateral and longitudinal control remained insufficient. As in the meantime the Sikorsky R-4 had succesfully completed its tests and entered service with the Army Air Forces, action was initiated on 7 April, 1945, to cancel all contracts with Platt-LePage. Shortly after, the XR-1 was bailed to the manufacturer for additional trials and possible development as a civil design. The last flight was made on 21 June, 1946, and after being flown for a total of 91 hr 45 min this historic machine was donated to the Smithsonian Institution. It is now part of the collection of the National Air and Space Museum in Washington.

Platt-LePage had submitted a proposal for the construction of a modified helicopter on 26 April, 1941, and this XR-1A (serial 42-6581) was ordered on 29 October, 1941, under Contract AC4609. It was characterized by revised rotor hubs with fairing around the drive system; enlarged and strengthened tail surfaces; a full Plexiglass nose covering which replaced the 'bird cage' nose and canopy of the XR-1; and the relocation of the pilot from the front to the rear seat. Powered by a 450 hp Pratt & Whitney R-985-AN-1, the XR-1A was first flown at Eddystone on 27 May, 1943, and found to be smoother to fly than the XR-1. However, it still lacked adequate control and possessed surprising and unpredictable characteristics when it was delivered to Wright Field in June 1944. The XR-1A was damaged in an accident on 26 October, 1944, due to the failure of a pinion bearing support in the starboard rotor hub, and was shipped back to Platt-LePage. Declared surplus at the end of the war

50

before completion of repairs, the XR-1A was acquired by Helicopter Air Transport Co (HAT) of Camden, New Jersey, which repaired, over-hauled, and modified it for commercial use. In 1946 it received the experimental civil registration NX6950 but its subsequent fate is unknown.

The much modified XR-1A which was tested by the USAAF until 1946. *(Air Force Museum)*

In January 1944, motivated in part by its desire to avoid further criticism from members of Congress who claimed that Sikorsky had received preferential treatment, the Army Air Forces gave a Letter Contract to Platt-LePage for seven YR-1A helicopters which, essentially similar to the XR-1A, were intended for service test. The formal contract was approved in October 1944 and the first YR-1A was to have been delivered in January 1945. However, no YR-1A had been completed when the contract was terminated in April 1945. The Platt-LePage Aircraft Co did not survive for long the cancellation of XR-1 and YR-1A contracts and was wound up in 1946.

Rotor diameter 38 ft 5 in (11.71 m); length 29 ft 4 in (8.94 m).
Loaded weight 4,730 lb (2,145 kg) XR-1 and 5,300 lb (2,404 kg) XR-1A; rotor loading 4.1 lb/sq ft (19.9 kg/sq m) XR-1 and 4.6 lb/sq ft (22.3 kg/sq m) XR-1A; power loading 10.8 lb/hp (4.9 kg/hp) XR-1 and 11.8 lb/hp (5.3 kg/hp) XR-1A.
Maximum speed 110 mph (177 km/h) XR-1 and 100 mph (161 mp/h) XR-1A.

Hughes D-2

As Howard Hughes apparently did not authorize the release of information on the D-2 and as company records pertaining to this twin-engined aircraft were either destroyed or sealed in the archives of Summa Corporation, the initial development history of this aircraft has long remained shrouded in mystery. Fortunately, repeated attempts to sell the D-2 or derivatives thereof to the Army Air Corps/Army Air Forces resulted in records of the subsequent history of this aircraft being kept by the AAF.

The first evidence of the existence of this project is contained in a letter dated 5 December, 1939, and addressed to the Chief, Materiel Division, in which Howard Hughes offered to enter into a contract with the Air Corps. For a consideration of $50.00 and co-operation from the Air Corps in furnishing installation drawings and data necessary for construction of a military aircraft, Hughes Aircraft Company would submit a report on the performance of a 'pursuit type airplane' then under construction, together with a report on estimated performance after incorporation of changes required to meet military specifications.

Before recounting the response of the Air Corps to this unsolicited proposal and the protracted negotiations which ensued, it is appropriate to attempt to foresee likely events leading to the submission of a proposal

Howard Hughes inspecting the port engine installation of the D-2 on 7 April, 1943. The three executives on the left are Glenn Oderick, Stanley Bell, and Kenneth Riley. *(Summa Corporation)*

by the upstart aircraft manufacturer. As told in the corporate history chapter, by the mid-thirties Howard Hughes had become an avid aviation enthusiast and, flying his 1B Racer, had set a landplane speed record in September 1935 and a US transcontinental record in January 1937. In addition, sometime in 1936 he became attracted by the idea of setting a round-the-world record and acquired the sole Douglas DC-1 and a Sikorsky S-43-W for possible use in a globe-circling flight. In the end he decided to use a faster Lockheed 14-N2 and with this twin-engined transport set a new record of 91 hr 14 min (elapsed time) and 71 hr 11 min (flying time) in July 1938. Remarkable as this record was, Howard Hughes felt that it could be easily surpassed with a purpose-built aircraft.

Although lacking documentary evidence, the author believes that Dick Palmer, the designer of the 1B Racer, had begun preliminary design for such an aircraft before severing his association with Hughes to become chief engineer with Vultee Aircraft Inc in early 1938. After his round-the-world record flight, Howard Hughes is believed to have had a small team led by Stanley A Bell resume work on the project to obtain an aircraft capable of surpassing by a good margin the time set with the Lockheed 14-N2 and not, as later claimed during negotiations with the Army Air Corps, to develop a 'pursuit type airplane.' From the onset, the design team is thought to have spared no effort to minimize drag, selecting a twin boom and small fuselage configuration[1] and deciding to use Duramold plywood (plastic bonded plywood moulded under heat and pressure) for most of the airframe. It would also appear that accommodation was initially to be provided for a crew of five (as in the Lockheed 14-N2) and that a conventional retractable undercarriage gear was to be fitted (later changed to a nosewheel design).

Violent military and economic changes occurred a few months after work on the D-2 began. In Europe, war had started in September 1939 and in the United States the supply of aircraft engines and specialized aviation equipment were increasingly subjected to government intervention. For Howard Hughes this meant that attempting a round-the-world flight would be impossible in the short term unless a longer routing via Africa and the South Atlantic was chosen and that critical parts and equipment needed to complete the D-2 would be difficult to obtain without government approval. Thus, as pointedly noted later in a memorandum signed by the Chief, Engineering Division, Materiel

[1] According to one of the many legends surrounding Howard Hughes and his early aviation activities, he would later express much displeasure because 'Lockheed had copied the D-2 design and been rewarded with the P-38 contract. Howard Hughes was too intelligent to have made such a claim seriously. He undoubtedly knew that the XP-38 proposal had been submitted to the Army Air Corps in April 1937 before preliminary design on the D-2 had been started. Conversely, it is likely that Hughes was aware that the D-2 configuration bore a striking resemblance to that of the similarly-sized Fokker G.I which had been shown at the 1936 Salon de l'Aéronautique in Paris and had first flown on 16 March, 1937.

Command, Hughes was apparently hoping to benefit in two ways from his offer to sell drawings and engineering data to the Air Corps for a nominal amount. First, he hoped to be allowed to purchase the powerful Wright Tornado engines which had been selected to power the D-2 and, second, he opened an opportunity for his company to sell the D-2 if or when he no longer could use it as originally planned. Initially it appeared that Hughes would achieve the first objective of his manoeuvre as in 1940 the Air Corps informed him that there was no objection to his purchase of two Tornado forty-two-cylinder engines. However, in November 1940 when

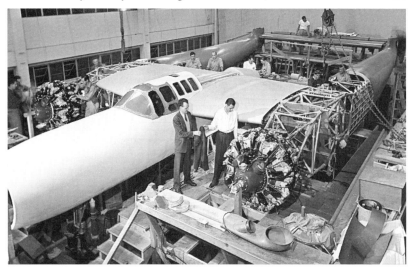

Howard Hughes and Glenn Oderick standing by the port Pratt & Whitney R-2800 engine of the D-2. The smooth finish made possible by the use of Duramold is noteworthy. *(Summa Corporation)*

Pratt & Whitney was forced to terminate the development of its XH-2600 engine (two of which were to have powered the Lockheed XP-58), the Air Forces diverted the Tornado engines to Lockheed, and Hughes was left without engines for the D-2 until the Materiel Command made arrangements to supply three Pratt & Whitney R-2800-49s. These three engines, two for installation in the D-2 and one to be used as a spare, were shipped to Hughes in March 1942.

In answer to the Hughes proposal, the Materiel Division requested a complete description and model number of the aircraft and approximate delivery date of the engineering reports before preparing a contract. Even though such information was not provided fully, a Purchase Order in the amount of $50 was forwarded to Hughes Aircraft Company on 22 May, 1940. By then, the reports to be submitted no longer applied to a 'pursuit type airplane' but were for the 'Hughes Duramold Bombardment airplane.' This was but the first of several changes in the type of military missions for which the D-2 was proposed. By May 1941, the aircraft was considered suited for 'bomber convoy and protection.' Thirteen months later, on 30 June, 1942, specifications termed it a fighter and the AAF 'considered it advisable to call it XP-73 for purpose of administrating the contract.' However, two days later the proposed military derivative of the D-2 (which may have been given the company designation of D-3) was reclassified as an attack aircraft and designated XA-37 by the Army Air Forces. These tergiversations would tend to lend

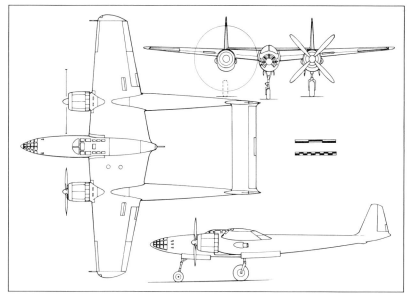

Hughes XA-37

credence to the contention that the D-2 had not been designed as a military aircraft and hence could not meet well defined mission requirements. Notably, it quickly became apparent that its ability to carry bombs internally was insufficient to make it into a satisfactory attack or light bomber and that its poor manoeuvrability rendered it unsatisfactory as a fighter.

While the search for a mission was going on, negotiations between Hughes and the Army Air Forces proved equally frustrating with Hughes's alternating between periods during which he pushed for a quick decision by the AAF and others during which he ignored AAF requests. In the end, Howard Hughes quite abruptly changed his mind and, after pressuring the Goverment to purchase the D-2, decided to retain it pending completion of initial trials.

Except for the Engineering Division at Wright Field which initially expressed some curiosity in the method of Duramold construction used for the D-2 but soon recommended against plywood structures for high performance aircraft, the aircraft never appeared to have been considered seriously by operating commands of the Army Air Forces. In particular, as the D-2 had not been designed to military specifications, Materiel Command had little use for it and favoured the similarly sized and configured Lockheed XP-58 which was of all-metal construction and complied with these specifications. Thus, the initial request by Hughes's representatives that the AAF commit itself to purchasing the D-2 if the aircraft could be modified to meet specifications was rejected outright in October 1941. Moreover, possibly displeased by the industrialist's insistence that his project be kept secret and that specific officers be designated for liaison with the Hughes Aircraft Company, Materiel Command also recommended in January 1942 that the Air Corps discontinue further aircraft projects with Hughes. Apparently, however, Howard Hughes had friends in high places.

On 16 June, 1942, Lieut-Gen H H Arnold, Commanding General, US Army Air Forces, instructed personnel at Wright Field to procure the private venture D-2 as a prototype for possible future bomber development. Moreover, after a telephone conversation with Howard Hughes, Gen Arnold felt compelled on 17 July, 1942, to inform President Roosevelt that an agreement had been reached whereby the AAF would absorb the D-2 development costs if it was sufficiently interested in the aircraft after inspection and testing; conversely, Hughes had accepted to take the loss if the aircraft failed to interest the AAF. Notwithstanding high level interest, this agreement became void less than two weeks later when suddenly Howard Hughes informed the AAF that he no longer wished to sell the aircraft before flying it himself. Accordingly, the proposed procurement of the D-2 became a 'Hold Project' requiring no further action from Materiel Command.

Components for the D-2 were built by Hughes in its Culver City plant located in the western outskirts of Los Angeles and final assembly was undertaken far from prying eyes at Harper Dry Lake, a site in the Mojave Desert which was even more remote than the AAF facility at Muroc Dry Lake. Built mostly of wood and powered by two 2,000 hp Pratt & Whitney R-2800-49 radial engines driving three-blade propellers, the D-2 (also referred to as the DX-2 and XD-2 in AAF documents) was of twin boom configuration with a narrow fuselage mounted centrally and was fitted with a hydraulically-operated nosewheel undercarriage with the main and nose units retracting to the rear and the nosewheel turning 90° to lie flat in the small fuselage. Also noteworthy, as it represented one of the earliest examples of the use of such devices, was the installation of a hydraulic control surface boost mechanism acting on the elevators, rudders, and ailerons.

Although the Hughes Aircraft Company had apparently designed its own installation of two turbosuperchargers per engine and had planned to install a pressurization system for the cabin which had accommodation for a crew of two or three, neither were installed before the start of ground trials at Harper Dry Lake. When these began in the spring of 1943 it almost immediately became necessary to postpone flight tests as control was found insufficient when the boost system was inoperative and as there was an excessive amount of friction in the control systems. Moreover, high speed taxi-ing tests, during which Howard Hughes lifted the D-2 off the ground on some 30 occasions, revealed that small aileron deflections resulted in a sudden reversal of force and aileron instability. Accordingly, new ailerons of 40 per cent greater chord were installed, thus increasing wing area from 600 to 616 sq ft (55.74 to 57.23 sq m), before flight trials could begin.

After installation of the new ailerons, the D-2 was at last considered ready to fly. On 20 June, 1943, Howard Hughes took it up twice, once for 15 minutes and then, after minor control adjustments, for another 35 minutes. During these two flights Hughes noticed high aileron control forces and a considerable tendency for the D-2 to roll with power on and undercarriage retracted. To correct these deficiencies, the wingtips were extended (increasing wing area to 634 sq ft/58.9 sq m and aspect ratio from 6 to 6.3), the ailerons were extended into the new tips but shortened inboard to remove them from the slipstream, and outboard flaps were provided in place of the removed aileron sections. Subsequent flights, which brought total flying time to over nine hours, were not more encouraging and Hughes was forced to consider major modifications including a complete redesign of the laminar-flow wings involving notably a switch from the NACA 16-1 aerofoil series to the NACA 66-2 series and increases in area to 775 sq ft/72 sq m and aspect ratio to 7.5. Furthermore, the structure of the wing centre section, which was continuous through the fuselage nacelle, was to be revised to double the size of the proposed bomb bay. Following incorporation of the planned changes the aircraft was to be designated D-5.

General Arnold once again intervened by stating on 27 June, 1943, that the lack of de Havilland Mosquito night fighters and reconnaissance aircraft might necessitate resorting to the Hughes design to fill these needs and by requesting two days later that the D-2 be flown to Bolling Field, DC, for inspection. Hughes could not comply with this request as the D-2 was being modified and was unsafe for a cross country flight. Nevertheless, he confidently submitted specifications, production schedules, and facility requirements for three versions of the D-5: (1) a two-seat unarmed reconnaissance aircraft with a top speed of 488 mph at 30,000 ft (785 km/h at 9,145 m) and a 3,600-mile (5,790-km) range; (2) a three-seat light bomber fitted with four 0.50-in guns in a remotely controlled turret at the rear of the central nacelle and a bomb load of 4,000 lb (1,814 kg); and (3) a two-seat escort fighter with the same gun turret and six forward-firing 20-mm cannon. Unimpressed, Materiel Command recommended against encouraging further development of the D-2/D-5 and on 13 August, 1943, advised that no further action was to be taken with the Hughes Company. These recommendations were approved by the Chief of Air Staff on 21 August. Were it not for further high level intervention, development of the Hughes twin-engined aircraft would have ended then. However, as detailed in the XF-11 chapter, it was given a new lease on life almost immediately.

Before the D-2 could be brought to the proposed D-5 configuration, it was lost in a mysterious fire in November 1944 when a lightning bolt—a most unusual occurrence at that time of the year in the desert—struck the wooden hangar in which it was kept at Harper Dry Lake. By then, however, the loss was of no importance as the XF-11, the derivative of the D-2/D-5 which Hughes had finally succeeded in having the AAF order as a long range, high speed reconnaissance aircraft, had evolved into a new and larger design of metal construction which only retained the basic twin-boom/central fuselage nacelle configuration of its wooden forebear.

D-2 characteristics and estimated performance
(as communicated by Howard Hughes to Capt Charles R Hawks, the AAF officer representing the Materiel Command, Western Procurement District, and recorded in an AAF confidential memorandum dated 3 July, 1943):

Span 60 ft (18.29 m); wing area 616 sq ft (57.23 sq m).
Loaded weight 31,672 lb (14,366 kg); wing loading 51.4 lb/sq ft (251.0 kg/sq m); power loading 7.9 lb/hp (3.6 kg/hp).
Maximum speed 433 mph at 25,000 ft (697 km/h at 7,620 m); cruising speed 274 mph (441 km/h); initial climb rate 2,620 ft/min (13 m/sec); service ceiling 36,000 ft (10,975 ft); range 1,000 miles (1,610 km) with 2,200 lb (998 kg) load.

McDonnell XP-67

The McDonnell Aircraft Corporation, following its incorporation in July 1939, assembled a small team of engineers which began work in September. Soon after, James McDonnell approached the Army Air Corps concerning the possibility of obtaining a contract for fighter aircraft and submitted proposals to the Materiel Division. Although none of these proposals matched current Air Corps requirements, McDonnell Aircraft's efforts were rewarded by its inclusion on the list of manufacturers invited to submit proposals in response to the Request for Data R-40C which was issued in March 1940. The McDonnell Model I

View of the XP-67 showing to good advantage the aircraft's unusual planform.
(WADC/National Archives)

proposal, which called for the development of a fighter to be powered by an Allison V-3420-B2 or Pratt & Whitney H-3130 mounted in the fuselage aft of the pilot and driving two pusher propellers by means of extension shafts and angled gear drive, failed to win this competition. It was, however, of sufficient interest for the Air Corps to purchase relevant data under a $3,000 Purchase Order dated 6 June, 1940. The fledgling McDonneli Aircraft Corporation had made its first sale to the Army Air Corps.

Encouraged by this modest accomplishment, the company continued its efforts and later in the same month submitted an unsolicited proposal for its Model II fighter with Continental I-1430 engines in a conventional

59

twin-engined arrangement and provision for a crew of two. Once again, the company was unsuccessful. However, during subsequent discussions between its staff and personnel from the Materiel Division, the design was revised and on 5 May, 1941, a proposal for the Model S-23-A was formally submitted. This time, McDonnell's perseverance was rewarded and on 2 August, 1941, the Chief of the AAF Experimental Engineering Section initiated an Authority to Purchase for two prototypes and associated data. Contract W535-AC-21218 for these two experimental aircraft was approved on 29 October, 1941.

Designated XP-67 by the Army Air Forces, the new single-seat long-range fighter was to be fitted with a pressurized cabin and was planned to carry an unusually heavy armament consisting of six 0.50-in machine-guns and four 20-mm cannon. This later specification was changed during detailed design to six 37-mm cannon with 45 rpg in the inboard wing sections. Comparative tests of a 75-mm gun installation were requested by the AAF but, in the event, no armament was ever fitted to the sole prototype to fly.

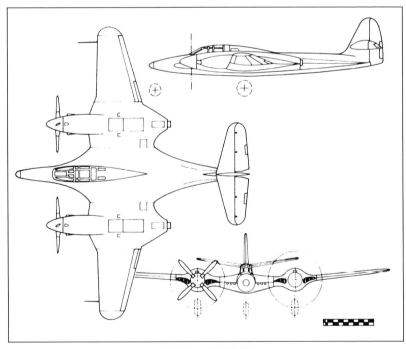

McDonnell XP-67.

The XP-67 mock-up, which was inspected between 15 and 17 April, 1942, revealed the aircraft's unique bat-like appearance[1] which stemmed

[1] Hence the nickname 'The Bat' later bestowed on the first McDonnell fighter.

from an attempt to maintain true aerofoil sections through most of the airframe by merging the centre fuselage and the rear portions of the engine nacelles. Power was to be provided by two Continental XI-1430 turbosupercharged twelve-cylinder inverted-vee liquid-cooled engines which were to be housed in long nacelles, to drive four-blade propellers rotating in opposite directions, and to use the exhaust for added thrust. With the XI-1430-17/19 engines as installed in the prototype and developing 1,350 hp for take-off and 1,600 hp at 25,000 ft (7,620 m) under military conditions, top speed was optimistically predicted to be 472 mph (759 km/h) at 25,000 ft.

Completed in early December 1943 but not fitted with either the intended cabin pressurisation equipment, oxygen system, or armament, the first XP-67 (serial 42-11677) had conventional ailerons instead of the planned drooping ailerons. It was slightly damaged during high-speed taxi-ing tests at Lambert Field, St Louis, on 8 December but, after being repaired, was trucked to Scott Field, Illinois, to be readied for its first flight on 6 January, 1944. The maiden flight, with E E Elliott at the controls, was of six minutes' duration and consisted of a quick circuit of the field and an emergency landing due to powerplant difficulties. The damaged turbo compartments were repaired and the second and third flights were accomplished without major incident. However, on the fourth flight on 1 February, 1944, the engines were unintentionally oversped and the bearings burned out. The XP-67 was then returned to St Louis where, while awaiting replacement engines, McDonnell reworked the ducts to improve cooling and raised the horizontal tail surfaces 12 inches (30.5 cm) to improve longitudinal stability characteristics. There followed a period of manufacturer's flight testing before the first flights made by AAF pilots on 11 May, 1944. The major difficulties which were encountered and corrected or improved during this period were

The XP-67, the first McDonnell aircraft ordered by the US Armed Forces.
(USAF)

engine roughness, improper aileron balance, and unsatisfactory main undercarriage door closure. After tailplane dihedral was increased from 5° to 7° and a small dorsal fin added, handling characteristics were found satisfactory. The powerplant installation, however, remained a source of numerous difficulties and on 6 September, 1944, the first prototype was damaged beyond economic repair when fire started in the right nacelle and forced an emergency landing. E E Elliott safely landed the XP-67, but wind blew the flames over the fuselage and caused major damage. At the time of the accident, 42-11677 had accumulated a total of 43 hours in the air and 42-11678, construction of which had been held in abeyance until flight performance had been obtained on the first prototype, was approximately 15 per cent completed. McDonnell and AAF representatives agreed on 13 September, 1944, that the contract should be terminated and a formal termination notice was issued six weeks later.

Before and during the flight trial programme, various plans had been devised to improve performance. For the second prototype and the first production variant, these proposals included the relatively simple substitution of contra-rotating propellers for the handed propellers as fitted on the first aircraft and the use of I-1430 engines with ratings increased to 2,100 hp under war emergency conditions. The use of a mixed powerplant arrangement, with the front of each nacelle housing either a Packard V-1650 or Allison V-1710 inline engine with two-speed supercharger and the aft portion being occupied by an I-20 turbojet, was proposed for later production models. Nothing came of these plans as before the advent of jet fighters the AAF requirement for long range fighters was expected to be satisfied initially by Republic P-47Ns and North American P-51Hs, prototypes of which had flown in July 1944 and February 1945, and later by the more promising North American P-82.

Span 55 ft (16.76 m); length 44 ft 9^1/$_4$ in (13.65 m); height 15 ft 9 in (4.80 m); wing area 414 sq ft (38.46 sq m).
Empty weight 17,745 lb (8,049 kg); loaded weight 23,114 lb (10,031 kg); maximum weight 25,400 lb (11,521 kg); wing loading 53.4 lb/sq ft (260.8 kg/sq m); power loading 8.2 lb/hp (3.7 kg/hp).
Maximum speed 405 mph at 25,000 ft (652 km/h at 7,620 m); cruising speed 270 mph (435 km/h); rate of climb 2,600 ft/min (13.m/sec); service ceiling 37,400 ft (11,400 m); maximum range 2,384 miles (3,835 km).

FH-1 of VMF-122 off Cherry Point, North Carolina, in 1948. *(USMC)*

McDonnell FH-1 Phantom

In 1942, when the Bureau of Aeronautics became seriously interested in jet propulsion and began searching for a manufacturer to design and build the Navy's first carrier jet fighter, all traditional suppliers of naval aircraft were fully engaged in designing new or improved combat aircraft and their manufacturing facilities were in full production. Consequently, to design its new jet aircraft the Navy was forced to select the young McDonnell Aircraft Corporation which, although inexperienced, had a capable and inventive engineering team and adequate manufacturing facilities. Moreover, the Navy derived confidence from its knowledge of McDonnell-funded jet fighter studies. Thus, the development of the first McDonnell aircraft to bear the name Phantom is a classic example of being in the right place at the right time.

Having received an attractive proposal from McDonnell in January 1943, BuAer, prompted by the pressure of war, bypassed the more conservative approach of first ordering a jet-powered research aircraft and on 7 January issued Letter of Intent NOa(s)-161 to McDonnell Aircraft, instructing the manufacturer to proceed with the design of a jet fighter and the manufacture of two XFD-1 prototypes (BuNos 48235 and 48236) and a static test airframe. The aircraft's intended role was defensive combat patrol, operating from a carrier, and flying at 15,000 ft (4,570 m) over or near the carrier. Speed, range, and armament, however, were not specified.

In designing the XFD-1, the engineering team led by Kendall Perkins decided at an early stage that two fundamental design policies were to be followed throughout. First, the aircraft was to be designed on a conservative basis in every respect, except for the engines and other special features dictated by their use. Second, design simplicity was to be emphasized to ease production and maintenance, and to minimize weight. These considerations led to the adoption of conventional wing and tail surfaces, with marked dihedral on the tailplane to keep it out of

63

the jet efflux, and of a short and sturdy nosewheel undercarriage to keep the hot jet exhaust off the wooden deck as then used on most USN carriers. Furthermore, the armament and cockpit were to be sited in the forward fuselage. Whilst these design features presented no particular problems, the powerplant installation constituted a challenge as engines had to be selected from 'paper' designs proposed by Westinghouse[1].

The initial design employed six wing-mounted engines of 9.5-in (24.1-cm) diameter providing a static thrust of 275 to 340 lb (125 to 154 kg) each and a wing area of 187 sq ft (17.37 sq m); performance calculations, however, indicated that this aircraft would only have marginal take-off, climb, and wave-off performance. The next step was to compare arrangements using six, eight, or ten of these engines and a larger wing with an area of 230 sq ft (21.37 sq m). Following this exercise, a

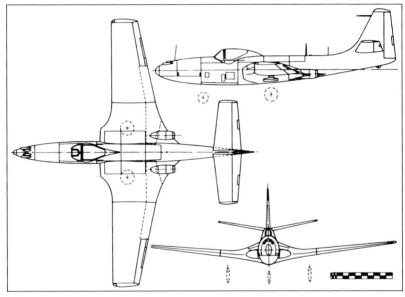

McDonnell FH-1 Phantom.

comparison was made between designs having eight engines of 9.5-in (24.1-cm) diameter, six engines of 11-in (27.9-cm) diameter, four engines of 13.5-in (34.3-cm) diameter, or two engines of 19-in (48.3-cm) diameter. The twin-engined configuration was found to be superior as it resulted in a lighter aircraft, simpler control and instrumentation problems, and easier manufacture of folding wings. Accordingly, further

---

[1] Westinghouse Electric Corporation had received a Navy study contract for a jet engine in December 1941 and a contract for the manufacture of prototype engines in October 1942. The Westinghouse X19A first ran in March 1943 and successfully passed its 100-hour endurance test on 10 July, 1943.

studies were limited to this configuration and design work proceeded to define the best engine location. After considering engines in wing nacelles or in the fuselage, it was decided to install the two engines in the wing root fillets as this location freed the centre fuselage for the large fuel tanks required if the aircraft was to have sufficient endurance in spite of the high fuel consumption of these early turbojets. Moreover, this location resulted in short inlets and tail-pipes and would thus minimize thrust loss.

Mock-up inspection took place between 31 May and 3 June, 1943, and the finalized Contract NOa(s)-161 was signed on 30 August. The design, however, was not fully defined until early 1944, and initial structural release, marking the start of construction, did not occur until 25 January 1944. Thereafter progress of the XFD-1 was rapid, but development of its intended powerplant, the Westinghouse WE-19XB-2B turbojet, had fallen behind to such an extent that by October 1944 only one engine had arrived at McDonnell. Until 4 January, 1945, when the second WE-19XB-2B was delivered, McDonnell was forced to conduct XFD-1 taxi-ing tests on the power of only one turbojet. Even though only 1,165 lb (528 kg) of thrust was available, a short hop over the runway was made

With the completion of the XFD-1, McDonnell began a long association with the US Navy as the prime supplier of carrier-borne jet fighters. *(MCAIR)*

on 2 January, 1945. Finally, following installation of a second turbojet, trials began at Lambert Field, St Louis, on 26 January when test pilot Woodward Burke made two flights, totalling 49 minutes.

Teething troubles with the novel powerplant resulted in a slow-paced programme as flight tests had to be suspended for over a month after one of the turbojets suffered a bearing failure. Thus, by April 1945, the first XFD-1 had only made nine flights for a total of 5 hours in the air. With the exception of another engine failure, which this time was attributed to ingestion of foreign materials, contractor's preliminary evaluation was encouraging as the only unsatisfactory characteristics (excessive aileron system friction, slight directional oscillation at high speed, and deterioration of stick-free longitudinal stability at high speed) were considered easy to correct.

In a first attempt at correcting the directional instability encountered at high speed, the incidence of the stabilizer was changed before completion of the second XFD-1 in June 1945, while more extensive changes were incorporated in the first XFD-1. However, BuNo 48236 was damaged in a belly landing on 24 August 1945, and Woodward Burke was killed in the crash of BuNo 48235 on 1 November, 1945, as the result of an aileron failure. Nevertheless, development of the Navy's first pure jet proceeded and on 19 July, 1946, during trials aboard the uss *Franklin D. Roosevelt* (CVB-42), Lieut Cdr James Davidson made the first carrier take-off and landing by a US jet aircraft.

BuNo 111756, the eighth FD-1, at the Naval Air Test Center. *(Hal Andrews)*

Phantom production had been initiated before these accidents as Contract NOa(s)-6242 for 100 FD-1s (BuNos 111749/111848) had been issued on 7 March, 1945. Due to post V-J Day cutbacks, however, the production contract was first reduced from 100 to 30 aircraft and plans for an FD-1N night fighter variant were dropped. Later, production of the day fighter variant was boosted back to 60 aircraft to provide enough Phantoms for test activities, service evaluation, and two operational squadrons. Most of these 60 aircraft were delivered under the FH-1 designation after McDonnell was awarded the constructor's letter H to avoid confusion with Douglas which was again using the letter D in naval fighter designations following the award of a contract for three XF3D-1s night fighters on 3 April, 1946.

Powered by two 1,600 lb (726 kg) thrust Westinghouse J30-WE-20s (the production version of the WE-19XB-2B turbojets) and armed with four 0.50-in machine guns in the upper nose decking, the FH-1 differed from the XFD-1 in having a slightly longer fuselage, square-tipped vertical tail surfaces of increased area, and more fuel capacity. Internal

BuNo 111760, the second FD-1, at the Naval Air Test Center. *(Hal Andrews)*

capacity was increased from 260 to 375 US gallons (984 to 1,420 litres) and provision was made for one flush-fitting 190- or 295-gallon (719- or 1,117-litre) ventral tank.

Service history

Delayed by the non-availability of engines, the first FH-1 (BuNo 111749) was first flown on 28 October, 1946, and was delivered in January 1947; the last Phantom (BuNo 111808) was accepted by the Navy on 29 May, 1948. Phantoms were first assigned to VF-17A at NAS Quonset Point, Rhode Island, beginning in July 1947. Ten months later, on 5 May, 1948, the pilots of this Atlantic Fleet squadron completed their carrier qualifications aboard the uss *Saipan* (CVL-48); VF-17A (renumbered VF-171 in August 1948) thus became the first operational shipboard jet

An FH-1 Phantom of VF-17A during the unit's carrier qualifications aboard the uss *Saipan* (CVL-48) in May 1948. *(NA&SM)*

fighter squadron in the world. A few FH-1s also went to VF-1L (soon redesignated as part of VX-3) at NAS Atlantic City, New Jersey, and to VF-172 at NAS Jacksonville, Florida. Phantoms also became the first jets assigned to the Marine Corps and equipped VMF-122 at MCAS Cherry Point, North Carolina, between November 1947 and July 1950.

With the Navy, the Phantom's career as a first-line aircraft ended in 1949 when F2H-1s were delivered to VF-171. Thereafter, FH-1s were distributed to Naval Reserve units around the country to be used until July 1953 for jet pilot indoctrination. Later, FH-1s were operated by three civil contractors. The Cornell Aeronautical Laboratory in Buffalo, New York, had one; the Teterboro School of Aviation in New Jersey had another which was registered N4282A in the late fifties; and Progressive Aero Inc, held title to three Phantoms (N4282A, N4283A, and the non-flyable ex-BuNo 111761) with which it offered a multi-engine jet rating school at the Hollywood-Fort Lauderdale International Airport in the mid-sixties. One of these historic aircraft (BuNo 111769, N4283A) has since been preserved in the Marine Corps Aviation Museum in Quantico, Virginia, and another has gone to the Naval Aviation Museum in Pensacola, Florida.

	XFD-1	FH-1
Span, ft in	40 9	40 9
(m)	(12.42)	(12.42)
Span (wings folded), ft in	16 3	16 3
(m)	(4.95)	(4.95)
Length, ft in	37 3	38 9
(m)	(11.35)	(11.81)
Height, ft in	14 2	14 2
(m)	(4.32)	(4.32)
Wing area, sq ft	276	276
(sq m)	(25.64)	(25.64)
Empty weight, lb	6,156	6,683
(kg)	(2,792)	(3,031)
Loaded weight, lb	8,625	10,035
(kg)	(3,913)	(4,552)
Maximum weight, lb	9,531	12,035
(kg)	(4,323)	(5,459)
Wing loading*, lb/sq ft	31.3	36.4
(kg/sq m)	(152.6)	(177.5)
Power loading*, lb/lb st	2.7	2.7
(kg/kgp)	(2.7)	(2.7)
Maximum speed, mph at sea level	487	479
(km/h at sl)	(784)	(771)
Cruising speed, mph	250	248
(km/h)	(402)	(399)
Climb rate, ft/min	4,960/1	4,230/1
(m/sec)	(25)	(21)
Service ceiling, ft	43,700	41,100
(m)	(13,320)	(12,525)
Normal range, miles	540	695
(km)	(870)	(1,115)
Maximum range, miles	750	980
(km)	(1,205)	(1,575)

* wing and power loadings are calculated at normal loaded weight and maximum take-off power.

McDonnell XHJD-1 Whirlaway

In seeking to find work for his fledgling company, James McDonnell was prepared to consider all logical alternatives and was willing to risk some capital to acquire know-how in new technology such as that required to develop rotary wing aircraft. To that end, he first made a small investment in the Platt-LePage Aircraft Company in mid-1942 and, a year later, he authorized Constantine M Zakhartchenko and a small group of engineers to undertake research on design and construction of rotors.

In return for his initial investment, McDonnell was allowed to have some of his engineers join the Platt-LePage design team to learn the techniques of helicopter engineering. Moreover, he was appraised of Platt-LePage's preliminary work on a twin-engined, twin-rotor helicopter to meet Army requirements. Although that design eventually proved

The XHJD-1 hovering near an FH-1 in front of McDonnell's plant at Lambert Field, St Louis. *(MCAIR)*

unsuccessful in the Army competition (the AAF selected the Kellet XR-10), it fared better in a different guise as McDonnell, in return for an increase in his investment as finalized in June 1944, obtained Platt-LePage's agreement allowing the McDonnell Aircraft Corporation to initiate the parallel development of the twin-engined, twin-rotor concept. On the strength of both this agreement and the work accomplished by Zakhartchenko's team, McDonnell proposed a helicopter of this design to the Navy to serve either as a testbed or as an anti-submarine warfare platform. As a testbed, the proposed Model 65 was intended to be used for the study of the effects of rotor diameter, disk loading, variations in rotor blade flap and lag angles, and other variables. In the ASW role, it was to be able to carry an adequate load of detection gear and weapons.

Considering the side-by-side rotor arrangement proposed by McDonnell to be a most suitable configuration for large helicopters capable of operating in the ASW role, the Bureau of Aeronautics issued a Letter of Intent on 15 May, 1944, covering the design, construction, and testing of one XHJD-1. This Letter of Intent was confirmed on 23 March, 1945, when Contract NOa(s)-3703 was awarded. At the time of contract award, design of the Whirlaway, entrusted to a team led by Constantine Zakhartchenko, was well underway and ground testing was begun early in 1946. Piloted by Charles R Wood Jr, the XHJD-1 made its first hover flight at Lambert Field, St Louis, on 27 April, 1946.

Designed to carry up to ten occupants but normally flown as a two-seater with up to 1,800 lb (816 kg) of test instrumentation, the Whirlaway was fitted with twin side-by-side rotors mounted on pylons extending

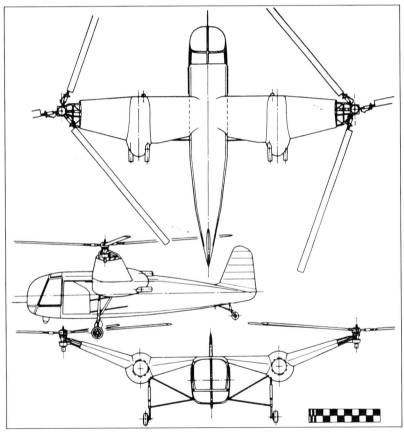

McDonnell XHJD-1 Whirlaway.

70

outboard of the engine nacelles. The nacelles, each housing a 450 hp Pratt & Whitney R-985-AN-14B seven-cylinder radial engine, were attached to short wings which supported approximately 10 per cent of the gross weight during cruise and as much as 30 per cent of the weight in power-off autorotation, with consequent substantial improvement in overall performance efficiency. Furthermore, this feature, combined with the ability to transmit power from either engine to both rotors by transmissions and gear boxes, enabled the XHJH-1 to maintain level flight at full gross weight on the power of only one engine.

From April 1946 until June 1951, the XHJD-1 was used for numerous flying research tests including the evaluation of performance, stability, balance and vibration characteristics peculiar to its twin-rotor configuration. In the process, the Whirlaway had its original 50-ft (15.24-m)

The XHJD-1 after addition of externally-braced horizontal tail surfaces. *(MCAIR)*

diameter rotors replaced by rotors of varying diameters and had a braced tailplane with externally balanced control surfaces added before translation flights began. Once vibration and resonance problems with its unsynchronized three-blade rotors were alleviated through the use of shock-absorbing rotor mounts, the XHJD-1 was considered to handle well and was flown some 250 hours without serious mishap. In the process, it was flown not only by McDonnell and Navy pilots but, after being fitted with a rescue winch, was also evaluated in November 1949 by

USAF pilots from the Arctic Rescue Helicopter Board. However, as helicopter technology had made significant progress since development of the Whirlaway had been initiated, neither the XHJD-1 nor its proposed Model 65C development was put into production. Upon completion of its trials programme, the XHJD-1—the first helicopter to bear the McDonnell name and the world's first successful twin-engined, twin-rotor helicopter—was donated to the National Air and Space Museum.

Rotor diameter 46 to 50 ft (14.02 to 15.24 m) depending on configuration; overall span 87 ft (26.52 m); fuselage length 32 ft 2 in (9.8 m); height 12 ft 3 in (3.73 m).

Empty weight 8,000 lb (3,629 kg); loaded weight 11,000 lb (4,990 kg); rotor loading 2.8 to 3.3 lb/sq ft (13.7 to 16.2 kg/sq m); power loading 12.2 lb/hp (5.5 kg/hp).

Maximum speed 120 mph at 5,000 ft (193 km/h at 1,525 m); cruising speed 90 mph (145 km/h); rate of climb 1,300 ft/min (6.6 m/sec); absolute ceiling 12,900 ft (3,930 m); range 300 miles (485 km).

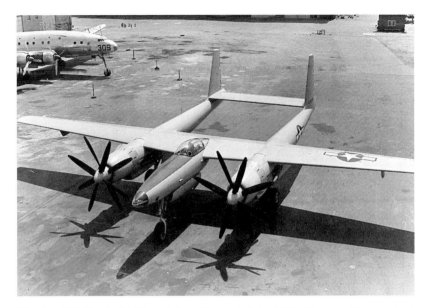

The first XF-11 (44-70155) at Culver City on 3 July, 1946. *(Summa Corporation)*

Hughes XF-11

Undeterred by the unsatisfactory results of initial trials with the D-2 and the Army Air Forces' initial rejection of the proposed D-5, Howard Hughes kept seeking a production contract for derivatives of his twin-engined aircraft. In so doing, his political connections proved helpful. In August 1943, Col Elliott Roosevelt[1] informed the Commanding General, Army Air Forces, that the Hughes D-5 was the only aircraft already designed which was suitable for photographic reconnaissance purposes. Accordingly, Gen Arnold issued a verbal directive to procure 100 D-5s. Col Roosevelt provided further support during a conference held on 8 October and attended by Jack Frye, as representative of Howard Hughes, and senior AAF officers, when he firmly stated that the 'procurement of 16 aircraft in 16 months would shorten the war by six to eight months.'

Notwithstanding sustained technical objections (with Wright Field personnel recommending the procurement of a reconnaissance version of the all-metal Lockheed XP-58 in preference to the Hughes aircraft of wooden construction), reservations regarding the adequacy of the

[1] Born in 1910, the second son of President F D Roosevelt joined the Army Air Corps in September 1940. Within a year he was a captain and, even though he was neither a graduate from the United States Military Academy nor of a military flying school, went on to command all Allied reconnaissance units in the Mediterranean Air Command during the closing stage of the North African campaign in the summer of 1943.

73

Hughes production facilities, and the stated concern that 'the many uncertainties and amount of money involved in this project might draw Congressional attention and public criticism upon the Army Air Forces,' a Letter Contract covering the purchase of 100 D-5s for an estimated $48,555,000, exclusive of a fixed fee not to exceed 4 per cent, was forwarded to the Hughes Tool Company on 11 October. One month later, the Letter Contract was approved by the Under Secretary of War and the aircraft was given the F-11 military designation.

Almost 10 months went by between the issuance of the Letter Contract and the formal award on 1 August, 1944, of Contract W33-038-ac-1079 covering two XF-11 prototypes (44-70155/44-70156), one static test airframe, and 98 production F-11s (44-70157/44-70254). Delays in finalizing the contract were caused by (1) contractual disputes (with Howard Hughes attempting to be reimbursed up to $3,919,000 for the development and testing of the D-2); (2) labour disputes (21 senior engineers, including Project Engineer Ed West, resigned in May 1944 when Hughes wanted to move them from the Brea engineering office to the main plant in Culver City and to place them under the direct supervision of General Manager F W Ayers and Chief Engineer K F Ridley); (3) the decision to switch production from a new plant to be built in Houston, Texas, as initially demanded by the Aircraft Production Board to locate production close to the Hughes Tool headquarters and in an area where labour was more easily available than in California, to the existing plant in Culver City, as approved in April 1944 to reduce costs; and, (4) major design changes.

While contract negotiations were taking place, the team led by Chief Engineer Stanley Bell and, until his resignation, by Project Engineer Ed West was kept busy. The task of turning the D-5 designed to Hughes standards into the F-11 meeting military specifications for a twin-engined, high-altitude reconnaissance aircraft (top speed of 450 mph, 724 km/h; maximum range of 5,000 miles, 8,000 km; self-sealing fuel tanks; and ultimate design load factor of 9) was quite daunting[2]. Early on, the design team was also forced to switch to 3,000 hp turbosupercharged Pratt & Whitney R-4360 radials as development of the complex Wright Tornado engine was abandoned. On the technical side, other major developments were (1) the change to all-metal construction which was decided in January 1944 as the Aircraft Laboratory at Wright Field had confirmed that wood or plywood would be unsatisfactory for operations under all climatic and maintenance conditions and (2) a marked reduction in the length and diameter of the centre nacelle with accommodation being provided for a normal crew of two or an alternate crew of three if a laboratory technician was added to process films in flight.

[2] AAF technical personnel remained firm and later rejected the Hughes request that only two-thirds of the tanks be made self-sealing but relented on their demand regarding the ultimate load factor requirement and allowed Hughes to complete the XF-11 to a load factor of 6.

By the time formal specifications were approved in March 1944 and the mock-up was inspected on 20 April, 1944, the all-metal XF-11 only retained the basic configuration of the wooden D-2, with twin boom tail and a central fuselage nacelle. Furthermore, it was much larger, with span going from 60 ft to 101 ft 4 in (18.29 to 30.89 m) and heavier, with loaded weight increasing from 31,672 to 47,500 lb (14,366 to 21,546 kg). It thus became increasingly difficult for Hughes and his representatives to justify their request that the D-2 development and construction costs[3] be included as reimbursable items in the F-11 contract. This long simmering dispute was finally settled in favour of the Army Air Forces as Hughes never could prove that the D-2 had been a prototype[4] for the F-11.

In early 1944, Hughes and the AAF had planned that the first XF-11 would be completed in November 1944 and that a peak production rate of 10 F-11s a month would be achieved by March 1945. However, in addition to being delayed by the previously mentioned contractual, labour, and technical problems, the programme suffered from late delivery of engines (the first R-4360-31 was shipped to Hughes in September 1945 instead of February 1945 and even then was not yet approved for flight operations), late delivery of wings (the sub-contractor, Fleetwings Division of Kaiser Cargo, Inc, in Bristol, Pennsylvania, supplied the first set of wings in April 1945 instead of December 1944 as scheduled), the loss of priority status following the end of the war in Europe (which also caused the cancellation of the production contract for 98 F-11s), and major labour troubles immediately after the war ended. Thus, the first XF-11 (44-70155) was still lacking some of its electrical and hydraulic systems when it was conditionally accepted on 5 April, 1946.

Powered by two turbosupercharged Pratt & Whitney R-4360-31s (instead of the originally specified R-4360-4As) rated at 3,000 hp for take-off and at 40,000 ft (12,190 m) and driving contra-rotating propellers, the XF-11 was first taken on taxi-ing tests by Howard Hughes on 15 April but immediately ran into trouble when propellers reversed pitch without apparent reason. Corrective measures were taken and on 24 April the aircraft was flown 20 ft (6 m) above the runway but full flight trials had to await replacement of propellers. After this was accomplished, the first flight took place at Culver City on 7 July, 1946, with Howard Hughes at the controls. The flight had been scheduled to last 45 minutes and, per a written AAF instruction, was not to exceed one hour in duration.

[3]   There even was an attempt to include a portion of the cost of Howard Hughes's personal Boeing Stratoliner in the development costs as it was claimed that a study of the pressure cabin of the four-engined airliner had provided useful information for that of the F-11.

[4]   Today, the D-2 would be considered as a 'proof-of-concept vehicle.' Even so, the cost of its development probably would not be included in a contract unless its construction had been originally ordered for military purposes. That was not the case with the D-2 which had been started as a private venture and, quite probably, for the personal use of Howard Hughes.

However, possibly distracted by undercarriage retraction problems[5], Howard Hughes extended his flight. One hour 15 minutes after take-off, when the XF-11 was in level flight, the starboard rear propeller went into reverse pitch, suddenly increasing drag on that side. The aircraft crashed near a golf course[6] and Howard Hughes was seriously injured. Subsequently, the Investigation Board attributed the crash primarily to the pilot who had extended his flight beyond the approved duration and who, instead of reducing power on the bad engine to let it windmill, had reduced power on the good engine. The loss of hydraulic fluid and the resulting sudden propeller pitch reversal were given only as contributory factors.

The second XF-11 (44-70156) at Muroc Dry Lake on 15 December, 1947. *(AFFTC)*

Also powered by R-4360-31s, the second XF-11 (44-70155) differed from the first prototype in being fitted with conventional four-bladed propellers. Nevertheless, not wishing to risk a second accident in a populated area, the Army Air Forces instructed that the aircraft be trucked to Muroc Dry Lake. It was first flown by Howard Hughes from this desert base on 5 April, 1947, and was accepted at Wright-Patterson AFB, on 14 April, 1948. Redesignated XR-11 in July 1948, the aircraft remained in Ohio until the end of that year when it was flown to Eglin AFB, Florida, to undergo testing by the Air Proving Ground Command until July 1949.

No armament had been planned for the F-11 but provision had been made for the installation of up to 12 cameras in the nose of the central nacelle and in the tail booms aft of the wings. However, it is unlikely that a full complement of cameras was ever installed before the aircraft was transferred to Sheppard AFB, Texas, on 26 July, 1949, to be used as a ground maintenance trainer by the 3750th Technical Training Wing.

[5]   Howard Hughes later informed the AAF that his only radio call during the flight had been a request for an aircraft to fly alongside to watch the operation of the undercarriage.

[6]   Contrary to what has been frequently written, Howard Hughes, as he informed the AAF during the crash investigation, had not attempted to make an emergency landing on the golf course.

44-70156 in flight over the San Fernando Valley during manufacturer's trials in 1947. *(MDHC)*

Finally, the sometime unsavoury saga of the Hughes twin-engined aircraft ended when the XR-11 was dropped from the Air Force inventory at Sheppard AFB in November 1949. It is reported to have cost $14,155,235 to taxpayers and, including D-2 costs, at least a quarter of this amount to Hughes.

Estimated F-11 characteristics and performance based on final specifications approved on 13 March, 1944.

Span 101 ft 4 in (30.89 m); length 65 ft 5 in (19.94 m); height 23 ft 3 in (7.09 m); wing area 983 sq ft (91.32 sq m).

Empty weight 39,392 lb (17,868 kg); loaded weight 47,500 lb (21,546 kg); maximum weight 58,315 lb (26,451 kg); wing loading 48.3 lb/sq ft (235.9 kg/sq m); power loading 7.9 lb/hp (3.6 kg/hp).

Maximum speed 450 mph at 33,000 ft (724 km/h at 10,060 m); initial climb rate 2,025 ft min (10 m/sec); service ceiling 42,000 ft (12,800 m); normal range 4,000 miles (6,435 km); maximum range 5,000 miles (8,045 km).

BuNo 126392, an F2H-3 Banshee of the Royal Canadian Navy with HMCS *Bonaventure* beneath the bridge. *(Public Archives of Canada)*

McDonnell F2H (F-2) Banshee

With the FH-1 Phantom, the US Navy had proved the feasibility of operating jet fighters from carriers; however, even though it was faster (speed differences ranged from 35 to 100 mph, 56 to 161 km/h, depending upon altitude) than the Navy's Chance Vought F4U-4 Corsair, it was substantially slower than contemporary USAAF jet fighters and potential adversaries. Accordingly, while ordering jet fighter prototypes from other manufacturers, the Bureau of Aeronautics invited McDonnell to design a successor to the FH-1 and on 22 March, 1945, issued a Letter of Intent covering the development and manufacture of three XF2D-1s (redesignated XF2H-1s before delivery).

Sticking to the FH-1's proven formula, Herman D Barkey and his team designed an aircraft which was basically an enlarged Phantom powered by a pair of 3,000 lb (1,361 kg) thrust Westinghouse turbojets mounted in the wing-root fillets. The fuselage was lengthened to provide volume for larger fuel tanks (526 US gallons/1,991 litres for the XF2D-1 versus 375 gallons/1,420 litres for the FH-1), and the forward-firing armament—increased from four 0.50-in machine-guns to four 20-mm cannon—was relocated from atop the nose to the bottom of the nose cone to reduce the blinding effect on the pilot. This configuration and major internal details were cleared during mock-up inspection on 24-26 April, 1945. Construction of the prototypes (BuNos 99858 to 99860), delayed by postwar curtailments, began on 27 January, 1946. McDonnell, which emerged from the war as the leading manufacturer of advanced naval fighters, was thus saved from the mass cancellation of contracts which affected the producers of more conventional aircraft and went on to become a new star in the US aircraft manufacturing industry. Much of this success can be attributed to the FH-1 and its derivative, the XF2D-1 Banshee, with the latter leading to the manufacture of 892 production aircraft comprising six major models.

Production history

XF2D-1 (XF2H-1): First flown at Lambert Field, St Louis, on 11 January, 1947, with Robert M Eldholm at the controls, the Banshee prototype was powered by two 3,000 lb (1,361 kg) thrust Westinghouse J34-WE-22

The second XF2D-1 (BuNo 99859) at St Louis with the XHJD-1 seen beyond its tail. *(MCAIR)*

turbojets. Company's flight tests and Service evaluation, including carrier qualification trials, proved successful but some minor control problems brought about a decision to use a tailplane without dihedral on the production aircraft whereas the XF2H-1s had dihedral tailplanes. The last XF2H-1 (BuNo 99860) was delivered on 29 May, 1948.

F2H-1: The aircraft from this first production batch differed from the prototypes in having their fuselage length increased from 39 ft (11.89 m) to 40 ft 1.8 in (12.24 m) and no dihedral on their tailplanes. Internal fuel capacity was increased from 526 gallons (1,991 litres) to 877 gallons (3,320 litres). Ordered on 29 May, 1947, 56 F2H-1s (BuNos 122530/122559 and 122990/123015) were delivered between August 1948 and August 1949. They were initially powered by two 3,000 lb-thrust J34-WE-22s, but were later re-engined with 3,150 lb-thrust J34-WE-30s. The

The first F2H-1 (BuNo 122530) during a test flight on 6 September, 1950, after it had been fitted with after burning engines and extended wing trailing edge. The McDonnell-designed afterburners boosted the static thrust of each Westinghouse J34 by 34 per cent. *(MCAIR, courtesy of Dr F. W. Roos)*

first production aircraft (BuNo 122530) was bailed back to the manufacturer and was used as a testbed for the McDonnell-designed afterburner developed for the XF-88A. It was later fitted with extended trailing edge to serve as a development aircraft for the F2H-3 series.

BuNo 123333, an F2H-2 from the 5th Block, being doused with foam following an engine fire aboard the uss *Lake Champlain* (CVA-39) off Korea on 13 June, 1953. *(USN/National Archives)*

F2H-2: The 306 F2H-2s (*see* Appendix C for list of BuNos) were fitted with 200-gallon (757-litre) tip tanks and were also equipped with external racks for two 500-lb (227-kg) bombs or six 5-in (127 mm) HVAR rockets. As a result of these changes, normal loaded weight was increased from 16,200 lb (7,348 kg) for the F2H-1s to 20,555 lb (9,324 kg for the F2H-2s but was partially offset by the use of 3,250 lb (1,474 kg)-thrust J34-WE-34 turbojets. F2H-2s were first ordered in May 1948 and the first (BuNo 123204) flew on 18 August, 1949.

F2H-2B: Specially developed for use in the nuclear strike role, the 27 F2H-2Bs were externally identical to the F2H-2s. Their wings were strengthened locally to enable a 1,650-lb (748-kg) Mk 7 or 3,230-lb (1,465-kg) Mk 8 bomb to be carried beneath the port wing. BuNos assigned to F2H-2Bs were in the 125030/125662 range and these aircraft were produced alongside F2H-2s and F2H-2Ps starting with the 378th and ending with 'ship number' 433. Details are given in Appendix C.

F2H-2N: The first Navy single-seat, jet-powered, carrier night fighter, the F2H-2N differed from the day fighter in having a 2ft 9.6 in (0.85 m) longer nose housing an AN/APS-19 radar. The first three aircraft (BuNos 123300/123302) respectively started as the 66th to 68th F2H-2 airframes and were delivered as the 78th, 106th, and 117th aircraft. The next 11

BuNo 123301, the second F2H-2N, in the markings of the Tactical Test Division, Naval Air Test Center, at Patuxent River. *(MCAIR, courtesy of Dr F. W. Roos)*

F2H-2Ns (BuNos 123303/123313), which completed the small production run of night fighters, came off the line one at a time in the midst of batches of F2H-2s. The F2H-2N first flew on 3 February, 1950.

F2H-2P: The first aircraft (BuNo 123366) of the reconnaissance version was started as the 184th F2H-2 but was modified during production and was delivered as the 197th Banshee. It was first flown on 12 October, 1950. The nose of the aircraft was widened and extended 2 ft 4.3 in (0.73 m) to provide space for six vertical and oblique cameras and all armament was removed. For night photography, provision was made for

An F2H-2P (BuNo 125078) of VC-62 in flight near NAS Jacksonville, Florida, on 26 September, 1951. *(USN, courtesy of Hal Andrews)*

the carriage of a container for 20 flash cartridges beneath each wing, outboard of the flaps.

Production of the F2H-2P, the first jet-powered reconnaissance aircraft built for the US Navy, totalled 89 units which, excluding the aforementioned development aircraft, bore the BuNos 125072/125079, 125680/125706, 126673/126695, and 128857/128886. The 436th and last -2 Banshee, an F2H-2P, was delivered on 28 May, 1952.

Four F2H-2Ps from VFP-61 over southern California in February 1958. *(USN/ National Archives)*

F2H-3 (F-2C): Designed as a single-seat, all-weather fighter, the F2H-3 had an 8-ft 1.6-in (2.48-m) longer fuselage than the F2H-2 to provide

82

space for a Westinghouse AN/APQ-41 radar in the nose and more fuel in the fuselage—internal capacity being increased to 1,102 gallons (4,171 litres). The capacity of the tip tanks was decreased to 170 gallons (644 litres) but these tanks were infrequently carried. M12 or M16 20-mm cannon replaced the M3 guns of earlier variants, and the number of rounds per gun was increased from 150 to 220 for the upper cannon and to 250 for the lower cannon, with the guns being moved aft. Four weapon racks for bombs of up to 500 lb (227 kg) or HVAR and HPAG rockets were provided beneath each wing. Alternative weapons included a

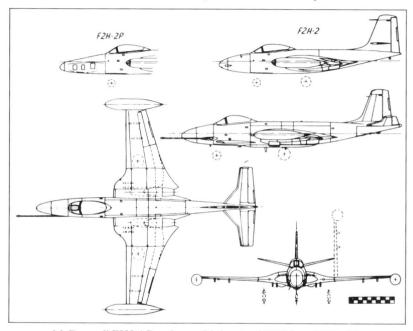

McDonnell F2H-4 Banshee, with insets of F2H-2 and F2H-2P.

nuclear store beneath the port wing or a Sidewinder air-to-air infrared-guided missile beneath each wing. The vertical tail surfaces were redesigned and the chord of the inboard wing was extended. The tailplane, which now had 10-deg dihedral, was moved down to the rear fuselage cone. In service, F2H-3s were retrofitted with a 'horsal' extension forward of the tailplane leading edge to eliminate a flutter problem.

An F2H-2N (BuNo 123311) was modified to serve as aerodynamic prototype and the first production F2H-3, which had been ordered on 4 July, 1950, made its first flight on 29 March 1952. The last of 250 F2H-3s (BuNos 126291/126350, 126354/126489, and 127493/127546) was delivered on 31 October, 1953. In service, some of these aircraft were fitted

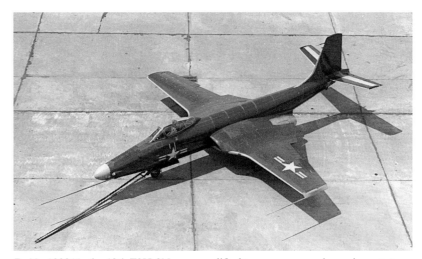

BuNo 123311, the 12th F2H-2N, was modified to serve as aerodynamic prototype for the F2H-3 series. The nose is still that of the F2H-2N but the extended wing trailing edge and tail surfaces are those of the F2H-3. In addition, the aircraft appears to have been fitted with afterburning engines. *(MCAIR, courtesy Dr F. W. Roos)*

with an air refuelling probe replacing the port upper cannon and protruding forward of the radome; the modification also entailed the installation of a ventral fairing. Thirty-nine F2H-3s not modified for air refuelling were transferred to Canada beginning in November 1955 and served with Royal Canadian Navy units until September 1962. During that same month, the few F2H-3s still in storage were redesignated F-2Cs.

F2H-3P: This proposed reconnaissance version of the F2H-3 was not built.

F2H-4 (F-2D): Following the modification of an F2H-3 (BuNo 126319) as the prototype of an improved all-weather Banshee with the more reliable Hughes AN/APG-37 radar, 150 F2H-4s (BuNos 126351/126353 and 127547/127693) were built. The last F2H-4 was delivered on 24 September, 1953. Except for the new radar, the F2H-4s were identical to the F2H-3s. Like the F2H-3s, most -4s were fitted in service with horsals and several were equipped with an inflight refuelling probe. F2H-4s still in storage were redesignated F-2Ds in September 1962.

Service history

Delivery of Banshees began in August 1948 to enable VX-3 at NAS Atlantic City to undertake service evaluation before the assignment of the first F2H-1s to VF-171 at NAS Cecil Field, Florida, in March 1949. However, the F2H-1s were soon transferred to reserve units after making headlines with two unusual events. On 9 August, 1949, Lieut J L Fruin's F2H-1 went out of control while performing aerobatics at 500 mph and

Three F2H-4s of VF-11 in February 1955. The first aircraft is still in the anodized finish in which it was delivered, the second has been repainted in the standard Navy blue finish, and the third has received the new non-specular light gull grey/glossy insignia white finish. *(USN, courtesy of Hal Andrews)*

An F2H-1 (BuNo 12533) flying over the Mississippi River on 20 March, 1952. *(USN)*

A McDonnell F2H-2 of VF-172 on the forward elevator of the USS *Essex* (CV-9) during operations off Korea on 25 August, 1951. *(USN/National Archives)*

30,000 ft (805 km/h and 9,145 m) and the pilot was forced to eject, thus becoming the first US pilot to use an ejection seat for an emergency escape. During the same month, another F2H-1 was flown to 52,000 ft (15,850 m) to set an unofficial altitude record for jet-powered aircraft while enabling the Navy to disprove the Air Force contention that the Convair B-36 strategic bomber could fly higher than contemporary fighters and was thus immune to interception.

The Banshee's good altitude and climb performance (the F2H-2 had an initial rate of climb more than 20 per cent greater than that of the Grumman F9F-2 Panther, 7,300 ft/min versus 6,000 ft/min—37 m/sec versus 30 m/sec) led to its use in Korea as an escort fighter. Arriving off Korea with VF-172 aboard the USS *Essex* (CV-9) in August 1951, F2H-2s first escorted Air Force Boeing B-29s on 25 August during an attack against the marshalling yard and railway depot at Rashin on the east coast of North Korea. After completing their first combat cruise in November 1951, F2H-2s did not return to the war zone until the autumn of 1952 as Banshees were assigned in priority to Atlantic Fleet squadrons for deployments to the Atlantic and Mediterranean aboard carriers of the Sixth Fleet. In the final year of the Korean War, however, F2H-2s returned to the fray with VF-11 deploying aboard the USS *Kearsarge* (CV-33) in September 1952 and with VF-22 and VF-62 arriving on the line aboard the USS *Lake Champlain* (CVA-39) in June 1953. Following the end of the war, the F2H-2s were rapidly supplanted in first-line squadrons by higher performance day fighters and went on to serve for a few years with reserve squadrons. Before the type's disappearance from the scene, however, the F2H-2 gained attention once more when Ensign Varner of VF-34 flew nonstop from NAS Los Alamitos, California, to NAS Cecil Field, Florida, covering the 1,900 miles (3,060 km) in 3 hr

Two F2H-2s of VF-172 over North Korea in the fall of 1951. *(USN)*

58 min *without* refuelling in flight. The rarer F2H-2Ns and F2H-2Bs had even shorter operational lives during which night fighters only deployed

twice [with a VC-4 detachment aboard the USS *Franklin D. Roosevelt* (CVB-42) and with VF-82 aboard the USS *Lake Champlain* (CVA-39)] while strike fighters were operated at sea from several carriers by detachments from VC-3 and VC-4.

In Korea, the fighters had been preceded by photographic reconnaissance Banshees as a detachment of three F2H-2Ps from Composite Squadron 61 (VC-61) had embarked aboard the USS *Valley Forge* (CV-45) in June 1951. Thereafter, detachments from VC-61 and VC-62 operated from several Task Force 77 carriers as well as from Sixth Fleet carriers until replaced in the mid-fifties by swept-wing Grumman F9F-6Ps and F9F-8Ps. Besides being operated in their intended role, some photographic Banshees were used for special tests including one on 16 December, 1952, when two F2H-2Ps were launched from the USS *Princeton* (CVA-37) and radio guided a Regulus missile, which had also been catapulted from the carrier, to a target on San Nicolas Island off the coast of Southern California.

BuNo 127508, a Block 11 F2H-3 without tip tanks, and BuNo 126373, a Block 4 F2H-3 with tip tanks, of VC-3 during a WestPac deployment with Carrier Air Group Twenty-One (CVG-21) in October 1955. *(USN, courtesy of Hal Andrews)*

From mid-1952, when VC-4 received the first F2H-3s, until 30 September, 1959, when VF(AW)-11 relinquished its last F2H-4s, Banshees were the fleet's standard all-weather carrier fighters. In the

These two photographs were taken aboard the USS *Ticonderoga* (CVA-14) in September 1955. The Banshees on the port side are F2H-2Bs of VF-101 (with the tail code T of Carrier Air Group One, CVG-1) and those on the starboard side are F2H-4s of VMF(N)-533 (with the tail code AI). *(MCAIR, courtesy of Dr F. W. Roos)*

process, both of these models were among the first USN aircraft to be launched from the deck of the USS *Hancock* (CV-19) during initial operational tests of the new steam catapult in June 1954. Following its phase-out from first-line units, the 'Old Banjo', as the Banshee was affectionately nicknamed, continued in service with reserve units until

1961, when the last were retired at NAS Oakland. Although extinct when the new Tri-Service designation system was adopted in September 1962, the F2H-3 and F2H-4 were then nevertheless redesignated F-2C and F-2D.

With the Marine Corps, F2H-2s were operated by VMF-122 and VMF-224, and F2H-2Ps served with VMJ-1 and VMJ-2. However, only the F2H-2Ps saw combat operations in Korea, with VMJ-1 operating from Pohang Airfield (K-3) from March 1952 until after the signing of the Armistice at Panmunjon in July 1953. Postwar, all-weather F2H-4s were operated for a few years by VMF-114, VMF-214, and VMF-533 before ending their life with the reservists at NAS Niagara Falls, New York.

To replace the Hawker Sea Fury F.B.11 piston-engined fighters equipping Nos 870 and 871 Squadrons, the Royal Canadian Navy had long considered acquiring Banshees. However, by the time funding was available, McDonnell was no longer producing F2Hs, and the RCN was forced to content itself with 39 F2H-3s transferred from USN stocks[1]. RCN pilots collected the F2H-3s at NAS Quonset Point, Rhode Island, between 30 November, 1955, and 16 June, 1958, and ferried them to

A pair of F2H-3s (BuNo 126446, No. 108, and BuNo 126343, No. 118) from VF-870, Royal Canadian Navy. *(Public Archives of Canada)*

Shearwater, Nova Scotia, for assignment to two operational squadrons, VF-870 and VF-871, and one test squadron, VX-10. In Canadian service, Banshees had a high attrition rate and by the summer of 1962 most aircraft had been destroyed in accidents in flight, ashore, and aboard HMCS *Bonaventure*. When the remaining eleven F2H-3s were struck off strength on 12 September, 1962, VF-870, the last RCN fighter squadron, was disbanded.

[1] BuNos 126294/126295, 126306, 126310, 126313, 126327, 126330/126331, 126333/126335, 126337, 126339, 126343, 126346/126347, 126361, 126381/126382, 126390, 126392, 126400, 126402/126403, 126414/126415, 126422, 126428/126429, 126434, 126443/126444, 126446, 126449, 126454, 126464, 126469, 126488, and 127510.

Two F2H-4s of Composite Squadron Four (VC-4) indulging in some aerobatics in December 1955. The aircraft are fitted with a refuelling probe. *(MCAIR, courtesy of Dr F. W. Roos)*

DIMENSIONS:	F2H-1	F2H-2	F2H-2P	F2H-3
Span, (with tip tanks), ft in	NA	44 11.9	44 11.9	45 0
(m)	(NA)	(13.71)	(13.71)	(13.72)
Span (without tip tanks), ft in	41 7.4	41 8.8	41 8.8	41 8.8
(m)	(12.68)	(12.72)	(12.72)	(12.72)
Span (wings folded), ft in	18 5	18 5	18 5	18 5
(m)	(5.61)	(5.61)	(5.61)	(5.61)
Length, ft in	40 1.8	40 0.4	42 5.2	48 2
(m)	(12.24)	(12.20)	(12.93)	(14.68)
Height, ft in	14 5.5	14 5.5	14 5.5	13 11.4
(m)	(4.41)	(4.41)	(4.41)	(4.25)
Wing area, sq ft	294.1	294.1	294.1	294.1
(sq m)	(27.31)	(27.31)	(27.31)	(27.31)
WEIGHTS:				
Empty, lb	9,794	11,146	–	13,183
(kg)	(4,442)	(5,056)	(–)	(5,980)
Loaded, lb	16,200	20,555	20,600	21,200
(kg)	(7,348)	(9,324)	(9,344)	(9,616)
Maximum, lb	18,940	21,000	–	28,500
(kg)	(8,591)	(9,525)	–	(12,927)
Wing loading*, lb/sq ft	55.1	69.9	70.0	72.1
(kg/sq m)	(269.1)	(341.4)	(342.1)	(352.1)
Power loading*, lb/lb st	2.7	3.2	3.2	3.3
(kg/kgp)	(2.7)	(3.2)	(3.2)	(3.3)

PERFORMANCE:

Maximum speed, mph at sea level	586	586	529	527
(km/h at sl)	(942)	(942)	(851)	(847)
Cruising speed, mph	351	501	475	461
(km/h)	(565)	(806)	(764)	(742)
Climb rate, ft/min	7,300	5,950	5,930	5,900
(m/sec)	(37)	(30)	(30)	(30)
Service ceiling, ft	49,300	48,500	48,500	46,500
(m)	(15,025)	(14,785)	(14,785)	(14,175)
Normal range, miles	1,278	1,200	1,200	1,170
(km)	(2,055)	(1,930)	(1,930)	(1,885)
Maximum range, miles	–	1,475	1,475	1,716
(km)	–	(2,375)	(2,375)	(2,760)

* wing and power loadings are calculated at normal loaded weight and maximum take-off power.

McDonnell XH-20 Little Henry

The diminutive XH-20 Little Henry was developed by a team led by Marvin Marks in close co-operation between the Helicopter and Propulsion Division of McDonnell and the AAF/USAF Rotor Wing Branch, Propeller Laboratory and Rotary Wing Unit, Aircraft Projects Section, Wright-Patterson AFB. At the time of its inception, the XH-20 was unique in being powered by two McDonnell-developed $7^{1}/_{4}$ in (18.42 cm) ramjet units weighing only 10 lb (4.5 kg) each, mounted at the tips of the two-blade rotor and fed from tanks beside the pilot. The fuel, originally propane but later gasoline (motor car petrol), was boosted through a feed line to a delivery valve on the rotor head. From there centrifugal force took over to convey the fuel through the blades to the tip-mounted ramjets.

Having undertaken privately-funded studies of ramjets as powerplants

The extreme simplicity of the Little Henry's airframe is clearly illustrated in this view. *(Wide World Photo)*

93

for helicopters, McDonnell submitted an unsolicited proposal to the Air Materiel Command at Wright Field in the spring of 1946 and in July was awarded a contract for the development and testing of two experimental machines. It was then hoped that the novel powerplant would make it feasible to build small, lightweight helicopters by reducing or eliminating complex and heavy engine parts, gear systems, and transmissions. Furthermore, it was claimed that this powerplant installation would result in increased efficiency and would completely eliminate the need for a conventional anti-torque rotor. Accordingly, the two XH-20s were ordered as flying test-beds and were not intended as production prototypes. Their airframe was kept as simple as possible and consisted of welded tubes carried on three vertical legs ending with free-castoring

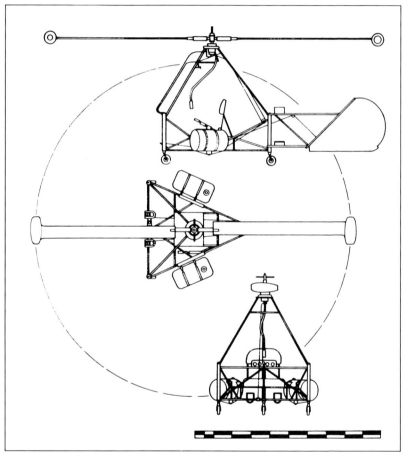

McDonnell XH-20 Little Henry.

wheels. Conventional helicopter controls were fitted, and the pitch lever incorporated a motorcycle-type throttle to regulate the fuel flow.

Fitted as a single-seater, the first of two prototypes (46-689 and 46-690) made both its first tethered flight on 5 May, 1947, and its first free flight on 29 August in St Louis with Charles R Wood Jr at the controls. With the project team then benefitting from the experience of Friedrich von Dobhloff, the Austrian engineer who had pioneered the application of jet principles to helicopters during the war, tests continued for four years. During that time, one of the two XH-20s was modified as a two-seater and, like the single-seater, proved generally satisfactory. However, the ramjet units had excessive fuel consumption, which drastically limited range and endurance when compared to conventionally-powered helicopters, and rate of descent in autorotation was excessive. Accordingly, the Air Force terminated the programme in 1951. The first XH-20 was preserved and is now part of the collection of the Air Force Museum at Wright-Patterson AFB, Ohio.

Rotor diameter 18 ft 0$^1/_4$ in (5.49 m); length 12 ft 6 in (3.81 m); height 7 ft (2.13 m). Weights not recorded. Cruising speed 50 mph (80 km/h); endurance 50 min.

The Hughes HFB-1 in Long Beach Harbor after its short flight on 2 November, 1947. *(Summa Corporation)*

Hughes HFB-1 (H-4) Hercules

Although it only flew once or, more accurately, briefly remained airborne some 70 ft (21 m) over the water during high-speed taxi-ing trials in November 1947, the huge Hughes flying-boat caught the fancy of the public and, put on permanent display in 1983, remains a money-making venture in Southern California, an area already quite rich in tourist attractions of unequal merit. From the aeronautical point of view, this eight-engined flying-boat did incorporate a number of exceptional features, foremost among which was size (its span is still unsurpassed even by that of the Antonov An-225 Mriya, 320 ft versus 290 ft—97.54 m versus 88.40 m)[1]. From the practical point of view, however, the Hughes Hercules must be regarded as an achievement of questionable value.

Alarmed by the high loss rate inflicted by U-boats on British merchantmen during the first years of the war and concerned about potential losses to Japanese submarines, noted US industrialist Henry J Kaiser, the 'father' of the Liberty ships, first proposed the development of a very large flying-boat early in 1942 as a means of more safely ferrying large numbers of United States troops and their weapons to Britain and Australia. Ranking USN officers and influential politicians saw merits in this concept, but Henry Kaiser, who did not control aircraft plants, failed to gain the support of US aircraft manufacturers who were already too busy with existing projects. Conversely, Howard Hughes, who had yet to

[1]   With a length of 219 ft, however, the Hughes flying-boat is shorter than the Boeing 747 (231 ft 4 in), Antonov An-124 (226 ft 8½in), Lockheed C-5 (247 ft 10 in), and Antonov An-225 (275 ft 7 in).

receive an aircraft contract, became keen on the large transport flying-boat project and he and Henry Kaiser organized the Kaiser-Hughes Corporation to promote the project and seek government support. By the autumn of 1942, with losses to enemy submarines mounting rapidly, they succeeded and on 16 November, 1942, were awarded an $18-million contract from the Defense Plant Corporation for the design and manufacture of three HK-1 flying-boats[2]. The HK-1s were then expected to be only slightly larger and heavier than the Martin XPB2M-1, the

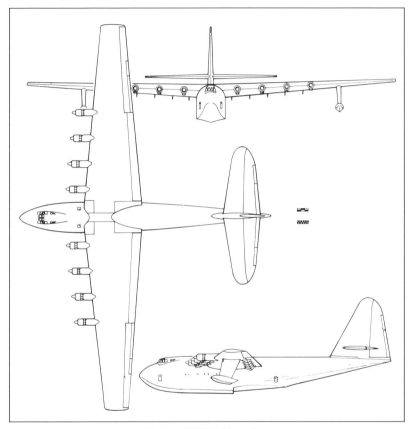

Hughes HFB-1 Hercules.

[2]   The fact that this contract was awarded by the Defense Plant Corporation, not as could have been expected by the Department of the Navy, was odd. So was the fact that no Navy BuNos or Army serial numbers were set aside for the three aircraft ordered in 1942. The only aircraft to be completed was given the experimental civil registation NX37802 before being flown. This would appear to indicate that the Hughes behemoth never gained favour with either the Bureau of Aeronautics or the Materiel Command and that its development had to be funded outside normal channels.

prototype of the Mars flying-boat which first flew on 3 July, 1942. (The XPB2M-1 had a wing span of 200 ft/60.96 m and weighed a maximum of 72 tons/65,317 kg). More notable by US standards of the time was the Government's insistence that the HK-1s be built of non-critical materials.

With Howard Hughes personally taking control of the project and Henry Kaiser slowly phasing out his involvement, the design of the flying-boat was entrusted to a team from the Hughes Aircraft Company led by Chief Engineer Rea E Hopper and including Kenneth Ridley, Roy Wendahl, and Gene Bandford as project design engineers and Eastman N Jacobs as chief aerodynamicist. Assistance in the design was also provided by specialized consultants and by personnel from the Langley Research Institute of the National Advisory Committee for Aeronautics (NACA), notably in selecting the wing section and minimizing hydro-dynamic drag.

To endow the flying-boat with the ability to operate over critical transatlantic sectors, or from California to Hawaii, while carrying a worthwhile payload (including such large and heavy items as the M4 Sherman tank), the designers were soon forced to increase the size and weight of the new flying-boat significantly. Moreover, the required use of non-critical material and the resulting selection of Fairchild's Duramold laminated birch wood as the primary material[3], resulted in a fairly heavy structure. To power the behemoth, the Hughes team selected Pratt &

Howard Hughes conferring with engineers on the flight deck of the HFB-1 Hercules. *(Summa Corporation)*

[3]   Even though birch, not spruce, was the principal type of wood used in its construction, the Hughes flying-boat was later unofficially and inaccurately nicknamed *Spruce Goose*.

With Howard Hughes (with hat atop the flying boat) carefully supervising the operation, the HFB-1 is launched in Los Angeles Harbor on 1 November, 1947.
(Carl Byoir & Associates/National Archives)

Whitney R-4360-4A twenty-eight-cylinder air-cooled radials which were fitted with single-stage variable-speed superchargers and rated at 3,000 hp for take-off, 2,500 hp at 5,000 ft (1,525 m), and 2,200 hp at 14,500 ft (4,420 m). Each of the eight engines was to drive a four-bladed constant-speed airscrew with a diameter of 17 ft 2 in (5.23 m), those on the four inboard engines having reverse pitch, and was to be fed from a collector tank in each wing. Fuel, however, was carried not in the wing but in fourteen 1,000-US gallon (3,785-litre) tanks located in the hull.

Always a perfectionist, Howard Hughes insisted on close attention being paid to every detail and careful consideration being given to the selection of major systems (this being notably the case with the 120-volt DC electrical system and hydraulically-boosted controls which were exceptionally advanced for the time). This care, combined with the facts that the flying-boat project had not been given priority status and that the number of prototypes had been reduced from three to one when the U-boat threat diminished and labour and factory space had to be made available for the production of F-11 reconnaissance aircraft, resulted in slow progress being made in its construction. Redesignated HFB-1 or simply H-4 after Henry Kaiser's withdrawal from the project, the large flying-boat thus remained unassembled in the Culver City plant when the war ended in August 1945.

Feeling under an obligation to complete the HFB-1 even though it was no longer needed in its intended role, Howard Hughes invested additional funds and selected a waterfront site at Terminal Island in Long Beach harbour on which to have the flying-boat assembled. Finally, in mid-June 1946, the fuselage, tail surfaces, and two wing panels—less engines, floats and control surfaces, were loaded on special flat bed

The HFB-1 in Long Beach shortly before its completion. *(Summa Corporation)*

trailers and transported 34 miles (55 km) from Culver City to Terminal Island. There, assembly and final preparation proceeded at a leisurely pace, especially so as Howard Hughes had been badly injured in the crash of the first XF-11 on 7 July, 1946, and was not there to lend impetus to the programme until Congressional hearings into his handling of wartime contracts were held in July and August 1947. Spurred by criticisms, notably from Senator Owen Brester, Howard Hughes put his staff on overtime and went on to have the flying-boat readied for trials[4].

Howard Hughes, co-pilot Dave Grant, two flight engineers, and guests from the press corps, boarded the H-4 (or HFB-1) at mid-day on 2

[4] As completed, the HFB-1 lacked both the clamshell doors and nose loading ramp which were to have been fitted for its intended use as a cargo transport and the 750 canvas seats as called for in the troop transport role. Instead, its forward upper deck was loaded with test instrumentation and ballast tanks were provided in various locations.

The HFB-1 on the eve of its first 'flight' near Terminal Island in Los Angeles Harbor. *(Carl Byoir & Associates/National Archives)*

101

The HFB-1 being towed to a temporary storage area in Long Beach Harbor after it had been acquired in 1976 by the Aero Club of Southern California. *(Wrather Corporation)*

November, 1947, for what was purported to be high-speed taxi-ing tests in San Pedro Bay. Speed on the way out reached about 40 kt (74 km/h) with the flying-boat displaying satisfactory water handling qualities and was increased to 75 kt (139 km/h) on the way back to the mooring point where all but one of the journalists deplaned before the next run was initiated. This time, flaps were lowered 15°, the predicted take-off setting, and at slightly over 73 kt (135 mph) the behemoth became airborne. It reached an altitude of 70 ft (21 m) and remained off the water for about a mile (1.6 km). Having proved that it could fly, the Hughes flying-boat was returned to its mooring. It never again was to fly as, after spending $17 million of his own money in addition to the $18 million which had been provided by the Defense Plant Corporation, Howard Hughes quirkily decided to place the flying-boat in storage. For the next 33 years, the H-4 remained in a specially built hangar in which temperature and humidity were carefully controlled.

In the autumn of 1976, less than six months after the death of Howard Hughes, Summa Corporation attempted to interest the US Navy in funding additional trials to obtain data for the proposed wing-in-ground-effect craft. Nothing came of this suggestion as NASA and other government agencies were not prepared to help the Navy fund this research programme. In the end, Summa Corporation sold the Hercules flying-boat to the Aero Club of Southern California. In co-operation with Wrather Corporation, the club had the flying-boat towed to a new site in Long Beach harbour where in May 1983 it was put on permanent display inside a purpose-built building next to the *Queen Mary*. Generating tourism revenue thus became the greatest achievement of the *Spruce Goose*.

Span, 320 ft (97.54 m); length, 219 ft (66.75 m); wing area, 11,075 sq ft (1,029 sq m). Loaded weight, 400,000 lb (181,437 kg); wing loading, 36.1 lb/sq ft (176.3 kg/sq m); power loading, 16.7 lb/hp (7.6 kg/hp).
Maximum speed, 234 mph at 5,000 ft (377 km/h at 1,525 m); service ceiling, 17,500 ft (5,335 m); maximum range, 3,000 miles (4,825 km).

McDonnell XF-85 Goblin

Representing yet another attempt at providing the USAAF with an escort fighter combining speed with range for strategic operations, the XP-85 (redesignated XF-85 in June 1948 when the USAF replaced the prefix P for pursuit by F for fighter) was something of an innovation. True, the concept of the parasite fighter had been proved in the United States and the USSR during the 1930s and, persisting along this development line, the Soviet Union had made limited use of parasite

The second XF-85 on its ground handling trolley. *(MCAIR)*

fighters early in the war against Germany. In the United States, where work on parasite fighters had been discontinued before the Second World War, it was the limited endurance of early jet fighters which prompted a resurgence of the concept.

On 20 January, 1944, seeking a jet fighter to escort its heavy bombers, the AAF directed the Air Technical Service Command to undertake studies and to invite the industry to submit concept proposals. As they were busy producing conventional aircraft and working on more promising projects, the major US aircraft manufacturers were not keen on the idea. Hence, only the young and hungry McDonnell Aircraft Corporation answered with any enthusiasm by having a team led by Herman D Barkley initiate work on its Model 27 during the autumn of 1944. However, the initial McDonnell proposal for a small but rather conventional fighter aircraft to be carried partially within a parent Boeing B-29, Convair B-36, or Northrop B-35 heavy bomber was rejected in January

104

1945 as by then the AAF had concluded that the fighter would have to be carried entirely within the B-35 or B-36.

Undaunted, McDonnell completely revised its design and on 19 March, 1945, submitted a proposal for the Model 27D, a diminutive aircraft with egg-shaped fuselage, triple vertical tail surfaces, tailplane with pronounced anhedral, and vertically-folding wings with 37 deg of leading-edge sweep[1]. The aircraft was to be powered by a Westinghouse J34 axial-flow turbojet with nose air intake and straight-through exhaust, and was to be armed with four 0.50-in machine-guns in the forward fuselage sides.

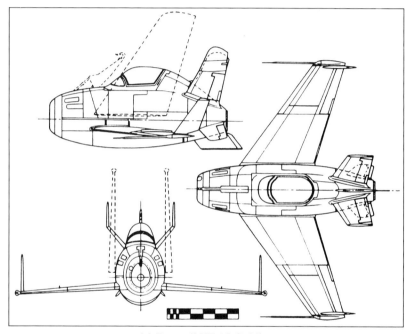

McDonnell XF-85 Goblin.

The Model 27D parasite fighter proposal was favourably received and, in spite of the postwar curtailment of military aircraft orders, on 9 October, 1945, McDonnell received a Letter of Intent for a design study, two prototypes of the XP-85 Goblin tailored for carriage in the B-36

[1] McDonnell's proposed use of wing sweep was quite daring as it predated both the availability of German engineering data on this subject and North American's recommendation for redesigning the original straight-wing XP-86 into the swept-wing Sabre. In the United States, however, the use of wing sweep for fighter aircraft had already been incorporated by Northop in the piston-powered XP-56, which was first flown on 6 September, 1943, and on the jet-powered XP-79, which was still under construction when McDonnell proposed its XF-85.

bomb bay, and a static test article. The mock-up successfully underwent inspection between 10 and 12 June, 1946, and, in March 1947, the Letter of Intent was confirmed by the award of Contract W33-038-ac-13496 in the amount of $2,393,126 including a fixed fee of $129,052. In parallel with the development of the XF-85, the AAF and its successor, the USAF, planned that the 24th and subsequent B-36s would be capable of carrying one F-85 plus bomb load while some of the bombers would be modified to carry three fighters but no bomb load. Conditional upon the results of flight trials with the two XF-85s, the USAF intended to order an initial batch of 30 parasite fighters; however, before completion of the first XF-85, this plan was shelved and procurement was limited to the two experimental aircraft. This cautious approach, although depriving McDonnell of its first Air Force production contract for fighter aircraft, later proved to be well-founded as flight trials with the XF-85 demonstrated that recovery aboard the parent bomber would have been quite arduous for most pilots.

Intended to be launched and recovered from a retractable trapeze beneath the parent bomber, the XF-85 was not fitted with an undercarriage but had a retractable hook in the fuselage forward of the pressurized cockpit. For emergency landings, the Goblin was provided with a retractable steel skid beneath the fuselage and its wingtips were protected by small steel runners. For flight trials, the aircraft, which was powered by a 3,000 lb (1,361 kg) thrust Westinghouse J34-WE-7 turbojet, was to be carried aloft by a specially modified Boeing EB-29B (44-8411), as no B-36 could yet be spared for this type of development work.

As the first prototype (46-523) had been damaged at Moffett Field,

The diminutive XF-85, showing the retractable hook. *(USAF)*

106

California, when it was dropped while being mounted in the wind tunnel at NACA's Ames Laboratory, it was the second aircraft (46-524) which was used for initial flight trials beginning on 23 August, 1948. After making three captive flights with the XF-85 remaining attached to the trapeze of the EB-29B, the initial free flight was made by Edwin Schoch on 28 August. Launched from the EB-29B at 20,000 ft (6,095 m) above Muroc Dry Lake, Schoch evaluated the XF-85's handling for 15 minutes before attempting to engage the Goblin's hook to the trapeze of the EB-29B. In the process, the XF-85 was caught in violent turbulence beneath the parent aircraft, struck the trapeze, and shattered its canopy. Fortunately, Schoch was unhurt and, in spite of the loss of his helmet and oxygen mask, managed to retain control and succeeded in making an emergency landing on a dry lake bed.

Following repairs, the second XF-85 made three flights on 14 and 15 October, 1948, with successful recovery by means of hook and trapeze. During the fifth flight, however, the aircraft ran into new problems when the removal of the temporary fairing around the base of the hook resulted

The Goblin about to hook up with *Monstro*, its parent Boeing EB-29B. *(USAF)*

in severe turbulence and loss of directional stability, forcing Schoch to make another emergency landing. Notwithstanding the addition of auxiliary vertical surfaces at the wingtips to improve directional stability while flying in turbulent air beneath the bomber, the sixth flight also ended with a landing on a dry lake. The same fate awaited the first Goblin when on 8 April, 1949, it made its only flight.

In spite of its small size and unusual configuration, the XF-85 earned favourable comments regarding its stability, control, and spin recovery characteristics, thus prompting McDonnell to remain confident and recommend that flight tests be resumed as soon as a satisfactory trapeze system could be developed. To Air Force personnel, however, it was obvious that even with major improvements the Goblin would remain quite a handful for the average squadron pilot due to the difficulty of retaining control while attempting to engage the hook to the bomber's trapeze. Furthermore, by the autumn of 1949 a major shortage of development funds made it increasingly difficult to justify more development work on the Goblin when its performance would soon be markedly inferior to that of foreign interceptor fighters. Accordingly, on 3 October, 1949, the Air Materiel Command recommended terminating the XF-85 project. On 17 October, Headquarters USAF concurred and, on 24 October, McDonnell was issued a termination notice.

Test pilot Edwin Schoch in front of the XF-85 on 9 October, 1952. *(MCAIR)*

Although the two XF-85s had been flown only 2 hr 19 min, the limited experience gained during the seven free flights proved invaluable when the USAF sponsored the development of the Republic RF-84K Thunderflash which saw limited service as a parasite reconnaissance aircraft carried by the Convair GRB-36F. This contribution alone justified keeping the first XF-85 in the collection of the Air Force Museum at Wright-Patterson AFB, Ohio.

Span 21 ft in (6.43 m); length 14 ft 10 in (4.52 m); height 8 ft 4 in (2.54 m); wing area 100.5 sq ft (9.34 sq m).
 Empty weight 3,984 lb (1,807 kg); loaded weight 5,600 lb (2,540 kg); wing loading 55.7 lb/sq ft (271.9 kg/sq m); power loading 1.5 lb/lb st (1.5 kg/kgp).
 Calculated performance: maximum speed 648 mph (1,043 km/h) at sea level and 581 mph (935 km/h) at 35,000 ft (10,670 m); initial climb rate 12,500 ft/min (63 m/sec); service ceiling 48,000 ft (14,630 m); cruising endurance 32 min; combat endurance 20 min.

After being fitted with afterburning Westinghouse XJ34-WE-15 turbojets, the second Voodoo was redesignated XF-88A. *(USAF)*

McDonnell XF-88 Voodoo

Although the advent of jet propulsion did much to boost the speed of combat aircraft, the new type of powerplant initially suffered from a major drawback: its apparently insatiable thirst for fuel. Thus, the first jet-powered aircraft were short ranged and, more significantly when considering performance requirements for escort fighters, had a limited endurance.

For the USAAF, which during the Second World War had been the foremost proponent of long-range fighter escort, the characteristics of the early jet engines created a new set of problems: continued use of piston-engined aircraft, which had the required endurance, as escort fighters would place them at the mercy of substantially faster jet-powered interceptors whereas the use of the first types of American jet fighters would preclude the USAAF from being able to escort its bombers all the way to and from most strategic targets. Initial attempts to develop new escort fighters combining the speed of jet fighters with the endurance of piston-engined aircraft (*eg* the Bell XP-83 jet fighter and the Consolidated-Vultee XP-81 with a General Electric XT31-GE-1 propeller-turbine in the nose and a General Electric J33-GE-5 turbojet in the tail) had been disappointing. Consequently, in early 1946 the AAF informally requested proposals for a 'penetration fighter' with a combat radius of at least 900 miles (1,450 km) and performance over the target good enough to cope with anticipated enemy opposition. Optimistically, the AAF sought to have the combat gross weight of the aircraft kept below 15,000 lb (6,800 kg) in spite of the weight of fuel required to achieve the desired range.

109

Work on the Model 36 was initiated by McDonnell on 1 April, 1946, and resulted on 7 May in the company being awarded a Letter of Intent for this large twin-jet aircraft. As proposed, the aircraft was to be powered by two 3,000 lb (1,361 kg) thrust Westinghouse J34 turbojets mounted side-by-side in the lower part of the centre fuselage with straight air intakes in the wing roots and exhausts beneath the rear fuselage. This powerplant installation was selected as it freed most of the volume within the fuselage for the large fuel tanks which would endow the aircraft with the endurance required for the long-range penetration mission. Other major design features retained early during the conceptual phase were the adoption of 35 deg of sweep and 7.9 per cent thickness for the wing, the location of the cockpit well forward of the wing, the use of V tail surfaces, and the provision for six 20-mm cannon in the forward fuselage[1]. Following mock-up inspection between 19 and 22 August, 1946, Project Engineer E M Flesh and his team progressively refined the design as the result of wind-tunnel testing. Notably, the wing root intakes were given 40 deg of sweep to increase the critical speed of the lips, a boundary layer ramp was added on the intakes to improve pressure recovery, and the V tail surfaces were replaced with conventional swept surfaces to avoid a predicted adverse rolling moment and insufficient longitudinal stability near the stall. Satisfied, the AAF approved Contract W33-038-ac-14582 on 14 February, 1947. Two XP-88 prototypes (46-525 and 46-526 which were redesignated XF-88s in June 1948 when the USAF replaced the prefix P for pursuit by F for fighter) were to

The first XF-88 (46-525) at the time of its completion. *(MCAIR)*

[1] To avoid the weight and handling difficulties associated with the use of a separate 250-round box for each gun, McDonnell proposed building the boxes integrally with the structure and developed an electrically-operated loading device for feeding ammunition belts from a ground cart backward through the feed chutes into the boxes. Using a mock-up, it was demonstrated that two men could reload all boxes and prepare guns for firing in 12 minutes. Since then, this ammunition handling technique has been adopted by several other fighter aircraft manufacturers.

be built and tested for an amount of $5.3 million, including a $258,809 fixed fee.

Powered by two 3,000 lb (1,361 kg) thrust Westinghouse XJ34-WE-13 axial-flow turbojets and piloted by Robert M Edholm, the unarmed XF-88 Voodoo (46-525) first flew at Muroc Dry Lake on 20 October, 1948. Fortunately, minor difficulties encountered early in the flight programme were easily rectified. Thus, a thrust loss on take-off due to choking in the S-shaped air ducts was eliminated by fitting spring-loaded blow-in doors in the wheel well section of the ducts. Insufficient rolling power was partially corrected by increasing aileron chord by 26 per cent but full resolution of this deficiency was found to require an increase in torsional rigidity of the wing over and above that made before the XF-88 first flight[2]. Excessive buffeting with the dive-brakes[3] in the full open position was promptly eliminated by perforating the brakes with $3/4$-in (1.9-cm) diameter holes and reducing the maximum opening from 65 to 45 deg. Finally, as no practical change in aerodynamic configuration could be made to correct inadequately damped directional oscillations and objectionable roll coupling, the McDonnell team was forced to devise artificial means of stabilization and to adopt a yaw damper system using a yaw rate gyro and controlling the rudder.

Whereas most handling characteristics were generally satisfactory and those few needing improvements were expected to be easily corrected, performance was disappointing due in part to the demanding range requirements and in part to weight increases since design inception. To achieve the required range, McDonnell had planned to supplement the 734-US gallon (2,778-litre) internal capacity[4] with 350-gallon (1,325-litre) tip tanks. However, wind tunnel testing revealed that a serious stall condition would be encountered with tanks on. Various modifications were evaluated in the wind tunnel but no satisfactory solution could be found, thus preventing the XF-88 from getting anywhere close to meeting the Air Force range requirement. Furthermore, early weight estimates, including a combat weight of 16,500 lb (7,485 kg), had proved unduly optimistic and by the time of the first flight loaded weight had increased by about 11 per cent. The installation of additional equipment, as requested by the Air Force, and various modifications required as a result of flight tests were expected to boost weight increases to nearly 22 per cent over the original specification. Not surprisingly, the XF-88 proved

[2]   During final design, the torsional rigidity of the wing had been increased by about 60 per cent over that required by strength considerations, primarily by increasing skin gauge but resulting in a 200 lb (91 kg) weight penalty, in order to prevent a loss in aileron effectiveness due to wing flexibility.

[3]   Mounted on the rear fuselage sides, the XF-88 dive-brakes were unusual as, in an attempt to get maximum drag and minimize operating power, they were hinged at the rear.

[4]   It is worth noting that the internal fuel capacity of the XF-88 was substantially greater than that of jet fighters then in USAF service, that of the Lockheed F-80C, Republic F-84D, and North American F-84 ranging between 416 and 435 gallons (1,575 and 1,647 litres).

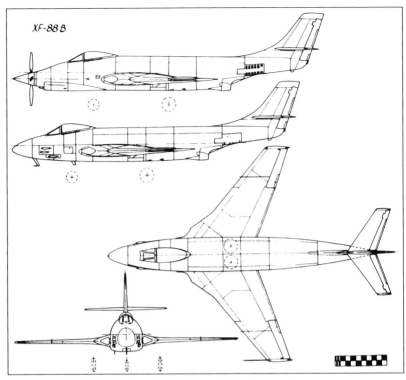

XF-88 B

McDonnell XF-88A and XF-88B Voodoo.

slower than anticipated (at sea level, its top speed of 641 mph (1,032 km/h) fell between that of the Republic F-84E—613 mph, (986 km/h) and that of the North American F-86A—679 mph (1,093 km/h) both already in production).

Before the first flight of the XF-88 and after considering various forms of liquid injection to boost the J34's power, McDonnell suggested two approaches to improve performance. Afterburners were to be fitted to the J34s powering the second Voodoo prototype and production F-88s were to be powered by 6,000 lb (2,722 kg) thrust Westinghouse J46 afterburning turbojets. Funding for the J46 installation never became available but approval was given for the second Voodoo to be delivered in the XF-88A configuration with afterburning J34s. This powerplant installation, however, proved difficult to realize as neither the turbojet manufacturer, Westinghouse, nor specialized component manufacturers considered the power increase which could be obtained from an afterburner with a length of 52 in (1.32-m)—the maximum which McDonnell could allow due to ground clearance considerations—sufficient to warrant development. In the end, McDonnell was forced to undertake the development of the afterburner on its own and did so

The XF-88A over the Mississippi River during a test flight in August 1953. *(MCAIR)*

successfully. With an installed length of only 30 in (0.76 m) and weighing 218 lb (99 kg), the McDonnell-designed afterburner boosted the thrust of each Westinghouse XJ34-WE-15 from 3,600 to 4,825 lb (1,633 to 2,189 kg).

Powered by a pair of these afterburning engines and fitted with bladder fuel cells in the wings to increase internal capacity by 100 gallons (379 litres) to 834 gallons (3,157 litres), the XF-88A (46-526) was first flown on 26 April, 1949. Soon, the second Voodoo demonstrated promising performance improvements (maximum speed at sea level was increased to almost 700 mph—1,125 km/h, time to climb to 30,000 ft was cut by two-thirds to four minutes, and take-off run was reduced by 20 per cent). Unfortunately for McDonnell, these improvements came too late. By then, the Air Force had to contend with a reduced budget, changing priorities, and confusion.

In addition to the XF-88, designs vying to meet the Air Force requirement for penetration fighters included the Lockheed XF-90, an all-new twin-jet design ordered in June 1946 and first flown on 3 June, 1949, and the North American YF-93A, a more powerful and larger derivative of the F-86 ordered in December 1947 under the P-86C designation and first flown on 25 January, 1950. At first, placing much value on commonality with other Sabre variants[5], the Air Force had favoured the North American design and, before any of the penetration fighter prototypes had flown, had supplemented the contract for two F-86C prototypes with one for 118 production aircraft. Accordingly, in December 1948 McDonnell was instructed to stop design and development work for the F-88 but to continue flight testing the two Voodoo prototypes.

However, the F-86C production contract was cancelled in February 1949 as a result of (1) a reduction in military budget, (2) the decision to

[5]   In the end, this consideration appears to have been ill-founded as the Air Force reported spending a total of $11.5 million for the two YF-93As versus $5.1 million for the two XF-90s and $6.6 million for the two Voodoo prototypes (including the cost of the XF-88B test-bed.)

give priority to interceptors and strategic bombers, and (3) the recommendation by a Senior Officers' Board that a penetration fighter should not be selected for production until after competitive testing and evaluation. In July 1950, the Senior Officers' Board changed course and this time recommended that Republic F-84Fs be purchased as interim escort fighters and that ten additional Lockheed XF-90s be procured to expedite development of a penetration fighter based on this type. Meanwhile, the Air Proving Ground Command had gone ahead with organizing the previously mandated competitive testing of the XF-88, XF-90 and YF-93. These tests took place between 30 June and 8 July, 1950, resulting in the Evaluation Board reporting on 15 August that the XF-88A was the winner. The apparent hopelessness of the situation surrounding the selection of a penetration fighter was finally cleared by

The XF-88B landing with its propeller, driven by an Allison XT38-A-5 turbine, in feathered position. *(MCAIR)*

wartime pressures mandating that priority be given to the procurement of existing types for use in Korea. Accordingly, none of the penetration fighters were to be put into production.

For McDonnell, however, this did not end the development of its Model 36 as, at the request of the Air Materiel Command (AMC), work on a propeller research vehicle had begun in July 1949. Seeking a test-bed for transonic and supersonic propellers, AMC insisted that airframe modifications be kept to a minimum while provisions were to be included for testing 27 combinations of two-, three-, and four-bladed airscrews ranging in diameter from 4 ft (1.22 m) to 10 ft (3.05 m) and driven by an Allison T38 turbine through a gear box operating at 1,700, 3,600, or 6,000 rpm.

In October 1949, after completing Phase I tests at Edwards AFB, the first XF-88 was returned to McDonnell to be modified as the XF-88B propeller research vehicle. To that end, the aircraft was to be fitted with a 2,650 shp Allison XT38-A-5 propeller-turbine mounted offset to port in

First flown on 24 April, 1953, in St Louis, the XF-88B was later transferred to NACA's Langley Memorial Aeronautical Laboratory. *(MCAIR)*

the nose and its nosewheel moved to starboard, the non-afterburning XJ34-WE-13s were to be replaced by afterburning XJ34-WE-15s, a fuel cell was to be installed in the wing as done for the XF-88A, and the fuselage fuel cell capacity was to be reduced to 543 gallons (2,055 litres) to provide space for flight test equipment. Moreover, 240 lb (109 kg) of

This view of the first F-101A and the XF-88A provides a good comparison of the respective sizes of the two types named Voodoo by McDonnell. The aircraft on the assembly lines in the background are Demons for the US Navy. *(USAF)*

115

ballast was to be placed in the rear fuselage to balance the weight of the nose-mounted propeller-turbine.

Modification work began with the installation of afterburning turbojets. However, before the propeller-turbine could be mounted, 46-525 had to be returned to the Air Force to replace the XF-88A (46-526) which had been damaged on 16 June, 1950. Thus, installation of the XT38 and related flight-test equipment was not completed until early 1953. Ground testing of the propeller-turbine started on 16 February and the novel powerplant was first tested in flight on 24 April. Thereafter, the XF-88B spend much of its time at the Langley Memorial Aeronautical Laboratory where NACA, which also received the damaged XF-88A in February 1955 as a source of spares for the XF-88B, completed the testing of the propeller research vehicle in 1956.

Span 39 ft 8 in (12.09 m); length 54 ft 1$\frac{1}{2}$ in (16.5 m); height 17 ft 3 in (5.26 m); wing area 350 sq ft (32.52 sq m).

Empty weight 12,140 lb (5,507 kg); loaded weight 18,500 lb (8,391 kg); maximum weight 23,100 lb (10,478 kg); wing loading 52.9 lb/sq ft (258 kg/sq m); power loading 3.1 lb/lb st (3.1 kg/kgp).

Maximum speed 641 mph (1,032 km/h) at sea level; cruising speed 527 mph (848 km/h); climb to 35,000 ft (10,670 m) in 14$\frac{1}{2}$ minutes; service ceiling 36,000 ft (10,975 m); range 1,737 miles (2,795 km).

Trailing shock waves from the afterburner of its Allison J71-A-2 turbojet, this F3H-2N carries two drop tanks beneath the fuselage and two 2-in rocket pods beneath each wing. *(MCAIR)*

McDonnell F3H (F-3) Demon

When the MiG-15 made its combat debut over Korea on 1 November, 1950, the only operational fighter aircraft of Western design capable of matching it on fairly even terms was the North American F-86A Sabre which had entered USAF service 20 months earlier. The MiG-15, however, thoroughly outperformed the most recent US Navy carrier fighters, the Grumman F9F-2 Panther and McDonnell F2H-2 Banshee. Fortunately, even though the MiG-15 itself had come as almost a total surprise to Allied intelligence, the appearance of Soviet high-performance combat aircraft had been anticipated by the Navy. A Request for Proposal for a carrier-based interceptor had been issued by the Bureau of Aeronautics on 21 May, 1948, and seven months later the McDonnell Model 58 had been selected from among eleven competitors submitted by six manufacturers as the winner of this design competition. Thereafter, with the issuance on 3 January, 1949, of a Letter of Intent covering initial design of the McDonnell XF3H-1, BuAer had taken precautionary steps to safeguard the Navy's ability to achieve air superiority. In spite of this early action, however, the Navy was not able to form its first squadron of F3Hs until March 1956, almost five and a half years after the appearance of the MiG-15 in Korea!

The January 1949 Letter of Intent had initiated the development of the USN's first sweptwing carrier fighter and its mock-up had been inspected between 13 and 15 July, 1949. Designed by a team led by Richard Deagen, the XF3H-1 was proposed as a single-engine, single-seat fighter with lateral air intakes and sweptback wing and tail surfaces. Following mock-up inspection and some redesign to reduce weight, two XF3H-1s were ordered on 30 September, 1949, by Contract NOa(s)-10260. At that time, McDonnell agreed to using the Navy-sponsored J40 turbojet which was under development by Westinghouse. More than any other design decision, the selection of this powerplant was to cause unsurmountable problems which considerably delayed the programme, cost the Navy an additional $200 million, forced Westinghouse out of the aero engine business, and almost resulted in cancellation of the third McDonnell Naval fighter.

While the XF3H-1 was under construction (initial structural release being authorized on 23 August, 1950) BuAer redirected the programme by instructing McDonnell to design production aircraft as all-weather

The first XF3H-1 (BuNo 125444) taking off at Lambert Field, St Louis, with slats and flaps down. *(MCAIR)*

general-purpose fighters instead of day interceptors as originally scheduled. A modified F3H-1N mock-up incorporating the required changes was inspected between 11 and 13 July, 1951, while construction of the prototypes remained unaffected as they were intended to serve essentially as aerodynamic test vehicles. However, modifications dictated by trials with the prototypes and the change in mission delayed the programme significantly. The first F3H-1N Demon, which had been ordered in March 1951, was not flown until December 1953. Thirteen months earlier, however, the Navy had authorized McDonnell to undertake a design study for replacing the unreliable Westinghouse J40 with a more powerful Allison J71. This eventually led to the decision to switch to the J71 turbojet beginning with the 61st production Demon. Although saving the programme from outright cancellation, this decision resulted in further delays.

As the intended 9,200 lb (4,173 kg) afterburning thrust Westinghouse

J40-WE-8 was not available for installation in the first XF3H-1, BuNo 125444 was powered by a 6,500 lb (2,848 kg) thrust XJ40-WE-6 without afterburner when Robert M Edholm took it for its maiden flight at St Louis on 7 August, 1951. The similarly powered second prototype (BuNo 125445) first flew in January 1952 and a year later was re-engined with a 10,500 lb (4,763 kg) thrust afterburning J40-WE-8. Both versions of the Westinghouse axial-flow turbojet proved unreliable and resulted in the first aircraft being damaged in a landing accident in August 1952 and in both prototypes being temporarily grounded on two occasions. Flight trials also revealed that forward visibility was not as good as desired for a carrier-borne aircraft and that lateral stability and roll rate were unsatisfactory. To correct the first problem, McDonnell redesigned the nose section of production models. To correct the roll rate deficiency the ailerons of the XF3H-1s were moved inboard, as proposed for the production aircraft. Once fitted with afterburning engine and modified ailerons, the second prototype was used for preliminary evaluation at the Naval Air Test Center, Patuxent River, Maryland, beginning in August 1953 and for initial carrier trials aboard the USS *Coral Sea* (CVA-43) on 28 October, 1953. However, full evaluation of the Demon had to wait until the first F3H-1Ns became available.

The first F3H-1N (BuNo 133489) was flown at Lambert Field on 24 December, 1953. After trials were suspended during a three-month period in the spring of 1954, following the loss of an F3H-1N during evaluation at NATC Patuxent River in March, NPE (Navy Preliminary

F3H-1N (BuNo 133490) powered by the troublesome Westinghouse J40-WE-8 turbojet. *(MCAIR)*

Evaluation) and BIS (Bureau of Inspection and Survey) trials respectively began in July 1954 and February 1955. Engine thrust and reliability remained below expectations and further operational testing had to await availability of J71-powered Demons. Finally, the first F3H-2N (BuNo 133520, the 32nd F3H-1N airframe modified before completion) flew on 23 April, 1955, and the first F3H-2M (BuNo 133569) flew on 23 August.

BIS trials for the F3H-2N began in September 1955, carrier qualifications were undertaken aboard the USS *Ticonderoga* (CVA-14) on the 12th of that month, and the Fleet Indoctrination Program was begun in January 1956. With FIP completion on 3 March, 1956, the Demon was at last ready for service use.

Production history

XF3H-1: When first flown on 7 August, 1951, the XF3H-1 (BuNo125444) was powered by a 6,500 lb (2,848 kg) thrust Westinghouse XJ40-WE-6 which was fed by large intakes protruding on each side of the cockpit (photographs initially released were retouched and showed what appeared to be small flush intakes to mislead anyone trying to guess engine thrust from inlet size). The same non-afterburning version of the Westinghouse turbojet also initially powered the second XF3H-1 (BuNo 125445) but was replaced in January 1953 by a J40-WE-8 which was fitted with an afterburner and had a maximum thrust of 10,500 lb (4,763 kg).

Modifications dictated by flight trials included the removal of the fence from each outboard wing panel, the relocation of the ailerons further inboard with a corresponding decrease in the length and area of the trailing-edge flaps, and the addition of an autopilot. The first XF3H-1 was lost in flight on 18 March, 1954, as the result of an engine explosion, and the second prototype was permanently grounded shortly after. The second XF3H-1 was finally shipped to the Naval Air Development Center at Johnsville, Pennsylvania, to be used in barrier engagement tests.

F3H-1N: Urgently needing a high-performance carrier fighter to match the MiG-15 and having high expectations for the F3H-1N, the Navy had ordered its production by McDonnell before the first flight of the XF3H-1. Furthermore, the Navy had also awarded a contract, later cancelled, to the Temco Aircraft Corporation of Dallas, Texas, for an additional 100 aircraft (BuNos 133389/133488). Unfortunately, the Navy's hopes were to prove unduly optimistic as three pilots were killed, five aircraft lost, and other F3H-1Ns were damaged extensively in non-fatal accidents. Although partially traced to relatively minor airframe and system deficiencies, most of the crashes were attributed to persistent engine troubles, the Westinghouse J40 proving most unreliable and failing to develop its design thrust. Thus, even though 58 F3H-1Ns were built (BuNos 133489/133519, 133521, and 133523/133548), the type was not put into service and the surviving aircraft were either used as ground trainers or scrapped.

The F3H-1Ns differed from the prototypes with relocated ailerons in having the entire nose and cockpit sections tilted down 5 deg to improve forward vision during carrier approach and landing. Internal fuel capacity was increased from 1,148 to 1,506 US gallons (4,346 to 5,701 litres). The simple gun ranging radar as planned for the F3H-1 interceptor was replaced by the AN/APG-30 housed under an enlarged diaelectric nose cone, and armament consisted of four forward-firing 20-mm cannon

An F3H-1N being used as a maintenance trainer by the Naval Air Technical Training Unit in Memphis, Tennessee. *(USN)*

situated below and behind the air intakes. For initial trials the F3H-1N was powered by a 7,200/10,500 lb (3,266/4,763 kg) thrust dry/afterburning J40-WE-8 turbojet but, in its aborted production form, the aircraft was fitted with a 7,500/10,900 lb (3,402/4,944 kg) J40-WE-22 or -22A engine.

F3H-1P: Mock-up inspection for this proposed reconnaissance version, of which 24 (BuNos 137132/137155) had been ordered in September 1952, took place on 26/27 May, 1953. However, development of these J40-powered aircraft was abandoned in favour of that of J71-powered F3H-2Ps.

F3H-2N: As soon as it was evident that Westinghouse would not be able to turn the J40 into a reliable powerplant, R J Baldwin—who had

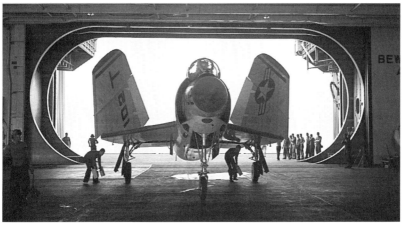

An F3H-2N of VF-14 being parked in hangar bay No. 1 aboard the uss *Forrestal* (CVA-59) on 24 June, 1956. *(USN)*

121

replaced Richard Deagen as project engineer—tried to convince the Navy to let McDonnell install a substitute engine. Eventually, in spite of its standing commitment to use the J40 in most of the Navy's advanced projects of the period, the Bureau of Aeronautics authorized McDonnell to study the feasibility of powering the Demon with the Allison J71. To that effect, a mock-up of the proposed F3H-2N was submitted for inspection on 10/11 August, 1953. Three months later the F3H-1N contract was amended to provide for the 32nd and 34th aircraft (BuNos 133520 and 133522) to be completed as J71-powered prototypes and for the 61st and subsequent production Demons to be powered by the

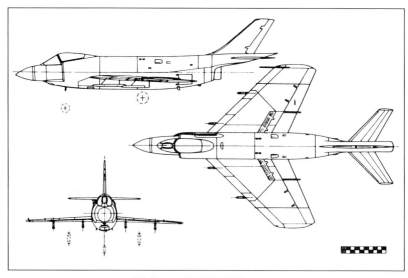

McDonnell F3H-2N Demon.

Allison engine. Moreover, to offset weight increases due to the redesign from a day interceptor into an all-weather general-purpose fighter, the J71-powered prototypes and production aircraft were to be fitted with larger wings. Wing area was increased from 442 to 519 sq ft (41.06 to 48.22 sq m) through the simple expedient of extending the chord at the wing root by 40 in (101.6 cm) by moving the trailing edge aft.

BuNo 133520, the first of two F3H-2N development aircraft, flew on 23 April, 1953, and 140 production aircraft (BuNos 133549/133568, 133570/133622, and 136966/137032) which had been ordered as F3H-1Ns were completed to the new standard with J71-A-2 turbojets with dry military rating of 10,000 lb (4,536 kg) and maximum afterburning thrust of 14,400 lb (6,532 kg). In service, these engines were upgraded to the similarly-rated J71-A-2A or -2B standard. The F3H-2Ns were fitted with AN/APG-51 radar, could carry two 262-US gallon (992-litre) drop tanks, and retained the primary cannon armament of the F3H-1Ns. Later they

122

were retrofitted to carry four AAM-N-7 Sidewinder I or IA infrared homing missiles.

In service, the Demon remained somewhat underpowered even after the installation of the J71, the two upper cannon were often omitted, especially when missiles or external stores were carried, and their blast tube was covered by a fairing plate. Moreover, as carrying two drop tanks under the fuselage resulted in a reduction in range and endurance due to the excessive drag of the closely mounted tanks and as the carriage of a single tank also resulted in shorter range than when the aircraft was flown in clean condition (endurance, however, was increased slightly), aircraft were more often than not flown without tanks. Hence, the fitting of a refuelling probe, which was developed in compliance with the September 1955 decision to have all Navy jet-powered fighters and attack aircraft fitted with probes for inflight refuelling, proved to be a much more satisfactory means of increasing both range and endurance. The removable probe was bolted on the starboard fuselage side above the air intake and, when extended upward and outboard during air refuelling, its tip was easily seen by the pilot.

One F3H-2N (BuNo 133573) was modified in 1957 as a test-bed for the AN/APQ-50 radar installation being developed for the F4H-1. Other F3H-2Ns still in service when the Department of Defense adopted a new Tri-Service designation system in September 1962 became F-3Cs.

F3H-2M: Produced in parallel with the F3H-2Ns, the 80 F3H-2Ms (BuNos 133569, 133623/133638, and 137033/137095) had their search radar specially modified to the AN/APG-51B configuration to guide AAM-N-2 Sparrow I semi-active radar homing missiles, four of which

A Block 7 F3H-2M in the markings of VX-5. *(USN)*

could be carried beneath the wings. The first F3H-2M flew on 23 August, 1955, and the model was redesignated MF-3B in 1962.

F3H-2: Whereas both the F3H-2N and F3H-2M models were built under existing contracts initially issued to cover the proposed production of F3H-1Ns, the F3H-2s were ordered directly as such in 1956-57. While

An F-3B of VF-193, CVG-19, USS *Bon Homme Richard* (CVA-31), landing at NAS Atsugi, Japan, on 6 November, 1962. *(Toyokazu Matsuzuki)*

retaining the ability to carry the more capable AAM-N-6 (AIM-7C after September 1962) Sparrow III and AAM-N-7 (AIM-9B) Sidewinder IA air-to-air missiles, the 239 F3H-2s (BuNos 143403/143492, 145202/145306, 146328/146339, and 146709/146740) were optimized as strike fighters and could carry up to 6,000 lb (2,722 kg) of conventional bombs, special stores, or rocket pods on two fuselage and six wing stations. They differed externally from previous models in having a slightly shorter beaver tail cone. The last of these aircraft, which were redesignated F-3Bs in 1962, was delivered on 8 April, 1960, and brought Demon production to a close. The impact of early development problems on the programme can be judged from the fact that, whereas 973 Demons (excluding the XF3H-1 prototypes but including the production aircraft which were to have been built by Temco) had been ordered, the last F3H-2 was the 519th production aircraft.

F3H-2P: In this proposed reconnaissance version of the Demon, radar and cannon were to have been replaced by cameras installed in four nose stations and one station in the former armament bay. The contract was cancelled before the completion of the first aircraft.

F3H-3: This projected version of the Demon was to have been powered by a 9,200/12,900 lb (4,173/5,851 kg) thrust General Electric J73-GE-3. Ninety F3H-3s (BuNos 143403/143492) were ordered but no J73-powered Demon was completed and the 90 airframes ordered as J73-powered F3H-3s were completed as J71-powered F3H-2s.

Service history
As already mentioned, the J40-powered F3H-1Ns were not put into service. Nevertheless, on 13 February, 1955, one of these aircraft piloted by McDonnell test pilot C V Braun, set an unofficial time-to-height record of 10,000 ft (3,048 m) in 71 seconds. A little over two months later the F3H-2N prototype was first flown and J71-powered aircraft entered service during the first quarter of 1956. An F3H-2M was delivered in

A McDonnell F3H-2 of VF-31, CVG-3, assigned to the uss *Saratoga* (CVA-60).
(Harry S Gann)

February to the Naval Missile Center at Point Mugu, California, and in March F3H-2Ns went to a development and training squadron (VC-3 at NAS Moffett Field, California) and an operational squadron (VF-14 at NAS Cecil Field, Florida).

F3H-2Ns were first deployed to the Mediterranean from January to July 1957 when VF-14 went aboard the uss *Forrestal* (CVA-59) and to the Western Pacific from April to September 1957 when VF-124 was embarked aboard the uss *Lexington* (CVA-16). Thereafter, Demons equipped 22 deployable squadrons—eight (VF-13, -14, -31, -41, -61, -82, -131, and -161) with the Atlantic Fleet and 14 (VF-21, -24, -53, -54, -64, -92, -112, -114, -122, -124, -141, -151, -193, and -213) with the Pacific Fleet, two replacement training squadrons (VF-101 and -121), and one composite and two evaluation squadrons (VC-3, VX-3, and VX-4).

F3H-2s from Blocks 12, 14, 16 and 18 over the uss *Saratoga* (CVA-60) in April 1962. *(USN)*

In service, even when carrying no external stores, the Demon was found to be short on range and endurance. Hence, as it would not have been able to operate for a normal 90-minute carrier cycle when carrying stores, the F3H was not used in its intended general-purpose role. In the more limited all-weather interceptor role, it was finally replaced by the Vought F-8E Crusader and by its McDonnell stablemate, the superlative F-4B. A West Coast squadron, VF-161 at NAS Miramar, became the last Demon squadron to complete its conversion to the Phantom II when in September 1964 it traded its F-3Bs for F-4Bs.

With the Fleet, the Demon performed dependably and gained the distinction of becoming the first carrier fighter to fire air-to-air guided missiles while deployed at sea, that event taking place on 8 December, 1958, when F3H-2Ms of VF-64 were operating from the USS *Midway* (CVA-41). Earlier during the same year, on 17 May, four Demons joined four Crusaders in becoming the first carrier fighters to fly the Atlantic nonstop with inflight refuelling to demonstrate the feasibility of delivering jet fighters from east coast stations to carriers of the Sixth Fleet in the Mediterranean.

F-3B (BuNo 143468) of the Naval Missile Center at NAS Point Mugu, California.
(Peter B Lewis)

In addition to its use as an operational fighter, the Demon was assigned to various Navy test facilities (Naval Missile Center at Point Mugu, Naval Ordnance Test Station at China Lake, Naval Air Test Center at Patuxent River, and Naval Air Test Facility at Lakehurst) and was used for several significant tests including the inflight launching of a Northrop XKDT-1 rocket-powered target drone by an F3H-2M operating from the Naval Missile Center at Point Mugu (3 September, 1957); the first airborne firing of the Hughes HIPEG (High Performance External Gun, a twin-barrel 20 mm cannon mounted in a pod) by an F3H-2N at the Naval Air Ordnance Test Station Chincoteague, Virginia (8 April, 1958); and the first launching of a two-stage Sparroair space probe which reached a peak altitude of 66 miles (106 km) after being released from an F3H-2M flying

126

An F3H-2M of VF-112 carrying the NH tail code of CVG-11. *(Harry S Gann)*

almost vertically at 30,000 ft (9,145 m) over the Pacific Missile Range (2 August, 1963).

Much maligned during the dark days of 1951-55 when the J40-powered aircraft failed to gain acceptance by the US Navy, the J71-powered Demon redeemed itself in service. In particular, pilots praised the aircraft's large wings with power-operated slats and large flaps which rendered it docile at high altitude as well as during carrier landings. Nevertheless, due to its long gestation period, the J71-powered Demon had a relatively short operational career lasting only eight and a half years. By comparison, the Vought Crusader, which in its F8U-1 version had entered service a year after the Demon, remained in service for 30 years as the last RF-8Gs were not phased out until 1987.

	F3H-1N	F3H-2
Span, ft in	35 4	35 4
(m)	(10.77)	(10.77)
Span (wings folded), ft in	25 4	25 4
(m)	(7.72)	(7.72)
Length, ft in	59 0	58 11½
(m)	(17.98)	(17.97)
Height, ft in	14 7	14 6.6
(m)	(4.45)	(4.43)
Wing area, sq ft	442	519
(sq m)	(41.06)	(48.22)
Empty weight, lb	18,691	21,287
(kg)	(8,478)	(9,656)
Loaded weight, lb	26,085	31,145
(kg)	(11,832)	(14,127)
Maximum weight, lb	29,998	39,000
(kg)	(13,607)	(17,690)
Wing loading*, lb/sq ft	59.0	60.0
(kg/sq m)	(288.2)	(293.0)
Power loading*, lb/lb st	2.4	2.2
(kg/kg)	(2.4)	(2.2)
Maximum speed, mph/ft	628/10,000	643/35,000
(km/h at m)	(1,011/3,050)	(1,035/10,670)
Maximum speed, mph at s.l.	616	716
(km/h at s.l.)	(991)	(1,152)
Cruising speed, mph	553	
(km/h)	(890)	

127

Climb rate, ft/min	10,900	14,350
(m/sec)	(55)	(73)
Service ceiling, ft	44,000	42,650
(m)	(13,410)	(13,000)
Normal range, miles	1,130	1,180
(km)	(1,820)	(1,900)
Maximum range, miles		1,370
(km)		(2,205)

* wing and power loadings are calculated at normal loaded weight and maximum take-off power.

The McDonnell Model 79 Big Henry. *(MCAIR, courtesy of Dr F. W. Roos)*

McDonnell 79 Big Henry

In 1950, after trials with the XH-20 had been terminated, McDonnell engineers remained convinced that for certain specialized applications the intrinsic simplicity of this system would outweigh its uneconomical fuel consumption rate. Hence, after failing to attract the interest of the Army in a proposed light scout and observation vehicle using a ramjet-driven rotor, they turned their attention to the agricultural market in the belief that an easily maintained, low cost helicopter would find a ready market.

As described in a specification report dated 26 September, 1950, the Model 79 was essentially similar in concept and construction to the Model 38 (XH-20) but was somewhat larger with the diameter of the two-bladed rotor being increased from 18 to 27 ft (5.49 to 8.23 m). It differed further from the Model 38 in having tail surfaces consisting of a fixed ground adjustable tailplane and a universally mounted movable rudder. Open accommodation was provided for a pilot, and alternate alighting gears, consisting of either a tricycle gear or twin skids, were offered. Power was provided by a pair of McDonnell 8RJ4 ramjets, one at the tip of each rotor blade, and 100 US gallons (379 litres) of fuel was carried in two tanks. For ferry purposes auxiliary tanks could be fitted to increase fuel capacity to 180 gallons (681 litres).

Designed as a utility helicopter, the Model 79 was intended to be used for pest or weed control, defoliation, fertilizing, seeding, or many other varied uses such as carrying mail or cargo. To that end, it could be fitted with either (1) dual liquid chemical tanks with a total capacity of 116 US gallons (439 litres) and dual spray booms; (2) dual dust or seed bins with a total capacity of 15.5 cu ft (0.44 m³) and a dust outlet pointing downward and aft of the rotor disc; or (3) dual mail or light cargo bins with a total volume of 40 cu ft (1.13 m³). As a further alternative, the design provided

James S McDonnell at the controls of the Big Henry. *(MCAIR, courtesy of Dr F. W. Roos)*

for the installation, either during construction or as rapid modification kits, of cockpit floor extensions and removable plastic panels to convert the single-seat Model 79 into the two-seat Model 79A with dual controls.

Charles R Wood Jr first flew the single seat Model 79 demonstrator, which was registered N12M, on 26 March, 1952. Although trials proved relatively uneventful and confirmed that the basic design was sound and easy to fly and maintain, development of the Model 79 had to be abandoned in mid-1953 as the type had failed to attract commercial interest due to high fuel consumption rate and noise level.

Rotor diameter 27 ft (8.23 m); fuselage length 15 ft 6 in (4.72 m); height, 8 ft 4 in (2.54 m). Empty weight 647 lb (293 kg); loaded weight 1,800 lb (816 kg); maximum weight 2,000 lb (907 kg).
Maximum speed 86 mph (138 km/h); rate of climb 1,060 ft/min (5 m/sec); hover ceiling in ground effect 3,800 ft (1,160 m); service ceiling 10,000 ft (3,050 m); endurance 62 min.

The XH-17 (50-1842) hovering over the runway at Culver City on 23 October, 1952. *(Summa Corporation)*

Hughes XH-17

By letter dated 31 January, 1946, Materiel Command requested qualified manufacturers to submit proposals for the development of a large experimental helicopter. This rotary-wing craft was to be capable of carrying externally an 8 ft by 8ft by 20 ft (2.44 m by 2.44 m by 6.10 m) cargo package weighing up to 10,000 lb (4,536 kg) at a top speed of 65 mph (105 km/h), to hover at an altitude of 3,000 ft (915 m), and to have a tactical radius of 100 miles (160 km) and an endurance of 30 minutes. It was intended for use in transfer of ordnance, equipment, supplies, and personnel, with loads to be lowered into or lifted out of areas in which even helicopter landings were impossible. Moreover, this sky crane helicopter had to be easily dismantled for transport on standard trailer trucks.

Advised by Friedrich von Dobhloff, the Austrian engineer who during the war had pioneered the application of jet principle to helicopters at the Wiener Neustädter Flugzeugwerke and who also worked with McDonnell on the XH-20 and other helicopters, the AAF Rotary Wing Branch recognized that achieving such capabilities would require major and risk-fraught technological advances and, accordingly, it encouraged bidders to consider using (1) a method of rotor construction other than conventional steel tube spar and wood; (2) gas-turbines and jet-driven rotors; and (3) servo controls, blade ailerons, or other devices to reduce the high control forces inherent in the use of a main rotor which was expected to have a diameter of 75 to 80 ft (22.86 to 24.38 m). Finally, to minimize costs, the Rotary Wing Branch recommended that the fuselage and other non-critical components of this flying test-rig be constructed in the simplest form possible.

As requested, the bidders submitted proposals for a two-phase programme with the first phase consisting of a design study and the second phase, which would be undertaken only after the AAF approved the design study, calling for the fabrication of a flying test-rig. After proposals evaluation, Kellett Aircraft Corporation of Upper Darby, Pennsylvania, was notified on 2 May, 1946, that it had won the design competition and soon after a contract for the first phase design study was negotiated.

The one-year design study phase revealed that technical problems would be even more difficult than anticipated, notably as the result of the need to use a rotor of much greater diameter, and hence more difficult to manufacture and control. Powerplant selection also proved arduous as,

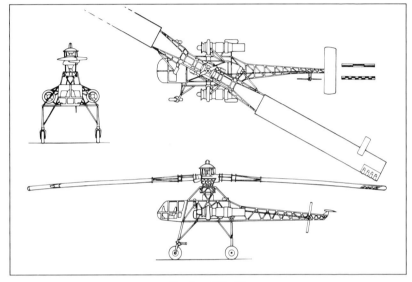

Hughes XH-17.

although concurring with AAF personnel at Wright Field that the use of gas-turbine and rotor-tip combustion was likely to provide the best solution, Kellett was eventually forced to recommend a twin-turbine installation instead of the single turbine favoured by the AAF. This and other technical recommendations were endorsed by the Air Materiel Command at the end of the design study phase and on 27 August,1947, Kellett was awarded Contract AC15011 to build a ground test-rig for the XR-17 (which became the XH-17 in June 1948 when the newly created USAF adopted a revised designation system). Provision was incorporated in the contract for the modification of the ground rig into a flying test-stand at the Air Force option.

While the XR-17/XH-17 ground test-rig was under construction, Kellett ran into financial difficulties and in 1948 sold the rights and partially completed rig to Hughes for $250,000. Pleased that work on the largest helicopter then under development would be continued, the USAF approved the transfer of the partially completed rig from Upper Darby to Culver City. At that time, key members of the Kellett design team were hired by Hughes and moved to California where work was resumed quickly and the test-rig completed in late 1949.

To save costs, as had been recommended in the request for proposals and provided in the Kellett design, Hughes incorporated components from other aircraft in the XH-17 test-rig. The two-seat cockpit came from a Waco CG-15, the single-wheel front undercarriage from a North American B-25, the twin-wheel main undercarriage from a Douglas C-54, and the 636-US gallon (2,407-litre) fuel cell from a Boeing B-29 bomb bay tank. Power was provided by two General Electric 7E-TG-180-XR-17A gas generators (modified J35 turbojets) with bleed air from the intermediate compressor stage being fed into the rotor hub and then through ducts to four tip burners at each blade tip, where fuel was added and burned. This dual powerplant installation was predicted to provide the equivalent of 3,480 hp when the rotor turned at its normal rate of 88 rpm. The 130-ft (39.62-m) diameter two-blade rotor relied on tension-torsion straps for blade retention.

Trials with the XH-17 ground rig were begun at Culver City on 22 December, 1949. Note absence of tail boom and tail rotor. *(WADC/National Archives)*

Ground running began on 22 December, 1949, and, as was expected from such a drastic advance in rotary wing size and complexity, soon brought to light a number of teething problems. Nevertheless, satisfactory progress was made until June 1950 when a cyclic gear failed, badly damaging the rig. Eight months earlier, however, Hughes and the Air Force had felt sufficiently confident in the project to proceed to the next phase and the manufacturer was funded under Contract AF8907 awarded in October 1949 to modify the ground rig into a flying test-stand. Hence, instead of merely repairing the rig after the June 1950 accident, Hughes also incorporated changes required to prepare the XH-17 for flight.

The large size of the XH-17 and the complexity of its rotorhead are shown to advantage in this photograph taken at the Hughes Airport in Culver City on 23 October, 1952. *(Summa Corporation)*

Notably, these pre-flight modifications included the fitting of a dual hydraulic system, each featuring three variable displacement hydraulic pumps, and the installation of a tail rotor. Due to the absence of driving torque resulting from the use of a pressure-jet cycle system to drive the main rotor, the diameter of the tail rotor could be reduced in comparison with that which would have been required for a conventionally-powered helicopter with the overall size of the XH-17, and for yaw control Hughes was able to use the tail rotor of a Sikorsky H-19 mounted on a tubular fuselage extension.

Ground testing resumed after a two-year hiatus during which these modifications were incorporated at a leisurely pace while design of the servo control was being refined. Finally, having received the Air Force serial 50-1842, the XH-17 was first flown by Gale Moore at Culver City on 23 October, 1952. That flight, however, had to be cut short after the XH-17 had been airborne for barely a minute as directional control forces were excessive. While correction of this deficiency could be made quickly, difficulties uncovered later in the trials required more time. In particular, high vibratory stresses in the main rotor blades were difficult to correct and the XH-17 was repeatedly grounded while modifications were incorporated. The off and on test programme ended when the rotor blades reached their design life in December 1955.

All in all, the XH-17 had validated the design concept and its development into a satisfactory sky crane would have been feasible had it not been for the high fuel consumption rate which could not be reduced to any significant extent and which precluded ever achieving the 100-mile

The XH-17 carrying a standard Air Force radar and communications trailer. *(MDHC)*

tactical radius requirement set back in 1946. On the positive side, this large sky crane helicopter possessed several remarkable assets, including its demonstrated ability to airlift a standard Air Force remote communication trailer and loads of up to 10,284 lb (4,665 kg). It was indeed ahead of its time in many respects apart from its obvious size. Pilots notably praised its exceptional responsiveness to collective and cyclic pitch control movements and the negligible level of vibration felt in the cockpit. Conversely, they complained about the sluggishness of its directional control.

Rotor diameter, 130 ft (39.62 m); fuselage length, 53.3 ft (16.25 m); height, 30.1 ft (9.17 m).
Empty weight, 28,562 lb (12,956 kg); maximum payload, 10,284 lb (4,665 kg); loaded weight, 31,270 lb (14,184 kg); maximum weight, 43,500 lb (19,731 kg); rotor loading, 2.4 lb/sq ft (11.5 kg/sq m); power loading, 9 lb/hp (4.1 kg/hp).
Maximum speed, 90 mph at 8,000 ft (145 km/h at 2,440 m); cruising speed, 85 mph (137 km/h); initial climb rate, 1,650 ft/min (8.4 m/sec); service ceiling, 13,100 ft (3,995 m); range with 10,284 lb (4,665 kg) load, 30 miles (48 km).

The XV-1 after addition of small steering rotors aft of the tail surfaces. *(MCAIR)*

McDonnell XV-1

Initially designated XL-25 in the liaison aircraft category, then XH-35 in the helicopter class, and finally XV-1 as the first type in the new vertical lift category of aircraft designations, this machine worked on the unloaded rotor principle. Designed by Friedrich von Doblhoff, the Austrian helicopter pioneer responsible for the wartime WNF 342, the XV-1 was the result of an experimental programme undertaken jointly by McDonnell, the US Army, and the USAF Air Research and Development Command.

Combining the features of a twin-boom, twin-tail, fixed-wing aircraft with those of a single-rotor helicopter, the XV-1 was powered by a 525 hp Continental R-975-19 seven-cylinder radial. For vertical flight this engine drove two compressors which fed air through tubes to small pressure jets at the tips of the three-blade rotor, with the pressure jets operating on the principle of ignition and expansion of the fuel gases. For forward flight, the engine drove a two-blade pusher propeller mounted aft of the fuselage between the tail booms while the rotor autorotated. The XV-1 was intended to take-off and land as a helicopter, with transition from helicopter flight mode to conventional flight being made by transferring power from rotor to propeller as soon as the forward speed exceeded the stalled speed of the wing. Side-by-side accommodation was provided for a pilot and a co-pilot with room behind them for test instrumentation. Alternatively, accommodation could have been provided for a pilot and three passengers or a pilot and two stretchers.

Initiated by a Letter of Intent dated 20 June, 1951, the XV-1 project proceeded through mock-up inspection in November 1951, and the first aircraft (53-4016) was completed some 22 months later. Project test pilot John R Noll began tethered hover flights on 11 February, 1954, but

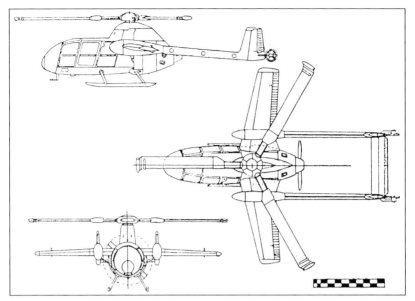

McDonnell XV-1.

difficulties with the pressure jet system delayed initial free flight until 14 July, 1954. The first successful transition from helicopter flight to conventional flight was made on 29 April, 1955. During the preceding months, the second XV-1 (53-4017) had joined the flight trials programme. This machine differed from the first prototype in having a bulkier but streamlined undercarriage and cut-down rotor pylon to reduce interference drag. Numerous detail improvements, including the addition of a small steering rotor behind each boom, were progressively incorporated.

Although on 10 October, 1956, the XV-1 had become the world's first rotary wing vehicle to reach a speed of 200 mph (322 km/h), the gain in performance over conventional helicopters did not warrant the added complexity of the convertiplane configuration. Furthermore, the potential of the McDonnell XV-1 was seriously limited by its use of a piston engine instead of gas turbines as adopted to power European convertiplanes which preceded or followed it[1]. Accordingly, the programme was terminated in 1957 after the two prototypes had been flown for a total exceeding 600 hours. The first XV-1 then went to the Army Aviation

1   In France, the SNCASO Farfadet, which used a Turboméca Artouste II to drive its propeller and a Turboméca Arius I to drive the compressor and feed air to its rotor, made the first successful transition from helicopter flight to conventional flight on 2 December, 1953, almost 17 months before this was accomplished with the XV-1. In Great Britain, the much larger and capable Fairey Rotodyne, which was powered by a pair of Napier Elands, did so on 10 April, 1958.

The first XV-1 convertiplane (53-4016) in front of the McDonnell plant at St Louis in 1954. This machine is now kept in the Army Aviation Museum, Fort Rucker, Alabama. *(MCAIR)*

Center Museum at Fort Rucker, Alabama, and the second was donated to the National Air and Space Museum, in Washington, DC.

Span 26 ft (7.92 m); length 50 ft 5 in (15.37 m); height 10 ft 9 in (3.28 m); rotor diameter 31 ft (9.45 m).

Empty weight 4,277 lb (1,940 kg); loaded weight 5,505 lb (2,497 kg); rotor loading 7.3 lb/sq ft (35.6 kg/sq m); power loading 10.5 lb/hp (4.8 kg/hp).

Maximum speed 203 mph (327 km/h); cruising speed 138 mph (222 km/h); maximum rate of climb 1,300 ft/min (6.6 m/sec) in 3.2 minutes; vertical rate of climb 308 ft/min (1.6 m/sec).

RF-101C-40-MC (56-0172) off the coast of the southeastern United States during the 1962 Cuban Missile Crisis. *(USAF)*

McDonnell F-101 Voodoo

Originally intended for service with fighter squadrons of the Strategic Air Command, the F-101 Voodoo went on to serve with most USAF combat commands including TAC, ADC, PACAF, and USAFE, as well as with the Air National Guard, the Royal Canadian Air Force/Canadian Armed Forces, and the Chinese Nationalist Air Force. With the various USAF commands the Voodoo performed reliably in a wide variety of roles—penetration/escort, tactical/nuclear strike, interception, reconnaissance, and conversion training—and can be regarded as one of the most versatile supersonic aircraft yet to be designed. For McDonnell, it marked an important turning point as it was its first aircraft to be accepted for production by the USAF.

During the early stages of the Korean War, when the USAF attempted to undertake strategic bombing missions in a manner similar to Second World War daytime operations—*ie* streams of bombers escorted by fighters, it found that its Republic F-84 Thunderjets escorting Boeing B-29s were no match for the faster and more manoeuvrable MiG-15s of the North Korean and Chinese Air Forces and that its North American F-86A Sabres lacked the range and endurance required of effective escort fighters. SAC then planned initially to re-equip its Fighter-Escort Wings with Republic F-84F Thunderstreaks but wanted longer ranged penetration fighters to escort its Convair B-36s. Thus, the Air Force issued a General Operational Requirement in February 1951 and five manufacturers—Lockheed, McDonnell, North American, Northrop, and Republic—promptly submitted proposals. That submitted by McDonnell, a more powerful and heavier version of the F-88, won the competition in May 1951, but a Letter of Intent for its development was not awarded until 3 January, 1952.

139

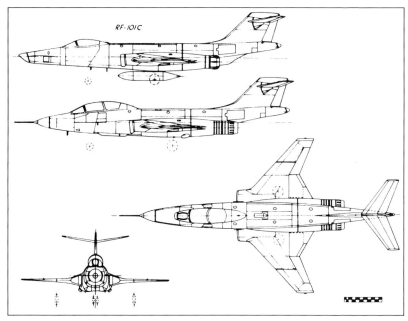

McDonnell F-101B Voodoo and side view of RF-101C.

To achieve the performance specified for the new escort fighter, which was designated F-101 in November 1951, the McDonnell design team led by Edward M Flesh studied several powerplant arrangements before recommending the use of Allison J71 turbojets in December 1951. With afterburner, these engines were expected to have three times the maximum thrust of the Westinghouse J34s powering the XF-88A and more than twice that of the Westinghouse J46s which had been proposed for the stillborn production version of the F-88. The Wright Air Development Center, however, pronounced itself in favour of using even more powerful Pratt & Whitney J57s, and Air Force Headquarters endorsed the WADC recommendation.

Fed by enlarged and redesigned intakes in the wing roots, the J57s were to be mounted in the same location as the engines of the earlier experimental aircraft and, besides being more powerful, were anticipated to have a markedly improved specific fuel consumption. Nevertheless, due to the greatly increased thrust, fuel requirement was also higher and forced the design team to lengthen and widen the fuselage to increase internal fuel capacity more than three fold (2,341 versus 734 US gallons—8,861 versus 2,778 litres). Internal tankage was to be supplemented by two 450-gallon (1,703-litre) external tanks and, for ferrying purposes, the ammunition boxes for the four 20 mm cannon could be replaced by a 226-gallon (855-litre) auxiliary fuselage tank. Furthermore, the F-101 was to incorporate provision for both types of flight refuelling systems used at

140

The NF-101A, the first F-101A modified as a test-bed for J79 turbojets, flying near Edwards AFB on 8 January, 1958. *(USAF)*

that time by the USAF. Accordingly, a retractable probe was mounted forward of the cockpit and a refuelling boom receptacle was installed on top of the centre fuselage. The most evident external features distinguishing the new aircraft from the XF-88 were the relocation of the all-movable tailplane almost to the top of the vertical tail surfaces and the increase in wing area (from 350 to 368 sq ft—32.52 to 34.19 sq m) obtained by increasing the chord on the inboard half of each wing panel. Other changes included a reduction in wing thickness and the relocation of the ailerons further inboard. Most of these design features were incorporated in the mock-up which passed inspection during July 1952.

On 28 May, 1953, the USAF awarded McDonnell an initial production contract for 29 F-101As. No prototypes were ordered as the new aircraft was a fairly straightforward development of the XF-88, and wartime needs justified bypassing the more usual prototype phase. By then, construction of the first aircraft (53-2418) was already well under way. However, the signing of the armistice at Panmunjon which ended fighting in Korea in July 1953 removed the urgency with which the programme had been proceeding. Moreover, changing requirements and the need to redesign the aircraft to enable it to undertake not only the originally planned escort mission but also that of nuclear strike prompted the Air Force to withdraw its authorization to proceed with quantity production until Category II tests had been completed and required design changes had been made.

After completing preliminary ground trials at St Louis, the first F-101A was shipped to Edwards AFB, California, where Robert Little reached Mach .9 at 35,000 ft (10,670 m) during the first flight on 29 September, 1954. Less than a month later, however, after level speed had been increased progressively to Mach 1.4, the aircraft experienced irregular air flow in its intakes while its engine proved prone to compressor stall. A redesign of the internal intake layout and engine compressor modifications soon solved these problems.

One month after the first first flight of the F-101, the Air Force lifted its production hold. Voodoos went on to be built as single-seaters for use in the escort/strike fighter and reconnaissance roles (a Letter of Intent for the development of this variant having been issued in January 1953) and as two-seaters for use in the all-weather interceptor role (production of this version being authorized in February 1955). Details of these production versions and of later conversions are as follows:

Production history

F-101A: Powered by two 10,200/15,000 lb (4,627/6,804 kg) dry/after-burning thrust Pratt & Whitney J57-P-13 turbojets, the 78 F-101A-1-MCs to F-101A-35-MCs (53-2418/53-2446 and 54-1438/54-1485) were optimized for the penetration escort role and constituted the USAF's WS-105A weapon system. These single-seaters were armed with four 20 mm cannon and could carry externally a 1,620-lb (735-kg) or 3,721-lb (1,688-kg) special store (nuclear bomb). The F-101As were equipped with the MA-7 fire control system as well as with LABS (Low Altitude Bombing System) computers for toss release of their nuclear bombs. The last F-101A was delivered on 21 November, 1957. In 1956, one of these aircraft (53-2432) was briefly flown by pilots from the NACA High-Speed Flight Station at Edwards AFB for familiarization.

JF-101A: The ninth F-101A (53-2426) was bailed to Pratt & Whitney to serve as a test-bed for the more powerful J57-P-55s selected for the

The JF-101A (53-2426) in which Maj Adrian E Drew set a new world speed record on 12 December, 1957. *(USAF)*

F-101B interceptor. With these engines, the aircraft set a new absolute world speed record of 1,207.6 mph (1,943.45 km/h) on 12 December, 1957.

NF-101A: In 1958 the first F-101A was bailed to General Electric to serve as a test bed for the J79-GE-1 turbojet. Given the N designation prefix to indicate that it had been permanently assigned for special tests, this aircraft was test flown with two J79s in 1958-59 before being sent to Amarillo AFB, Texas, to end its life as a ground maintenance trainer.

YRF-101A: While under construction, the 16th and 17th F-101A airframes were set aside for conversion as prototypes for the WS-105L weapon system, the USAF's first supersonic reconnaissance aircraft. Two additional airframes were ordered to complete the F-101 fighter contract. The YRF-101A-10-MC made its maiden flight on 30 June, 1955. The two YRF-101As (54-149 and 54-150), which retained the J57-P-13s of the fighter version, were characterized by their redesigned and longer nose housing four cameras for low-altitude photography. Two high-altitude cameras were mounted behind the cockpit in place of the ammunition boxes of the single-seat fighter variant.

RF-101A: The first production reconnaissance version of the Voodoo, of which 35 were built (54-1494/54-1521 and 56-155/56-161), was

Four RF-101As in service with the Chinese Nationalist Air Force. *(CNAF, courtesy of Paul D Stevens)*

generally similar to the YRF-101A. Like the two prototypes, these aircraft were unarmed and could carry up to six cameras. The RF-101A retained both flight refuelling systems as used on the fighters but the internal fuel tank arrangement was revised and resulted in a slightly reduced capacity of 2,250 gallons (8,517 litres).

NF-101B: This designation was given to the two-seat prototype for the long-range interceptor version described under the following heading. Unlike the airframes of production F-101Bs, which were stressed for 7.33g manoeuvres, that of the NF-101B was limited to 6.33g manoeuvres. Powered by two Pratt & Whitney J57-P-55s with longer afterburners and

143

a maximum thrust rating of 16,900 lb (7,666 kg), this experimental aircraft (56-232) was first flown at Lambert Field on 27 March, 1957.

F-101B: Development of an all-weather interceptor variant was first suggested by the Air Defense Command in autumn 1952. Initially regarded as too costly, this programme was again considered in spring 1953 to provide the Air Force with long-range interceptors to complement relatively short ranged North American F-86Ds. However, it was only after delays with the development of the Convair F-102B (redesignated F-106A in June 1956) made it imperative for the Air Force to obtain interim interceptors to bridge the gap between the barely supersonic

F-101B-90-MC of the 13th FIS at Davis-Monthan AFB, Arizona, on 11 March, 1968. Based at Glasgow AFB, Montana, the 13th FIS flew Voodoos from the summer of 1959 until deactivated in June 1968. *(Douglas D Olson)*

Convair F-102A and the Mach 2+ F-102B, that McDonnell began working in earnest on that aircraft. Competing proposals were also submitted in spring 1954 by North American and Northrop and in June of that year the McDonnell's entry was selected as the winner of this competition.

Before being awarded a development contract, McDonnell had considered both single-seat and two-seat configurations, studied various powerplant installations (including pairs of General Electric J79s, Pratt & Whitney J57s or J75s, or, as initially favoured, Wright J67s), and proposed alternative armament arrangements (folding-fin rockets and/or various types of guided missiles to be carried in a ventral bay) and fire control systems. In the end, after a mock-up of a single-seat cockpit had been inspected in November 1954 and engine and armament proposals had been thoroughly reviewed, the contractor and the Air Force agreed that the WS-217A long-range interceptor system would be based on a two-seat aircraft. It would be powered by Wright J67s (Bristol Olympus turbojets which in their Americanized version were expected to have a maximum afterburning thrust of around 22,000 lb/10,000 kg), fitted with

144

a Hughes MG-13 fire control system, and armed with guided missiles with conventional warheads.

An initial batch of two-seat interceptors was ordered under a Letter of Intent issued on 3 March, 1955. The number of aircraft on order was increased to 96 when contractual arrangements were finalized four months later. The new interceptor was officially designated F-101B in August 1955, and its mock-up was inspected on the 14th and 15th of the following month at a time when flight trials were still expected to begin in spring 1956. However, Wright ran into serious development troubles with its J67 turbojets and the F-101B programme was delayed until McDonnell and the Air Force agreed to have the interceptor powered by

N8234, the F-101B which had been used by the Colorado State University for research into severe storm conditions, at Buckley ANGB, Colorado, in November 1981. The aircraft still carried on its fuselage, forward of the intake, the unit insignia of its previous operator: the 116th Fighter Interceptor Squadron, Washington Air National Guard. *(René J Francillon)*

Pratt & Whitney J57-P-55 engines fitted with afterburners which were longer than those of J57-P-13s powering the tactical single-seaters and boosted maximum thrust rating from 15,000 to 16,900 lb (6,804 to 7,666 kg). With these engines, the NF-101B flew on 27 March, 1957, and F-101Bs entered service in January 1959, some 18 months later than initially planned. Following the NF-101B prototype, 400 F-101B-40-MCs to -120-MCs were built (*see* Appendix C for list of serial numbers). The last of these aircraft was delivered on 24 March, 1961.

Retaining the centre and rear fuselage sections and the wing and tail surfaces of the F/RF-101A, the interceptor had a revised forward fuselage housing the MG-13 fire control system with automatic search and track mode, a flight refuelling probe, a two-seat cockpit with the radar operator aft of the pilot, and all-missile armament. Inside the centre fuselage and wings, fuel capacity was reduced to 2,053 gallons (7,771 litres) to avoid c.g. location problems and provide added room for the armament and some electronic equipment. Armament consisted of six GAR-1 semi-active or GAR-2 infrared homing Falcon missiles carried on and

145

54-1512 an RF-101A-30-MC at Tan Son Nhut AB, Vietnam, in 1965. *(USAF)*

launched from a hydraulically-actuated rotary armament door covering the fuselage bay beneath and behind the rear cockpit.

Late production F-101Bs (blocks 115 and 120) were completed with modifed fire control system and with provision for carrying externally two MB-1 Genie unguided missiles with nuclear warheads in place of two of the Falcon missiles. From 1961, many earlier F-101Bs were upgraded to this standard under Project *Kitty Car*. Other modernization programmes saw a fair number of F-101Bs fitted between 1963 and 1966 with an infrared sensor in place of the retractable refuelling probe and other fire control system modifications as part of the Interceptor Improvement Program (also known as Project *Bold Journey*) while most were fitted between 1964 and 1968 with a modified pitch control system for their automatic pilot.

CF-101B (RCAF serial 17404, ex-USAF F-101B-115-MC 59-0404) at Wurtsmith AFB, Michigan, on 9 July, 1988. *(Douglas D Olson)*

CF-101B: A first batch of 56 Voodoos[1] was delivered to the Royal Canadian Air Force between July 1961 and May 1962. In RCAF/Canadian Armed Forces service, these aircraft were redesignated CF-101B and assigned Canadian serials using the last three digits of their USAF serials prefixed by the number 17 (*eg* 59-391 became 17391). In 1970-71 the 46 surviving CF-101Bs from this initial batch were exchanged for 56 ex-USAF Voodoos from earlier production batches which had been upgraded with infrared sensors and other fire control system modifications as part of Project *Bold Journey*. In Canadian service, this new batch of CF-101Bs and the second batch of CF-101Fs received consecutive serials in the 101001 to 101066 range with the serials assigned to CF-101Bs being 101008/101021, 101023, 101025/101051, and 101053/101066.

EF-101B: This unofficial designation was used in Canada to identify two Voodoos fitted with specialized electronic countermeasure equipment to serve as ECM aggressors. One was an ex-Canadian Armed Forces CF-101F (serial 101006) and the other was an ex-USAF F-101B which was specially purchased in 1982 and given the Canadian serial 101067.

RF-101B: In 1971, after being returned to the United States, 22 CF-101Bs from the first batch were modified by Martin Marietta Corporation at Greenville, South Carolina, as two-seat reconnaissance aircraft. The fire control system and armament of the interceptors were replaced by a battery of forward and vertical cameras in a nose of modified contour. With the exception of an ex-USAF F-101B-85-MC (57-301) which had been similarly modified before being assigned to the

RF-101B (57-0301) operated by the Air Force Logistics Command at the Donaldson Center. *(Jim Sullivan)*

[1] The first batch of Canadian Voodoos included 25 F-101B-115MCs with Fiscal Year 1959 serials 59-391/-392, -394/-399, -401/-406, -408/-411, -433/-436, and -438/h440, and 31 F-101B-120-MCs with 1959 serials 59-441/-442, -444/-448, -450/-453, -455/-457, -459, -461, -463/-464, -467/-471, -475/-477, and -479/-483.

Air Force Logistics Command as a test vehicle, all RF-101Bs[2] were operated by the Nevada ANG.

TF-101B: This designation identified F-101Bs which, instead of being upgraded to the latest operational standards, were modified by the Air Force and fitted with dual controls.

F-101C As changing requirements prompted the Air Force to decide that SAC would no longer have its own fighters, the F-101As were quickly transferred first to TAC and then to USAFE for use in the long-range strike role. However, F-101As were not well suited to low-altitude tactical operations as their structure was stressed only for manoeuvres not exceeding 6.33 g. Accordingly, the next single-seat fighter version of the Voodoo was tailored for use by TAC and structurally strengthened to allow manoeuvres of up to 7.33 g. Its MA-2 bombing system comprised the LABS (Low Altitude Bombing System) and LADD (Low Altitude Drogued Delivery) systems. On delivery, the 47 F-101C-40-MCs to -55-MCs (54-1486/54-1493 and 56-001/56-039) retained the powerplant, internal armament, and external nuclear bomb attachment of the F-101As. In service, however, one of the four 20-mm cannon was frequently removed to provide space for TACAN navigation equipment. The first F-101C flew on 21 August, 1957, and the last was delivered 10 months later. Ninety-six aircraft (56-040/56-135) ordered as F-101Cs were completed as RF-101Cs after the Air Force decided not to equip a second wing with single-seat Voodoo fighters.

RF-101C: Combining the strengthened wing structure of the F-101C with the camera installation of the RF-101A, 166 RF-101C-40-MCs to -75-MCs (56-040/56-135, and 56-162/56-231) were the last single-seat

F-101F-76-MC (56-0294) of the 165th Tactical Reconnaissance Squadron, 123rd Tactical Reconnaissance Wing, Kentucky ANG, at Shewmaker ANGB (Standiford Field), Louisville. *(KYANG)*

2   The ex-Canadian RF-101Bs were serials 59-391, -397, -398, -402, -403, -404, 410, -434, -436, -441, -447, -448, -450, -453, -457, -459, -463, -467, -477, and -481/-483.

Voodoos built for the Air Force. Final delivery was on 31 March, 1959.

F-101D and F-101E: These designations were reserved for projected versions which were to have been powered by two General Electric J79s. None were built.

F-101F: Produced alongside F-101B interceptors, the 79 F-101F-51-MCs to F-101F-121-MCs were operational and conversion trainers with dual controls. They carried the same missile armament as the F-101Bs and were combat capable. Serial numbers for these aircraft are given in Appendix C. Most F-101Fs were retrofitted with infrared sensors and other fire control system modifications as part of Project *Bold Journey*.

57-0327, an F-101F-91-MC of the 111th FIS, Texas ANG. *(J. Geer)*

CF-101F: Along with 56 F-101Bs, the RCAF received 10 F-101Fs[3] in 1961-62. In Canadian service, these two-seat combat-capable trainers were designated CF-101Fs and were given serials using the last three digits of their USAF serials prefixed by the number 17 (*eg* 59-478 became

McDonnell RF-101G (54-1460, ex F-101A-30-MC) of the 165th Tactical Reconnaissance Squadron, Kentucky ANG, at Shewmaker ANGB on 31 July, 1969.
(Paul D Stevens)

---

[3]   The first batch of Canadian CF-101Fs included four F-101F-116-MCs (59-393, 59-400, 59-407, and 59-437) and six F-101F-121-MCs (59-443, 59-449, 59-449, 59-460, 59-466, 59-472, and 59-478).

17478). Like the first batch of CF-101Bs, survivors of the first batch of CF-101Fs were exchanged in 1970-71 for refurbished F-101Fs with all the latest *Bold Journey* modifications. The 10 CF-101Fs from this second batch received Canadian serials 101001/101007, 101022, 101024, and 101052.

RF-101G and RF-101H: After USAFE had taken its single-seat Voodoo fighters out of service, 61 of these aircraft were modified by Lockheed Aircraft Service Company at Ontario, California, to serve as reconnaissance aircraft with three squadrons of the Air National Guard.

RF-101H (56-0004 ex F-101C-40-MC) of the 165th TRS, KY ANG, at Shewmaker ANGB on 31 July, 1969. *(Paul D Stevens)*

After their armament had been removed and new nose cones housing cameras had been installed, 29 F-101As were redesignated RF-101Gs while 32 F-101Cs became RF-101Hs.

Service history

Before entering service, the Voodoo had already gained some notoriety as an F-101A had been intentionally exposed to an H-bomb explosion during a flight over the Bikini testing ground in May 1956. However, it was mostly during its first two years in service that the big McDonnell fighter and reconnaissance aircraft attracted attention with a series of unusual and record breaking flights. The first of these record flights, which was undertaken as Operation *Sun-Run*, saw four RF-101As take off from Ontario, California, on 27 November, 1957, to set new transcontinental speed records. Refuelled in flight from KC-135As, two of the aircraft landed at McGuire AFB, New Jersey, while the two other flew back to California and landed at March AFB. In the process, 1st Lieut Gustav Klatt flew eastbound coast-to-coast in 3 hr 7 min 43 sec (average speed 781.7 mph, 1,257.8 km/h) and Capt Robert Sweet broke the westbound coast-to-coast record (3 hr 36 min 33 sec, 677.7 mph,

F-101B-85-MC and F-101B-90-MC of the 116th FIS, Washington ANG.
(WA ANG)

1,090.4 km/h) and Los Angeles–New York–Los Angeles record (6 hr 46 min 36 sec, 721.85 mph, 1,161.5 km/h). On 12 December, 1957, Operation *Fire Wall* saw Maj Adrian Drew of the 27th Fighter-Bomber Wing break the world's absolute speed record by flying the ninth aircraft (53-2426), which had been fitted with two J57-P-55s as a powerplant development aircraft for the F-101B, at a speed of 1,207.6 mph (1,943.45 km/h). During the same month, an RF-101A flew from Tachikawa AB, Japan, to Hickham AFB, Hawaii, in 6 hr 3 min to set a point-to-point record. Other record flights set by Voodoos included a 5,600-mile (9,012-km) circuit originating and terminating at Bergstrom AFB, Texas, which was flown in 11 hr 35 min by two air refuelled F-101Cs on 22 May, 1958; an Andrews AFB, Maryland, to Liège, Belgium, F-101C flight in 6 hr 12 min on 28 June, 1958; a flight by seven F-101Cs which were ferried nonstop from Bergstrom AFB to RAF Bentwaters, Suffolk, in 11 hr 2 min on 10 August, 1958; and, on 25 September, 1958, an F-101A flew 1,896 miles (3,051 km) between Carswell AFB, Texas, and Bermuda in Operation *Long Leap*, the longest nonstop/non-refuelled flight yet accomplished by a century series fighter. Finally, the RF-101C was used during 1959 to break two world closed-circuit records: Col Edward Taylor flew at an average speed of 700.047 mph (1,126.6 km/h) over a 1,000-km (621 mile) course on 8 April and Capt George Edwards flew at an average of 816.28 mph (1,313.6 km/h) over a 500-km (310.7-mile) course on 15 April.

These noteworthy early flights, which were matched by a remarkable safety record (notwithstanding a tendency to pitch up, a problem only partially solved through the installation of an active inhibitor, the F/RF-101 achieved the distinction of having the lowest first-year accident

151

The RF-101C-75-MC (56-0119) in which Col E H Taylor set a world's record by averaging 700.047 mph over a 1,000-km closed-circuit course at Edwards AFB on 8 April, 1959. *(USAF)*

F-101A-30-MC (54-1453) of the 92nd TFS, 81st TFW, USAFE, at Hahn AB, Germany, in May 1962. The 81st TFW was then based at RAF Bentwaters, England. *(David W Menard)*

rate of any operational fighter in Air Force history), soon gave place to the less glamorous service life. The first Voodoo delivered to an operational unit was an F-101A which reached the 27th Strategic Fighter Wing at Bergstrom AFB on 2 May, 1957. Two months later, this unit was transferred from SAC to TAC and was redesignated 27th Fighter-Bomber Wing, a designation retained while the wing received F-101Cs to supplement its F-101As and complete its conversion to Voodoos. However, before the last F-101C could be delivered, it was decided that TAC would transfer its single-seat Voodoo fighters to the 81st Tactical Fighter Wing, a USAFE unit based at RAF Bentwaters. The F-101As and F-101Cs served with the 81st TFW until replaced by F-4Cs in 1965-66 and were then returned to the United States where 61 were modified as RF-101G and RF-101H tactical reconnanissance aircraft. A few F-101Cs were last operated by ANG squadrons during their conversion to RF-101G/Hs in 1965.

152

The first RF-101A was delivered to the 17th Tactical Reconnaissance Squadron at Shaw AFB, South Carolina, on 6 May, 1957. With this and other squadrons of TAC's 363rd Tactical Reconnaissance Wing, RF-101As were supplemented by RF-101Cs and these aircraft flew their first low-level reconnaissance flights over Cuba on 23 October, 1962. For their role during the Cuban Missile Crisis, 15 pilots from the 363rd TRW were awarded Distinguished Flying Crosses, a clear indication of the RF-101's usefulness during a tense period. The last TAC RF-101Cs were phased out by the 31st TRTS, a replacement training unit in the 363rd TRW, on 16 February, 1971.

An RF-101C-40-MC (56-0163) parked in a revetment at Tan Son Nhut AB, Vietnam, in May 1967. *(USAF)*

RF-101Cs were first assigned to USAFE during spring 1958 when the 66th TRW at Laon AB, France, began its conversion from Republic RF-84Fs to Voodoos. These aircraft went on to serve with the 66th TRW until it was deactivated at RAF Upper Heyford, Oxfordshire, on 1 April, 1970. With PACAF, reconnaissance Voodoos first served with the 15th TRS/67th TRW at Kadena AB, Okinawa, which received its first RF-101C on 28 August, 1958. Aircraft from this squadron were initially deployed to South Vietnam in October-November 1961 to take part in Operation *Pipe Stem*, a series of intelligence gathering flights over South Vietnam and Laos from Tan Son Nhut AB. These were followed by similar *Able Mable* missions over South Vietnam and *Yankee Team* sorties over Laos which were flown by detachments of the 15th and 45th TRSs first from Bangkok's Don Muang Airport and then from Tan Son Nhut AB from November 1961 until spring 1964. *Yankee Team* reconnaissance sorties over Laos were resumed in May 1964 and during the following months RF-101Cs flew pathfinding and BDA (bomb damage assessment) sorties in support of strikes flown by F-100Ds against AAA sites in Laos. From then until November 1970, when the last Voodoos departed from the war zone, RF-101A/Cs from the 15th, 18th, 20th, and

RF-101C-50-MC (56-0196) of the 29th TRS, 363rd TRW, landing at Shaw AFB, South Carolina. *(Jim Sullivan)*

45th TRSs provided the bulk of air reconnaissance in Southeast Asia. A total of 33 RF-101Cs was lost in combat (24 to AAA and small arms fire, five to surface-to-air missiles, two to unknown causes, one to a MiG, and one in a sapper attack at Tan Son Nhut AB). In addition, six RF-101Cs were lost in operational accidents while in Southeast Asia.

With the Air National Guard, RF-101G/Hs were first operated in 1965 by the 154th TRS from Arkansas, the 165th from Kentucky, and the 192nd from Nevada. They were supplemented by RF-101A/Cs beginning in 1970 and by RF-101Bs from 1971. Reconnaissance Voodoos also served with the 107th and 171st TRSs from Michigan, the 153rd TRS from Mississippi, and the 184th TRS from Arkansas. The last RF-101C was withdrawn from use by the 153rd Tactical Reconnaissance Squadron in January 1979.

In addition to serving with the USAF, reconnaissance Voodoos also served with the Chinese Nationalist Air Force. Beginning in November 1959, when four aircraft were shipped to Taiwan, eight RF-101As were operated by the CNAF on routine operations as well as for covert flights deep into mainland China. When the CNAF retired its last RF-101As in the late 'seventies, one (54-1505, Chinese serial 5660) was preserved in a Taiwanese museum.

The operational life of the F-101B was equally long. Service with active squadrons of the Air Defense Command (Aerospace Defense Command after January 1968) began after the first F-101B was delivered to the 60th Interceptor Squadron at Otis AFB, Massachusetts, on 5 January, 1959. Thereafter, F-101Bs equipped 17 air defence squadrons (the 2nd, 13th, 15th, 18th, 29th, 49th, 59th, 60th, 62nd, 75th, 83rd, 84th, 87th, 322nd, 437th, 444th, and 445th FISs) as well as training squadrons (Combat Crew Training Squadrons or CCTS and Fighter Interceptor Training Squadrons of FITS). The last active duty interceptor squadrons to fly

59-0426, an F-101B-115-MC of the 60th FIS. *(Jim Sullivan)*

Three F-101Bs (57-0422, 58-0282, and 58-0336) and an F-101F (58-0318) of the 179th FIS, 148th FIG, Minnesota ANG. *(Maj Gen Wayne C Gatlin)*

F-101Bs were the 60th and 62nd FISs which were deactivated on 30 April, 1971. With the Air National Guard, F-101Bs were first delivered in November 1969 to Washington's 116th FIS and Maine's 132nd FIS. They were also operated in Minnesota (179th), New York (137th), North Dakota (178th), Oregon (123rd), and Texas (111th) and were retired by this last mentioned unit in 1981. The last Voodoo in US service (F-101B-105-MC, 58-300) was phased out by the 2nd FITS at Tyndall AFB, Florida, on 21 September, 1982.

As an interceptor, the Voodoo proved quite successful once teething troubles with its fire control system had been corrected. However, it was outshone by the faster and significantly more manoeuvrable Convair F-106A. Nevertheless, the F-101B gained an honest reputation in squadron service for its reliable performance and earned further recognition during out of the ordinary endeavours. Thus, on 9 June, 1958, an F-101B made the USAF's first supersonic intercept. Headlines were also made on 2 October, 1959, when a specially instrumented aircraft was

155

flown at 1,080 mph (1,738 km/h) over the the Canary Islands to record for 6 min 51 sec a total eclipse of the sun. Finally, the Colorado State University, as part of a research programme into severe storms, flew a civil registered (N8234, ex 57-410) F-101B-110-MC fitted with special instrumentation.

In Canada, the first 56 CF-101Bs and CF-101Fs entered service on 13 November, 1961, when No.410 Squadron at Ottawa began conversion. Other RCAF (later Canadian Armed Forces) units flying Voodoo interceptors were Nos. 409 Squadron (Comox, British Columbia), 414 Squadron (North Bay, Ontario), 416 Squadron (Bagotville, Quebec), and 425 Squadron (Chatham, New Brunswick). In 1970-71, the surviving CF-101Bs and CF-101Fs were traded to the USAF for refurbished and modernized Voodoos (Operation *Peach Wings*) and these aircraft remained in service with Nos. 409, 410, 416, and 425 Squadrons until replaced by McDonnell CF-18A/Bs. The last to convert, No 416

EF-101B (CAF serial 101067) of No. 414 Squadron, Canadian Armed Forces, in April 1987. *(Daniel Soulaine)*

Squadron, did so in early 1985. By then, however, No.414 Squadron had two EF-101Bs (101006 and 101067) on strength. The last of this unique duo was retired in 1986, 38 years after the first flight of the XF-88, thus bringing to an end the Voodoo saga.

	F-101A	F-101C	RF-101A	RF-101C	F-101B
Span, ft in	39 8	39 8	39 8	39 8	39 8
(m)	(12.09)	(12.09)	(12.09)	(12.09)	(12.09)
Length, ft in	67 5	67 5	69 4	69 4	67 5
(m)	(20.55)	(20.55)	(21.12)	(21.12)	(20.55)
Height, ft in	18.0	18.0	18.0	18.0	18.0
(m)	(5.49)	(5.49)	(5.49)	(5.49)	(5.49)
Wing area, sq ft	368	368	368	368	368
(sq m)	(34.19)	(34.19)	(34.19)	(34.19)	(34.19)
Empty weight, lb	24,970	26,277	25,335	26,136	28,970
(kg)	(11,360)	(11,919)	(11,492)	(11,855)	(13,141)

Loaded weight, lb	48,120	48,908	47,331	48,133	45,664
(kg)	(21,827)	(22,184)	(21,467)	(21,832)	(20,713)
Maximum weight, lb	50,000	51,000	51,000	51,000	52,400
(kg)	(22,680)	(23,133)	(23,133)	(23,133)	(23,768)
Wing loading*, lb/sq ft	130.8	132.9	128.6	130.8	124.1
(kg/sq m)	(638.6)	(648.9)	(627.9)	(638.6)	(605.9)
Power loading*, lb/lb st	1.6	1.6	1.6	1.6	1.4
(kg/kgp)	(1.6)	(1.6)	(1.6)	(1.6)	(1.4)
Maximum speed, mph at 35,000 ft	1,009	1,012	1,012	1,012	1,134
(km/h at 10,670 m)	(1,624)	(1,629)	(1,629)	(1,629)	(1,825)
Climb rate, ft/min	44,100	45,000	46,600	45,550	49,200
(m/sec)	(224)	(229)	(237)	(231)	(250)
Service ceiling, ft	55,800	55,100	55,800	55,300	54,800
(m)	(17,010)	(16,795)	(17,010)	(16,855)	(16,705)
Normal range, miles	1,900	1,315	1,100	1,715	1,520
(km)	(3,060)	(2,115)	(1,770)	(2,760)	(2,445)
Maximum range, miles	2,925	2,125	2,195	2,145	1,930
(km)	(4,705)	(3,420)	(3,535)	(3,450)	(3,105)

*wing and power loadings are calculated at normal loaded weight and maximum take-off power.

A float-equipped Hughes 300C on law enforcement duty. *(MDHC)*

Hughes 269, 200, and 300
and
Schweizer 300 and 330

In the mid-fifties, when helicopter technology reached a level sufficient to anticipate that small rotary-wing aircraft would soon enjoy the same degree of acceptance as light fixed-wing aircraft, numerous engineers and inventors, mostly in the United States, began to believe in the feasibility of 'placing a small helicopter in every garage.' Encouraged by this imagined but unsubstantiated market, they designed relatively inexpensive single- and two-seat helicopters to satisfy the hoped-for demand from private owners. For most manufacturers, however, these ill-guided efforts ended in bankruptcy or drained profit from other ventures. The major exception was Hughes which not only succeeded in putting its Model 269 into quantity production but also gained with it a firm foothold in the helicopter market. Even more remarkable is the fact that, more than a third of a century after the first flight of the Hughes 269, a derivative of this outstanding helicopter remains in production as the Schweizer Model 300C and that a turboshaft-powered derivative of this mid-fifties helicopter, the Schweizer Model 330, appears to have a promising future in the 'nineties.

As flight tests on the XH-17 were winding down, Hughes designers became interested in a small, three-bladed, tandem rotor helicopter designed by McCulloch Motor Corporation of Westchester, California. That helicopter, the MC-4 based on a design by 'Gish' Jovanovich, was never put into production but featured rotors of simplified design. Hughes, seeking to offer a low-cost helicopter to civil customers and

158

intending to enter the 'flying Jeep' light observation helicopter competition which the US Army had announced in 1955, bought the rights to the McCulloch/Jovanovich rotor design.

Beginning work in September 1955, a team led by Project Engineer Fred C Strible modified the McCulloch/Jovanovich rotor for use in the single-rotor Model 269. Accommodating two people side-by-side, this lightweight design differed from most helicopters in that its 180 hp Lycoming O-360-A flat-four engine was mounted horizontally, thus avoiding the need for modifications to the lubricating system. Power was transmitted from engine to transmission through eight belts eliminating a clutch and damping engine-to-transmission vibrations. Torque compensation was provided by a two-bladed tail rotor mounted on the port side of the truss tail boom assembly.

Completed within a year from the start of the project, the first Model 269 was registered N78P and was first flown by Gale Moore at the Hughes Airport in Culver City on 2 October, 1956. Both it and the second prototype (N79P) handled well and proved easier to fly than helicopters with fully-articulated rotors, thus encouraging Hughes to re-engineer the design for easier production and maintenance and to bring the second prototype to the Model 269A standard. The most obvious change was the substitution of a tubular tail boom for the truss unit of the Model 269, the relocation of the horizontal stabilizer farther aft, and the use of a cleaned-up and strengthened cockpit enclosure. Trials with the modified aircraft began in 1957 while work was already well-underway on five similarly-configured pre-production YHO-2-HUs for the Army. Evaluated in 1957 and 1958 by Army pilots at Fort Rucker, Alabama, and Air Force test flight teams at Edwards AFB, California, the five YHO-2s proved highly

The second YHO-2-HU (58-1325) at Edwards AFB. *(AFFTC)*

satisfactory and in its evaluation report the Army concluded that the small Hughes helicopter required less maintenance than contemporary observation helicopters, such as the Bell HO-13, and had outstanding manoeuvrability, simplicity, and economy of operation. Nevertheless, plans for its procurement or that of one of its competitors (the French-built Sud-Aviation YHO-1 Djinn and the Brantly YHO-3) had to be abandoned for budgetary reasons. Fortunately for Hughes, the Model 269A was given its FAA Type Approval in April 1959 and had a promising future in the commercial market. Full production was begun in July 1960 and the first production Model 269A was delivered in August 1961.

Production history

More than 3,000 of these piston-engined light helicopters have been produced, first by Hughes and then by Schweizer, in the following versions.

Model 269:   Two two-seat prototypes (N78P and N79P) were built in 1956. The three-bladed main rotor and the two-bladed tail rotor were

The first Model 269 (N78P) during initial trials in the autumn of 1956. *(Hughes, courtesy of Schweizer Aircraft)*

driven by a 180 hp Lycoming O-360-A horizontally-opposed four-cylinder air-cooled engine which was mounted below the side-by-side seats. The first flight was made at Culver City on 2 October 1956.

Model 269A: To serve as prototype for this production version, Hughes modified the second Model 269 by replacing its truss tail boom

160

with a one-piece aluminium tubular boom and introducing several minor modifications to improve handling and ease manufacture and maintenance. After five helicopters were built as YHO-2s for evaluation by the Army, the Model 269A was put into production during the summer of 1960. Customers could request the installation of dual controls and select the low-compression O-360-C2D (for use with 80/87 octane fuel), high-compression HO-360-B1B (for use with 91/96 octane fuel), or fuel-injected HIO-360-B1A versions of the Lycoming flat-four engine, all rated at 180 hp for take-off. Twenty-five US gallons (95 litres) of aviation gasoline were carried in a tank mounted externally aft of the cockpit and, if required, a 19-gallon (72-litre) auxiliary tank could be added on the opposite side. Including the prototype and three pre-production aircraft, but excluding five YHO-2s and 792 TH-55As built for the US Army, Hughes produced 307 Model 269As.

58-1325, a Hughes YHO-2 (Model 269A). *(AFFTC)*

YHO-2: Bearing the serials 58-1324 to 58-1328, five YHO-2s were evaluated by the US Army in the airborne command post and observation roles in 1957-58. However, as there were enough Bell HO-13s and Hiller H-23s in its inventory and funds were lacking, the Army was unable to have the HO-2 put into production.

TH-55A: This military version of the Model 269A, which was selected by the US Army in 1964 to become its standard training helicopter, retained the Lycoming HIO-360-B1A installation of the civil version but was fitted with military radio and instrumentation. An initial contract for 20 TH-55As was placed in 1964 and subsequent contracts under the Fiscal Year 1964 to 1967 budgets brought total Osage procurement to 792 (serials 64-18001/64-18020, 64-18025/64-18239, 65-18240/65-18263, 66-18264/66-18355, 67-15371/67-15445, 67-16686/67-17002, and 67-18356/67-18404). One TH-55A (67-16924) was experimentally fitted with an Allison 250-C18 turboshaft engine derated to 200 shp while another was fitted with a 185 hp Wankel RC 2-60 rotating-piston engine.

161

A TH-55A (64-18126) in the standard high-visibility markings (overall red with yellow band on the tail boom, and black letters and numbers) applied to these trainers. *(Hughes, courtesy of MDHC)*

TH-55J: This designation identified 38 Model 269As which were assembled in Japan by Kawasaki Jukogyo KK for delivery to the Nihon Rikujyo Jieitai (Japanese Ground Self-Defence Force) and given the Japanese military serials 61301 to 61338.

Model 200 (or 269A-1): Offered in both Utility and Deluxe versions— the latter featuring more attractive exterior styling, upgraded interior furnishing, electrical and longitudinal cyclic trim, and other refinements—this version was developed under the 269A-1 designation, certificated in August 1963, and marketed as the Model 200. Forty-one Model 200s were produced for civil operators and foreign military customers. They incorporated various improvements dictated by operational experience but were essentially similar to Model 269As. Model 200s were powered by 180hp Lycoming HIO-360-B1A or HIO-360-B1B engines and had a main fuel tank with a capacity of 25 or 30 gallons (95 or 114 litres).

Model 280U: This was a utility version of the Model 300 incorporating an electric clutch and an electric trim system. Normally delivered in a stripped-down single-seat configuration, the Model 280U could be fitted with agricultural spraying equipment.

162

Model 300 (or 269B):   Through a careful re-arrangement of the cabin, relocation of instruments and controls, and substitution of a contoured bench for the individual seats of earlier versions, Hughes was able to develop a three-seat variant without changing the exterior dimensions of its light helicopter. Initially designated Model 269B, the three-seater received its FAA Type Approval in December 1963 and was produced at the rate of one helicopter every working day beginning in 1964. Power was supplied by the 190 hp Lycoming HIO-360-A1A engine. The Model 300 was the first version which could be fitted with floats made of polyurethane coated nylon fabric in place of the standard skids on oleo-pneumatic shock-absorbers. A total of 463 Model 300s, 280Us, and 300 AGs was built by Hughes.

Model 300AG: This variant of the Model 300 was tailored for agricultural spraying with two 30-gallon (114-litre) chemical tanks, one on each side of the fuselage above the skids, and a 35-ft (10.67-m) spray boom.

Model 300B: To reduce exterior noise level to that of a light aeroplane, Hughes developed a quiet tail rotor. This QTR was installed during production beginning with helicopters delivered in June 1967 and was offered as a retrofit kit for early production Model 269s and 300s. The Model 300B designation was given in some company documents to QTR-equipped three-seat helicopters.

Model 300C (or 269C):   Powered by a 190 hp Lycoming HIO-360-D1A engine driving a three-bladed rotor of increased diameter (26 ft 10 in /8.18 m versus 25 ft 3½ in/7.71m), the Model 269C was first flown on 6

A German-registered (D-HCAP)Hughes 300C. *(MAP)*

March, 1969, received its FAA Type Approval on May 1970, and was put into production at Culver City. Production of the Model 300C was temporarily suspended during the summer of 1981 due to a decrease in demand but resumed in March 1982. However, after the manufacture of

The quiet Model 300CQ was specially developed for police patrol duty at night in urban area. *(Hughes, courtesy of MDHC)*

three prototypes and 1,162 production Model 300Cs and 300CQs, Hughes transferred the production of its light helicopter to Schweizer Aircraft of Elmira, New York, in November 1983. The first Schweizer-built Model 300Cs came off the new assembly line in June 1984 and Schweizer continued manufacturing Model 300Cs under licence even though McDonnell Douglas had acquired Hughes Helicopters in January 1984. Finally, in November 1986 Schweizer purchased all rights to the 269 and 300 series from MDHC. By the autumn of 1989, Schweizer had produced 250 Model 300Cs and TH-300Cs (the latter being a training

A Schweizer TH-300C trainer for the Türk Kara Kuvvetleri (Turkish Army). *(Schweizer)*

164

version for foreign military customers) and demand for both models appeared to be stronger than at any time since the early 'seventies.

In 1969, Nardi Costruzioni Aeronautiche Spa in San Benedetto del Trento, Italy, had acquired limited licence rights from Hughes Helicopters to manufacture the Model 300 and subsequently these rights, extended to include the Model 300C, were transferred to BredaNardi. During the 'seventies and 'eighties, the Italian firm went on to build Model 300s and 300Cs for civil customers and for the Greek Army.

Model 300 Sky Knight: This version, which was developed and built by Hughes as the 300QC and is still built by Schweizer, was specially

The prototype of the turboshaft-powered Schweizer 330. *(Schweizer)*

intended for urban police patrol activities. It differed from the Model 300C only in being fitted with sound deadening materials and a muffler to reduce emission of audible sound by 75 per cent.

Model 330: First flown on 14 June, 1988, the Schweizer 330 is a development of the 300C with the piston engine replaced by an Allison 250-C20W turboshaft derated to 200 shp. The cabin length and width have been increased respectively by 2ft (0.61 m) and 1 ft 5 in (0.43 m) to provide accommodation for a pilot and three passengers (two sitting on a bench slightly aft and between the two front seats) in the utility configuration or for an instructor and one or two students (with flight controls at all three positions) in the training configuration. Moreover, the cockpit enclosure has been streamlined, modern instrumentation has been provided, the aft fuselage has been faired, and a stabilizer with end plates added ahead of the tail rotor. Schweizer has actively marketed the

165

Model 330 to commercial customers, law enforcement agencies, and foreign civil and military operators, and in early 1990 was proposing it to the US Army for use at Fort Rucker as part of the Initial Entry Rotary Wing Integrated Training System. Thus, this turboshaft-powered version may well become the successor of its piston-engined TH-55 forebear. Moreover, in June 1989, Schweizer became a minority partner (35 per cent) in Jordan Aerospace, a company which may undertake assembly and manufacture of Model 330s in the Hashemite Kingdom of Jordan.

Service history

When making its debut in the civil market with the Model 269A, Hughes lacked the necessary business infrastructure to compete effectively and had to organize a distributor network and develop a financing package to win customers for its light helicopter. Working aggressively to achieve this goal, the manufacturer assembled a network of over 100 dealers, which spanned six continents and offered the two-seat helicopter to retail customers on time purchase or lease basis, and saw its efforts rewarded when it captured a 39 per cent share of the US commercial rotary-wing aircraft market less than two years after delivering the first 269A production model in August 1961. Encouraged by these results and the continued demand for its two-seater which was then selling for less than $23,000—about half the cost of most other rotary-wing aircraft, Hughes optimistically predicted that it would soon sell 500 light helicopters annually. The market, however, was not that large. Although doing better than its competitors, in 22 years Hughes delivered only 2,900 light

A Hughes Model 300C applying chemicals on vineyards in Germany's Mosel Valley in 1982. *(Hughes, courtesy of MDHC)*

helicopters, including more than 800 to military customers, before transferring production to Schweizer in July 1983.

Hughes 269As, 200s, and 300s were used, and continue to be used by civil customers for a variety of purposes. Customers notably included magazine and newspaper publishers, radio and television stations, utility and oil companies, engineering and construction firms, farmers and ranchers, and helicopter charter and taxi operators. For the agricultural role, in which Model 269As were first used by fruit and produce farmers in the San Joaquin Valley in California and by cotton growers in North Carolina, Hughes went on to develop the specialized Models 280U, and 300 AG.

In worldwide service, Hughes piston-engined helicopters gained a strong reputation for sturdiness and achieved an excellent safety record in spite of their lightweight construction. Their reliability was further demonstrated in June 1964 when Hughes used an unmodified Model 300 to set a world endurance class record of 101.1 hours. With two pilots relaying each other at the controls, refuelling was accomplished while hovering close to the ground—two dozen eggs being lashed to the underside of the skids to detect any unauthorized landings. None of the eggs were broken and the Model 300 remained airborne for the equivalent of over 6,300 miles (10,135 km).

Hughes 300 of the Taiwanese Police. *(MAP)*

With the Model 300, Hughes became the first manufacturer to focus on the application of helicopters to law enforcement patrol work. Project Sky Knight, which was initiated in December 1966 in co-operation with the City of Lakewood and the Los Angeles Sheriff's Department, saw Model 300s fitted with a searchlight and police radio provide round-the-clock support for routine patrol duty during which they brought a 10 per cent reduction in crime rates. As a result of this experiment, Model 300s and 300Cs subsequently sold to law enforcement agencies were provided with upgraded performance, crew protection, and communications capabilities. Furthermore, the Model 300CQ was specially developed to reduce community noise disturbance and to enable the scene of a crime to be approached unnoticed. During the last two decades, Model 300s, 300Cs, and 300CQs have been used extensively in the law enforcement role and those still in service at the beginning of the 'nineties are likely to be supplemented or replaced by Schweizer-developed Model 330s which, being powered by a turboshaft engine, will use cheaper and more readily available jet fuel.

In July 1964, the 269A was selected by the US Army as its new rotary-wing training aircraft. Designated TH-55A and officially named Osage, after the Indian tribe of the Missouri and Arkansas valley, the new trainer gained the unflattering nickname of 'sausage' soon after entering service at Fort Wolters, Texas, but was well liked by instructors and trainees. For the Army, it proved to be an effective choice because of its low initial cost and low cost of operation, and on account of the effective factory-direct logistic support programme provided by Hughes. Notably, the merits of this logistic support programme were brought out when the Army did not lose a single training day even after 47 per cent of the TH-55A fleet was damaged by a tornado. Remaining based at Fort Wolters during the duration of the Southeast Asia War, TH-55As were used to train the thousands of helicopter pilots then needed by the Army not only for assignment to units flying combat and support operations in Vietnam but also to units in the United States, Panama, and the German Federal Republic. After the war ended, the Army transferred its primary rotary-wing training activities from Fort Wolters to Fort Rucker and the

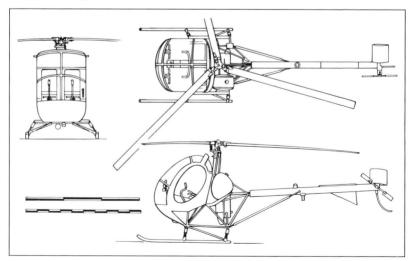

Hughes Model 300.

168

TH-55As made the move to Alabama in 1973. The Osages were finally phased out at Fort Rucker in 1987 and, pending selection of its Initial Entry Rotary Wing Integrated Training System for which the Schweizer 330 is a candidate, the Army has been forced to operate Bell UH-1s in the primary training role.

Abroad, Hughes piston-engined helicopters have been operated and, in numerous instances, continue to be operated by the air arms of the following nations: Algeria (269As with Al Quwwat al Jawwiya al Jaza'eriya); Brazil (269As and 269A-1s with the 1° Esquadrão de Helicópteros de Instrução, Força Aeronaval da Marinha do Brasil, at São Pedro da Aldeia); Colombia (ex-USA TH-55As and 300Cs with the Escuela de Helicópteros, Fuerza Aérea Colombiana, at BAM Luis F Pinto); Costa Rica (269Cs with the Sección Aérea, Ministerio de la Seguridad Pública); El Salvador (Schweizer-built 300Cs with the Fuerza Aérea Salvadoreña); Greece (BredaNardi-built 300Cs with the Helliniki Aeroporía Stratoú); Haiti (300Cs with the Corps d'Aviation d'Haïti); India (269Cs with INAS 562, Indian Naval Aviation, at Cochin); Indonesia (Schweizer-built 300Cs with the Tentara Nasional Indonesia-Angkatan Darat); Iraq (300Cs sold for civil duties but believed taken over by Al Quwwat al Jawwiya al 'Iraqiya for use in the military training role); Japan (Kawasaki-assembled TH-55Js with the Koki Gakko, Nihon Rikujyo Jieitai/Japanese Ground Self-Defence Force, at Akeno,

Hughes Model 269A-1 (Spanish designation HE.20, serial HE. 20-12) of Escuadrón 782, Ala de Enseñanza 78 (782nd Squadron, 78th Training Wing), Ejército del Aire Español, at Granada-Armilla, in April 1987. *(Christian Boisselon)*

A US-registered Schweizer 300C of the Cousteau Society equipped with floats for operations from the *Calypso* research vessel. *(Schweizer)*

Kasumigaura, and Iwanuma); Nigeria (unconfirmed transfer of ex-USA TH-55As); North Korea (300C acquired covertly through a West German dealer); Sierra Leone (ex-Swedish 300Cs with the Air Wing of the Republic of Sierra Leone Military Forces); Spain (269A-1s, designated HE.20s in Spanish service, with Escuadrón 782, Ejército del Aire Español, at Granada-Armilla); Sweden (269As and 300Cs, respectively designated Hkp 5As and Hkp 5Bs in Swedish service, with the Arméflygkar); Thailand (ex-USA TH-55As and Schweizer-built TH-300Cs); and Turkey (Schweizer-built TH-300Cs with the Türk Kara Kuvvetleri at Güverncinlik).

	TH-55A	200	300C	330
Rotor diameter, ft in	25 3½	25 3½	26 10	26 10
(m)	(7.71)	(7.71)	(8.18)	(8.18)
Overall length, ft in	28 2	28 2	30 10	30 10
(m)	(8.59)	(8.59)	(9.40)	(9.40)
Fuselage length, ft in	22 4	22 4	25 0	---
(m)	(6.81)	(6.81)	(7.62)	(---)
Height, ft in	8 2⅝	7 11	8 8⅝	8 7⅞
(m)	(2.51)	(2.41)	(2.66)	(2.64)
Rotor disc area, sq ft	502.3	502.3	565.5	565.5
(sq m)	(46.67)	(46.67)	(52.54)	(52.54)
Empty weight, lb	1,008	913	1,046	1,050
(kg)	(457)	(414)	(474)	(476)
Loaded weight, lb	1,670	1,670	2,150	2,150
(kg)	(757)	(757)	(975)	(975)
Rotor loading*, lb/sq ft	3.3	3.3	3.8	3.8
(kg/sq m)	(16.2)	(16.2)	(18.6)	(18.6)
Power loading*, lb/hp	9.3	9.3	11.3	10.7
(kg/hp)	(4.2)	(4.2)	(5.1)	(4.8)

Maximum speed, mph at s.l.	86	86	105	125
(km/h at s.l.)	(138)	(138)	(169)	(201)
Cruising speed, mph	75	66	77	115
(km/h)	(121)	(106)	(124)	(185)
Climb rate, ft/min	—	1,450	750	—
(m/sec)	(—)	(7.4)	(3.8)	(—)
Hover ceiling in ground effect, ft	6,400	4,700	5,900	18,000
(m)	(1,950)	(1,435)	(1,800)	(5,485)
Hover ceiling out of ground effect, ft	4,000	2,700	2,750	14,000
(m)	(1,220)	(825)	(840)	(4,265)
Normal range, miles	160	200	225	267
(km)	(260)	(320)	(360)	(430)
Endurance, hr	2.5	3.3	3.4	4.0

* rotor and power loadings are calculated at normal loaded weight and take-off power.

The Model 120, the last venture of McDonnell in the field of helicopters before the acquisition of Hughes Helicopters and the organization of the McDonnell Douglas Helicopter Company. *(MDC)*

McDonnell 120

Since 1949 the McDonnell Helicopter Engineering Division had attempted to develop a rotor system capable of high-speed operation. Such a system driven by tip-mounted pressure jets had been successfully tested on the XV-1 convertiplane and its use as a pure helicopter rotor was thought to offer many significant advantages, including (1) inherent angle of attack stability; (2) increased inherent pitch and roll damping; (3) greatly improved dynamic helicopter stability; (4) ability to start and stop in high winds; (5) no need for tracking and no dampers required; (6) no possibility of mechanical instability or ground resonance; (7) very low vibration; (8) low maintenance due to absence of highly loaded bearings, reduction gears, shafting, and anti-torque rotor; and (9) automatic rotor speed control. Accordingly, McDonnell decided in December 1956 to undertake as a private venture the design, development, and testing of a small single-seat crane helicopter using the XV-1 rotor.

The mock-up of the Model 120, which was designed by a team led by Project Engineer Lloyd R Novak, was completed in January 1957, and the first (N6081V) of two prototypes was flown on 13 November of that year by John R Noll. This helicopter was of simple design, with the pilot seated centrally and the fuel tanks mounted on each side of the upper fuselage beneath the rotor head. Three AiResearch GTC-85-135 gas-turbine compressors, which fed pressure jets at the tips of the three-blade

172

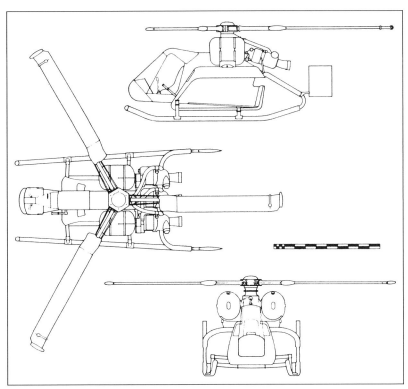

McDonnell Model 120.

rotor, were located below and behind the rotor head. A wide-spaced skid undercarriage enabled large loads to be slung beneath the centre of gravity, or specialized pods to be fitted to carry up to 12 troops, firefighting equipment, or cargo containers.

In spite of some powerplant teething problems, the Model 120 demonstrated a maximum load-to-weight ratio of 1.5:1. Unfortunately, in spite of having been judged 'one of the most outstanding helicopters evaluated to-date in its weight class' when flown at the Naval Air Test Center, NAS Patuxent River, in September 1959, the Model 120 remained experimental as McDonnell failed to win either military or civil orders for this competent design. The termination of this programme in February 1960 marked the end of McDonnell's independent efforts in this field as 13 months earlier the US Marine Corps had terminated the development of the XHCH-1 crane helicopter. McDonnell Douglas, however, came back to the helicopter field in 1984 with its acquisition of Hughes Helicopters, Inc.

Rotor diameter 31 ft (9.45 m); length 20 ft (6.1 m); height 9 ft 3 in (2.74 m).

Empty weight 2,450 lb (1,111 kg); loaded weight 5,000 lb (2,268 kg); maximum weight 6,300 lb (2,858 kg); rotor loading 6.6 lb/sq ft (32.3 kg/sq m).

Maximum speed 138 mph (222 km/h); cruising speed 109 mph (175 km/h); rate of climb 2,400 ft/min (12 m/sec); hover ceiling in ground effect 12,000 ft (3,660 m); range 98 miles (158 km).

An F-4S (BuNo 155834) from the 'Devil's Disciples' of VF-301 and an F-4J (BuNo 157254) from the 'Death Angels' of VMFA-235 flying off the port wing of a Douglas KA-3B of VAK-308 during a training exercsie over the Devil's Playground, south of Baker, California, on 10 December, 1981. *(René J Francillon)*

McDonnell F-4 (F4H) Phantom II

Only one other series of post Second World War aircraft of Western design has surpassed the McDonnell Phantom II in terms of quantity produced, the North American F-86 Sabre, its FJ Fury naval derivatives, and its foreign-built variants. However, even the superlative Sabre could not match the 'phabulous' operational longevity of the F-4.

Design of this great fighter began at McDonnell as a series of evolutionary studies undertaken in August 1953 and aimed at extending the production life of the F3H Demon by boosting its performance and increasing its versatility. Key among these early studies were those for (1) the Model 98A (also known as the F3H-E) to be powered by a Wright J67 turbojet and capable of Mach 1.69 at altitude versus Mach 0.988 for the J71-powered F3H-2; (2) the Model 98B (F3H-G with two Wright J65s and F3H-H with two General Electric J79s) fighter and its Model 98F photographic-reconnaissance variant, both with increased wing area, which were to reach Mach 1.52 with J65 turbojets and Mach 1.97 with the J79s; (3) Models 98C and 98D which were to be fitted respectively with delta and straight wings and powered by either a pair of Wright J65s or two GE J79s; and (4) the Model 98E (F3H-J) with a larger and thinner delta wing.

On the strength of these early studies, McDonnell submitted an unsolicited proposal to BuAer for a single-seat, all-weather fighter on 19 September, 1953. As no requirement for that type of aircraft had yet been issued by the Navy, McDonnell attempted to cover all alternatives by designing quickly exchangeable single- and two-seat nose sections so that versions of its proposed Model 98 could be suited to a variety of roles. To that end, the project team designed forward fuselages which could alternatively accommodate search radar, missile fire-control system, mapping radar, cameras, or electronic reconnaissance equipment as well as four 20-mm cannon or retractable packs for 56 two-inch FFAR rockets. Bombs, rocket pods, nuclear stores, missiles, and/or external tanks were to be carried on nine stations (four under each wing and one beneath the fuselage).

An F-4B-27-MC (BuNo 153047) of VF-74, assigned to Air Wing One for deployment aboard the USS *Forrestal* (CVA-59) in 1967. *(Jim Sullivan)*

Having kept in close contact with BuAer and operational personnel, the design team led by Herman D Barkey determined in the spring of 1954 that a fighter based on the Model 98B offered the best potential and obtained management approval to build a full-size mock-up. As had been hoped, the mock-up and estimated performance attracted much interest from the Navy. However, as the Grumman XF9F-9 and Vought XF8U-1 which had been ordered respectively in April and June 1953 appeared likely to fill the Navy requirements for supersonic fighters, BuAer encouraged McDonnell to submit a proposal for a single-seat, twin-engined, all-weather attack aircraft in competition with designs being submitted by Grumman and North American. On 18 October, 1954, after BuAer had reported favourably on the McDonnell proposal based on the F3H-H design, the Navy issued a Letter of Intent covering the planned procurement of two YAH-1s. Further review of Navy requirements during the ensuing seven months led BuAer to request on 26 May, 1955, that the two prototypes (BuNos 142259 and 142260) be completed not as YAH-1 cannon-armed, single-seat attack aircraft but as YF4H-1 missile-armed, two-seat all-weather fighters. For this mission, the aircraft was to be capable of staying on patrol for two hours at a distance of 250 naut miles (465 km) from the carrier and to remain airborne for two deck cycles (over three hours) without air refuelling. Go-ahead for the YF4H-1 was confirmed on 25 July, 1955, with the award of Contract NOa(s)55-272 covering not only the two previously-ordered prototypes but also five pre-production aircraft (BuNos 143388 to 143392).

When the YF4H-1 mock-up was inspected between 17 and 23 November, 1955, the aircraft was still planned around a wing with a quarter-chord sweep of 45 deg and constant anhedral. Power was to be

176

provided by a pair of General Electric J79 afterburning turbojets mounted in the lower portion of the fuselage and fed by fixed-geometry cheek intakes. Primary armament was to consist of four Sparrow III radar-guided missiles semi-submerged beneath the fuselage. As no provision was made for guns, the YF4H-1 became the first US all-missile fighter.

McDonnell RF-4EJ of the 501 Hikotai, Teisatsu Kokutai (Reconnaissance Wing), Nihon Koku Jieitai (JASDF) taking off at Hyakuri AB, Honshu, in 1979. *(Toyokazu Matsuzaki)*

Numerous design changes were made after extensive wind-tunnel testing revealed that the new fighter would encounter serious stability problems and would be limited to speeds below Mach 2. These changes resulted in the adoption of the now familiar F-4 shape characterized by the use of 12 deg dihedral on the folding outer wing panels, dog-tooth wing leading-edge, one-piece slab tailplane (stabilator) with $23^{1}/_{4}$ deg anhedral, and movable intake ramps. It took time to incorporate these changes in the final engineering drawings, and initial structural release was not authorized until 31 December, 1956.

Delays in the development of the General Electric J79-GE-8s which were to have powered the initial variants of the aircraft led to the installation in the first YF4H-1 of a pair of 14,800 lb (6,713 kg) trust J79-GE-3A engines on loan from the USAF to enable trials to begin in a timely fashion. With this powerplant, BuNo 142259 was flown by Robert C Little at Lambert Field, St Louis, on 27 May, 1958. Manufacturer's and Navy tests, during which it was found necessary to redesign the air intakes, culminated in December 1958 when the F4H-1 was declared the winner of the missile-armed, all-weather naval fighter competition which had pitted it against the single-seat, single-engined Vought F8U-3 Crusader III. As the result of this win, McDonnell, which on 19

177

December, 1956, had received an order for 16 more F4H-1s (BuNos 145307/145317 and 146817/146821), was awarded a follow-on contract for 24 F4H-1s (BuNos 148252/148275) on 17 December, 1958.

As the J79-GE-8s were still not available for the 45 F4H-1s which had been ordered before 17 December, 1958, these Phantom IIs[1] were each powered by two 16,150 lb (7,326 kg) thrust J79-GE-2 or -2As. To differentiate from later models powered by J79-GE-8s, the designation of

Phantom FGR 2 (XV460) of No. 31 Squadron, RAF Germany.

these 45 aircraft was first changed to F4H-1F, with the suffix F identifying the use of a special powerplant. On 18 September, 1962, the J79-GE-2/-2A powered F4H-1Fs were redesignated F-4As in accordance with the new Tri-Service designation system and the J79-GE-8 powered F4H-1s were redesignated F-4Bs.

During test and evaluation, changes were progressively incorporated in the F-4A and included (1) a redesign of the canopy to improve the view from the rear cockpit; (2) a revised radome to provide space for a new radar and its larger dish; (3) modified intakes with the upper lip extension removed and the fixed splitter plates replaced by a combination of variable (forward) and fixed (aft) ramps with bleed air holes on the fixed section; and (4) the installation of boundary-layer control through compressor air blown over the leading-edge and trailing-edge flaps (this device was first tested on BuNo 143392, the fifth pre-production

[1] The F4H-1 was named Phantom II on 3 July 1959, in a ceremony held on the McDonnell ramp in St. Louis during the celebration of the company's 20th anniversary. No one would have dared then to forecast that the aircraft would remain in production until the 40th anniversary of McDonnell Aircraft. In practice, the use of the roman numeral II was quickly, but unofficially, discontinued. There was no possibility of confusion as no FH-1 Phantoms remained in service when the F4H-1 Phantom IIs made their operational debut. Hence, from then on in this narrative, the roman numeral is more often than not omitted as the F-4 is generally known as the Phantom.

BuNo 145310, the ninth F4H-1F, carrying twenty-two 500lb bombs during external load testing in April 1961. *(MCAIR)*

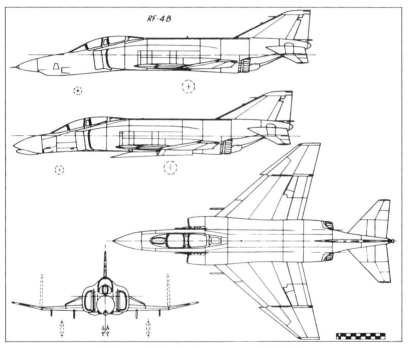

McDonnell F-4B Phantom II, with RF-4B.

F4H-1F). Not initially retained for production, but leading later to the development of the F-4C tactical fighter for the USAF, was the installation of multiple racks which enabled BuNo 145310, the ninth F4H-1F, to carry a total of 22 500-lb (227-kg) bombs beneath its fuselage and inner wing sections. Concurrent with this development work, F4H-1Fs were subjected to intensive evaluation by the Navy. The test programme included initial carrier suitability trials, with BuNo 143391 first being launched and recovered aboard the USS *Independence* (CVA-62) on 15 February, 1960, and Board of Inspection and Survey (BIS) trials which began at NATC Patuxent River in July 1960.

Impressed by the Phantom's spectacular performance and under pressure from the recently appointed and soon-to-be notorious Defense Secretary Robert S. McNamara, who wished to reduce defence expenditures through commonality of Armed Forces equipment, the USAF evaluated the Phantom in 1961 first as a potential successor to the Convair F-106A Delta Dart interceptors of the Air Defense Command[2] and then as a multi-role tactical fighter and tactical reconnaissance aircraft. In the interceptor role, the F4H-1 had much to commend it. During tests, it proved to be capable of carrying heavier loads than the F-106A over longer distances while having a 25 per cent greater radar range and requiring almost one-third less MMH/FH (Maintenance Man-Hour per Flight Hour). In the tactical fighter role, the F4H-1F was judged to be much more versatile than the Republic F-105D Thunderchief as it could carry similar external loads of conventional ordnance while being a much better air superiority fighter due to its lower wing and power loadings.

F-4B-9-MC (BuNo 149406), one of two Phantoms which were transferred by the US Navy to the Air Force for evaluation by Tactical Air Command as F-110As. This aircraft later received the Air Force serial 62-12169. *(MCAIR)*

---

[2]   McDonnell had initiated in-house studies of an interceptor version for the USAF in June 1957. This proposed aircraft, Model 98AD, was a two-seater with lengthened fuselage, J79-GE-X207A turbojets, and all carrier equipment omitted. Its armament was to have consisted of a quartet of GAR-2 or GAR-4 Falcon air-to-air missiles. The Air Force, however, was not yet prepared to give much consideration to versions of an aircraft first designed to meet Navy needs and Model 98AD, as well as many other F4H-1 derivatives proposed to the USAF during the late 'fifties, did not proceed past the drawing board.

The fact that, unlike the Thunderchief, the Phantom could not carry a special store internally was a moot point as the Kennedy Administration wanted to reduce dependency on nuclear retaliation and increase the Air Force's conventional and guerrilla warfare capabilities. In the tactical reconnaissance role, the Phantom promised better performance than the RF-101 and, unlike the Voodoo, could be fitted for night photographic operations.

In January 1962, President Kennedy requested Congressional approval for the procurement of F4H-1 derivatives for the Air Force including F-110A tactical fighters and RF-110A tactical reconnaissance aircraft. At the same time, DoD instructed McDonnell to deliver two F4H-1s (BuNos 149405 and 149406) to Langley AFB, Virginia, for evaluation by the Tactical Air Command. Painted in full TAC markings with the F-110A designation boldly applied on the nose and initially retaining their BuNos (they were later given Air Force serials 62-12168 and 62-12169), the two test aircraft were delivered on 24 January, 1962. Two months later, DoD announced that versions of the Phantom were to become the standard fighter and tactical reconnaissance aircraft of TAC, USAFE, and PACAF. Accordingly, McDonnell received a Letter of Intent for one F-110A (62-12199) on 30 March, 1962, and another for two YRF-110As (62-12200 and 62-12201) on 29 May. Full production of the RF-4C, as the RF-110A was redesignated on 18 September, 1962, was authorized on the last day of that year. Production of the F-4C, formerly F-110A, was covered by a modification of the RF-4C contract which was announced on 8 February, 1963.

Although no Phantoms, or for that matter any other type of jet fighter, were acquired by the US Army as DoD soon mandated that responsibility for providing air support to Army troops would remain with the Air Force, it is worth noting that work on two derivatives of the Navy fighter was initiated for the Army in March 1961. Models 98DA and 98DB were respectively proposed as two-seat and single-seat ground attack aircraft with built-in 20-mm M-61A1 cannon, but neither was built.

No better success attended initial attempts at developing export variants of the Phantom. The first of these was the Model 98BB for the Royal Canadian Air Force in May 1959. Following that were Models 98BH and BJ for the Luftwaffe in October 1959, and the Model 98CJ for the Royal Air Force in June 1960. Perseverance, and the superb performance of the Phantom in USN, USMC, and USAF service finally paid off in 1964 when the United Kingdom became the first F-4 export customer. Later export successes helped boost total F-4 production to 5,195 aircraft, with a peak production rate of two aircraft a day being reached in 1967-68. The 999th, 1,000th, and 1,001st Phantom IIs—respectively an RF-4B for the USMC, an F-4B for the USN, and an F-4C for the USAF—were delivered on 7 July, 1965. Other milestone aircraft were delivered as follows: No. 2000, an F-4D for the USAF, on 21 February, 1967; No. 3000, an F-4J for the USN, on 28 August, 1968; No.

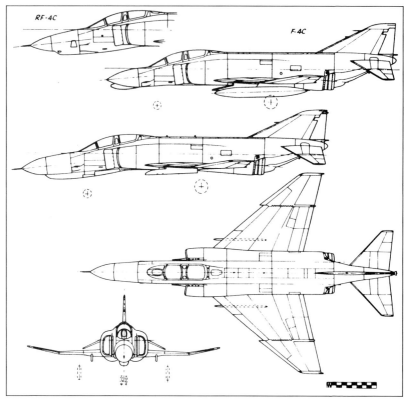

McDonnell F-4E Phantom II, with F-4C and RF-4C.

4000, an F-4E for the USAF, on 1 February, 1971; No. 5000, an F-4E for Turkey, on 24 May, 1978; and the 5,068th and last McDonnell-built Phantom II, an F-4E for Korea, on 25 October, 1979. The last Japanese-built F-4EJ was delivered on 20 May, 1981.

Phantom II variants

YF4H-1: The Phantom II prototypes (BuNos142259 and 142260) were powered by 9,300 lb (4,218 kg) thrust dry and 14,800 lb (6,713 kg) with afterburner General Electric J79-GE-3A turbojets fed by lateral intakes with curved lip and fixed ramp. The first flight, with Robert C Little at the controls, was made at Lambert Field, St Louis, on 27 May, 1958.

F-4A (F4H-1F): The 45 development and initial production F4H-1Fs[3] were powered by 10,350 lb (4,695 kg) thrust dry and 16,150 lb (7,326 kg) with afterburner J79-GE-2 or -2A engines. Pilot and radar intercept

---

[3]   BuNos 143388/143392, 145307/145317, 146817/146821, and 148252/148275 which were designated F-4A-1-MCs to F-4A-5-MCs in 1962.

182

The first YF4H-1 (BuNo 142259) at the time of its completion in April 1958.
(MCAIR)

officer (RIO) were seated in tandem under separate clamshell canopies
with the top line of the RIO canopy initially being flush with the top of the
fuselage. For the primary air-to-air mission, normal armament consisted
of four Sparrow III semi-active radar homing missiles carried semi-
recessed beneath the fuselage. Provision was also made for the carriage of
an additional Sparrow beneath each wing. For the secondary air-to-
ground mission, the aircraft was capable of carrying up to 16,000 lb (7,257
kg) of bombs, rockets, and other ordnance on four underwing and one
centreline stations. For the strike role, provision was made for the
external carriage of a single special weapon. External tanks could be
carried on the centreline station and the inboard wing stations to boost
usable fuel load from the 1,957 US gallons (7,408 litres) carried in six
fuselage and two wing tanks to a maximum of 3,297 gallons (12,480
litres). Moreover, a retractable inflight refuelling probe was provided in
the forward starboard fuselage side.

At first the F4H-1Fs were externally similar to the YF4H-1s, but
changes were progressively incorporated during manufacture or retrofitted as the result of flight tests. The most significant changes were (1) the
revised geometry of the air intakes with straight lips and fixed ramps
replaced by dual ramps (with a 10-deg variable ramp aft of a 5-deg fixed
ramp) ; (2) the installation of an infrared seeker beneath the nose ; (3) the
fitting of an enlarged radome housing the 32-in (81-cm) dish of an AN/
APQ-72 radar in place of the AN/APQ-50 Mod and its 24-in (61-cm) dish;
and (4) the use of a redesigned cockpit with raised canopies to improve
forward visibility for the pilot and increase headroom for the RIO. The
new intake configuration was first incorporated in BuNo 145307, the sixth
F4H-1F (F-4A-2-MC), and both the new radar installation and revised
cockpit were first fitted to BuNo 146817, the 17th F4H-1F (F-4A-3-MC).
In service, most late F-4As incorporating all of these changes were re-
engined with J79-GE-8s and brought almost to full F-4B standard.

BuNo 145307, the F4H-1F in which Lieuts Hardisty and DeEsch had set a world speed record at low altitude on 28 August, 1961, at the MCAIR plant in March 1968. The aircraft retains the air intake configuration (with a 10-deg variable ramp aft of a 5-deg fixed ramp) and low-set canopy with which it had been delivered. *(MCAIR)*

TF-4A: In service with two replacement training squadrons, VF-101 and VF-121, F-4As were sometimes designated TF-4As to reflect the fact that these aircraft were not to operational standards.

F-4B (F4H-1):   Powered by 10,900 lb (4,944 kg)/17,000 lb (7,711 kg) thrust J79-GE-8 turbojets and fitted with revised air intake ramps (the fixed ramp being set at 10 deg from the flight axis versus 5 deg for the modified F4H-1F intakes and the variable ramp having a maximum setting of 14 deg versus 10 deg), the F4H-1s (redesignated F-4Bs in September 1962) were otherwise similar to late production F4H-1Fs with APQ-72 radar and raised canopies. Provision was added for carrying four Sidewinder infrared air-to-air missiles on wing racks. Usable internal fuel load was increased slightly to 1,983 gallons (7,506 litres).

A total of 649 F-4B-6-MC to -28-MCs (BuNos are listed in Appendix C) was delivered to the USN and USMC between June 1961 and March 1967. Twenty-nine F-4Bs[4], included in the above total, were loaned to the USAF and temporarily received the Air Force serials 62-12168/62-12196. Notwithstanding the fact that the first two were conspicuously marked as F-110As, these aircraft retained their F-4B designation.

[4]   BuNos 149405/149406, 150480, 150486, 150493, 150630, 150634, 150643, 150649/150650, 150652/150653, 150994/150995, 150997, 150999/151000, 151002/151004, 151006/151007, 151009, 151011, 151014, 151016/151017, and 151020/151021.

BuNo 150481, a Block 14 F-4B of the Naval Air Test Center. The aircraft displays the air intake configuration (with a 14-deg variable ramp aft of a 10-deg fixed ramp) and high-set canopy as adopted for production models. *(Courtesy of Cloud 9 Photography)*

As described under the appropriate headings, 12 other F-4Bs were modified as F-4Gs, three became YF-4Js, 228 were upgraded as F-4Ns, and a few were modified as DF-4Bs, EF-4Bs, NF-4Bs, or QF-4Bs. Most, however, were operated as F-4Bs by the Navy and Marine Corps until struck off or sent to storage to the Military Aircraft Storage and Disposal Center (MASDC) at Davis-Monthan AFB, Arizona. In naval service, the F-4Bs were progressively upgraded and modified. Notably, as the result of combat experience in Vietnam, chaff dispensers were added above the rear fuselage sides and ECM capabilities were steadily improved with the addition of increasingly more effective Radar Homing and Warning Systems (RHAWS) and Deception Systems (*eg* AN/ALQ-51 and AN/ALQ-100). A number of F-4Bs were also retrofitted with slotted stabilators as fitted to F-4Js to shorten take-off distance and reduce approach speed.

Other appearance changes came about as the result of test programmes which saw F-4Bs modified for a variety of test and development projects. Notable among these projects was the Conformal Carriage Program sponsored by NavAir and the Air Force Systems Command. In this instance, BuNo 148371 was modified to flight-test a weapon carriage adapter developed by the David W. Taylor Naval Ship Research and Development Center in Bethesda, Maryland. Mounted flush beneath the fuselage, this adapter provided a matrix of adjustable hard points for

An F-4B of VF-114, which was then embarked aboard the uss *Kitty Hawk* (CVA-63), flying over North Vietnam in March 1968. *(USN)*

186

BuNo 148371, a modified F-4B assigned to NWC China Lake, carrying twelve inert Mk 82 bombs beneath its fuselage during the testing of the conformal weapon carriage adapter developed by the David W Taylor Naval Ship Research and Development Center. The wing pods contain cameras to record bomb separation. *(USN, courtesy of Jim Nichols and Hal Andrews)*

mounting various weapons and store combinations. Flight-test results substantiated wind-tunnel data and demonstrated that conformal carriage significantly reduced drag and led to significant improvements in level and climb speeds, supersonic acceleration, and manoeuvrability. Although revived briefly in 1983 when the Boeing Military Aircraft Company proposed to include it as part of its proposed F-4 modernization package, conformal weapon carriage was not adopted for the Phantom. The concept, however, has since been incorporated into the design of newer US and foreign types.

DF-4B: This designation identified a small number of F-4Bs modified by the Navy as drone director aircraft.

EF-4B: The EF-4B designation was given to a few F-4Bs (including BuNo 153070) which were modified for use by VAQ-33 in the electronic aggressor role with countermeasures pods and jammers carried beneath their wings.

NF-4B: This designation was given to a number of F-4Bs (including BuNo 152298) which were permanently modified as development and research aircraft.

187

QF-4B (BuNo 148365) target drone making a parachute-assisted landing at NAS Point Magu, California, in April 1972. *(USN)*

QF-4B: For use by the Naval Missile Center (NMC, later redesignated Pacific Missile Test Center, PMTC) at NAS Point Mugu, California, and the Naval Ordnance Test Station (NOTS, later Naval Weapons Center, NWC) at NAS China Lake, California, the Naval Air Development Center (NADC) at Warminster, Pennsylvania, converted the third F-4B (BuNo 148365) to QF-4B drone configuration and delivered this modified aircraft in the spring of 1972. Initially flown with a safety crew on board, the QF-4B was intended as a supersonic manoeuvring target for new missile developments. The weapons systems of the F-4B were replaced by radio and telemetry equipment. At least 44 additional F-4Bs were modified to the QF-4B configuration[5].

RF-4B (F4H-1P): Among initial Model 98 configurations studied during the summer of 1953, McDonnell had included a photographic-reconnaissance version, the Model 98P. Nothing initially came out of this work as the Navy's need for supersonic reconnaissance aircraft was then fulfilled by the acquisition of a version of the Vought Crusader, the

An RF-4B-25-MC of VMCJ-3 landing at MCAS El Toro, California. *(Peter J Mancus)*

---

5 Known QF-4B BuNos include 148365, 148378, 148386, 148409, 148414/148415, 148423/148424, 148428, 148431, 149409, 149414, 149423, 149428, 149431/149434, 149441, 149446, 149451/149452, 149461, 149466, and 149471.

F8U-1P. However, even though that aircraft was quite capable, it lacked the night reconnaissance capability which was being incorporated by McDonnell in early 1962 in the design of the RF-110A for the Air Force. Consequently, as it considered this capability desirable, the Marine Corps obtained authorization in February 1963 to order the first nine of an eventual 46 RF-4B-20-MCs to -43-MCs[6]. The first of these aircraft flew at St Louis on 12 March, 1965, and deliveries were made between May 1965 and December 1970, with all RF-4Bs going to the Marine Corps.

The first 36 RF-4Bs (BuNos 151975/151983 and 153089/153115) retained the powerplant installation and much of the F-4B airframe whereas the last 10 (BuNos 157342/157351) used the F-4J airframe and the F-4B engines. All were unarmed and, unlike the fighters, were fitted

RF-4B-25-MC (BuNo 153096) of VMCJ-3.

with an inertial navigation system. In place of the fighters' radar and specialized electronic equipment housed in the nose and fuselage, they were fitted with forward- and side-oblique cameras[7] (or alternatively with a mapping camera) in a nose which was 4ft 8⁷/₈ in (1.44 m) longer (that of the last three aircraft being more rounded) and could carry side-looking radar and infrared sensors. Film could be developed in flight and the cassettes ejected at low altitude for rapid dissemination of aerial intelligence to ground commanders. For night photography, photoflash cartridges were ejected upward from each side of the aircraft.

As part of Project *Sure* (Sensor Update and Refurbishment Effort) which had been initiated in 1975, one RF-4B was upgraded by McDonnell as a prototype for the 28 remaining RF-4Bs which underwent a Service Life Extension Program (SLEP) in the Naval Air Rework Facility

[6]   The designation F4H-1P, which had been used in proposals and during pre-contract negotiations before September 1962, was not used once this version was ordered.

[7]   Unlike the cameras of the Air Force RF-4Cs and export RF-4Es which were attached on fixed mounts and required that the aircraft follow a specific flight path, the cameras of the Marine RF-4Bs were on rotating mounts so that they could be aimed at targets off the flight path.

McDonnell F-4C-15-MC carrying four LAU-10/MK-24 flare pods at Edwards AFB, California, in July 1964. *(USAF)*

(NARF) San Diego at NAS North Island, California. Unlike F-4Bs and F-4Js which were redesignated F-4Ns and F-4Ss after undergoing SLEP, the updated RF-4Bs retained their original designation. In addition to having their airframe locally strengthened and their electrical wiring replaced, Project *Sure* aircraft were fitted with new systems including the AN/ASN-92 (CAINS) carrier aircraft inertial navigation system, the AN/ASW-25B data link, and intake-mounted ECM. Their J79-GE-8 engines were later replaced by -10Bs.

F-4C (F-110A): Retaining the folding wing and arrester gear of the F-4B and intended for the USAF as an air superiority fighter and conventional attack or nuclear strike aircraft, the F-4C was externally

F-4C (62-12169, ex F-110A, ex F-4B BuNo 149406) firing wing-mounted SUU-16/A gun pods. The 20-mm M-61A1 cannon in each SUU-16/A pod was mechanically-driven by means of a ram air turbine (seen extended beneath the pods) and was provided with 1,200 rounds. Cameras were carried beneath both wing outboard panels to record gun firing. *(AFFTC)*

almost identical to the naval Phantom but differed internally. It was fitted with dual controls in the rear cockpit as the USAF decided to fly it as a two-pilot aircraft. Other changes included the use of low-pressure tyres (the thicker wheels and tyres requiring deeper wells with a slight bulge above and below the inner wing panels), anti-skid systems, and a boom-type flight refuelling system with receptacle on top of the fuselage instead of the Navy's probe and drogue system with its retractable probe on the starboard side of the forward fuselage. The F-4C was powered by two 10,900 lb (4,944 kg)/17,000 lb (7,711 kg) thrust J79-GE-15 turbojets with built-in cartridge starting system. In addition, it had substantially different electronic equipment to suit it to its dual mission, including an AN/APQ-100 radar system, an AN/APA-157 radar set group, an AN/AJB-7 all-altitude bomb control system, an AN/ASN-48 inertial navigation system, and an AN/ASN-46 navigation computer.

Like the F-4B, the F-4C had no built-in guns and was basically armed with four AIM-7 Sparrow missiles in recesses beneath the fuselage. External stores included retarded and unretarded bombs (conventional, cluster, fire, chemical, leaflet, practice, laser or electro-optic guided, or nuclear), air-to-air missiles (AIM-4 Falcon or AIM-9 Sidewinder), air-to-ground missiles (AGM-12 Bullpup, AGM-45 Shrike, AGM-65 Maverick), rocket launchers, SUU-16/A or SUU-23/A gun pods, and/or mines for a maximum load of 16,000 lb (7,257 kg). Alternatively or in conjunction with other external stores, the F-4C could carry one 600-gallon (2,271-litre) tank on the centreline rack and/or one 370-gallon (1,401-litre) tank beneath each wing to supplement the internal tankage of 1,972 gallons (7,465 litres) in six fuselage bladders and two integral wing tanks.

A total of 583 F-4C-15-MC to -25-MCs (62-12199—the 310th Phantom II which was first flown on 27 May, 1963, 63-7407/63-7713, and 64-0654/64-0928) was delivered to the USAF between November 1963 and February 1967. Forty of these aircraft were transferred to Spain, and others became EF-4Cs.

EF-4C: The development of *Wild Weasel* defence suppression versions of the F-4C and Republic F-105F was begun in 1965 to counter the

An EF-4C (64-0757) of the 67th TFS, 18th TFW, taxi-ing at Kadena AB, Okinawa, on 30 October, 1972. *(Toyokazu Matsuzaki)*

191

North Vietnamese use of surface-to-air missiles. Whereas work on the EF-105F proceeded swiftly and resulted in the deployment of combat ready aircraft to Southeast Asia in May 1966, work on the EF-4C ran into problems due to insufficient internal space to house the required equipment, electronic interference, and vibration of the panoramic receiver pod mounted in the starboard rear Sparrow recess. A major redesign effort finally bore fruit during the summer of 1969 and led to the modification of 36 F-4Cs[8] to the *Wild Weasel 4* configuration with AN/APR-25 Radar Homing and Warning System (RHAWS) and AN/APR-26 SAM launch warning system. In addition, EF-4Cs frequently carried an AN/ALQ-119 noise and deception active ECM pod beneath the forward fuselage and were retrofitted in 1973 with AN/ALR-46 ECM receiver and AN/ALR-53 long-range homing receiver. Like previous *Wild Weasel* aircraft (modified F-100Fs, EF-105Fs, and F-105Gs), the EF-4C was intended to detect and attack the *Fan Song* track-while-scan radar used to guide SA-2 *Guideline* surface-to-air missiles. Primary armament for that mission consisted of AGM-45 Shrike anti-radiation missiles and cluster bombs.

YRF-4C (YRF-110A): In May 1962, concurrently with the issuance of Specific Operational Requirements 196 (SOR 196) for an all-weather reconnaissance version of the F-110A by the USAF, the Navy instructed McDonnell to proceed with the modification of six F-4Bs into YRF-110A prototypes (62-12200 and 62-12201, the 266th and 268th Phantom IIs) and RF-110A development aircraft (63-4770/63-4773) for the USAF. The mock-up for this version was reviewed in October 1962, and testing of

The first YRF-4C after it had been modified as part of the Precision Aircraft Control Technology (PACT) programme in 1972. *(AFFTC)*

8   Serial numbers for the F4Cs modified as EF-4Cs were 63-7423, 63-7433, 63-7437, 63-7440, 63-7443, 63-7447, 63-7452, 63-7459, 63-7462, 63-7467, 63-7470, 63-7474, 63-7478, 63-7481, 63-7508, 63-7512/63-7513, 63-7565, 63-7567, 63-7574, 63-7594, 63-7596, 63-7607, 63-7615, 63-7623, 64-0675, 64-0741, 64-0757, 64-0781, 64-0787, 64-0790/64-0791, 64-0815, 64-0840, 64-0844, and 64-0847.

optical and electronic reconnaissance systems was undertaken in 1963 at Holloman AFB with a bailed F-4B (BuNo 145310). The first YRF-4C, with extended nose but without cameras and other reconnaissance systems, made its maiden flight on 9 August, 1963; the second YRF-4C, with high and low panoramic and frame cameras but still lacking other systems, did so on 30 September, 1963.

After its original test programme, aircraft 62-12200 was successively modified to serve as the aerodynamic prototype for the F-4E version (first flying in this configuration on 7 August, 1965) and to test leading-edge manoeuvring slats as fitted to late production F-4Es. The YRF-4C was next fitted with a slotted stabilator and flown with a beryllium rudder and other composite materials components before being modified as a test bed for a fly-by-wire control system beginning in April 1972. Finally, as part of the Precision Aircraft Control Technology (PACT) programme, it was fitted with canard surfaces and special controls and first flew in this configuration on 29 April, 1974. In January 1979, at the end of its exceptionally useful life as a test bed, 62-12200 was donated to the Air Force Museum at Wright-Patterson AFB.

RF-4C: This was the production version of the USAF tactical reconnaissance version, of which 503 were delivered between May 1964 and January 1974 (serial numbers for these RF-4C-17-MC to -53-MCs are

RF-4C-27-MC (65-0903) of the 173rd TRS, Nebraska ANG. *(NE ANG)*

given in Appendix C). Twelve of these aircraft were subsequently transferred to the Spanish Air Force, two were loaned to Israel in 1970-71, and 12 ex-USAF RF-4Cs went to Korea in 1989.

The primary mission of the RF-4C was all-weather, day-night, high-low reconnaissance operation for which it had three camera stations in the nose (which was more rounded in the late production aircraft) and, at least initially, the capability of processing film in flight and ejecting cassettes. A photoflash ejection system was provided for night photography. In addition, the RF-4C had an AN/APQ-99 or -162 forward-looking radar and could be fitted with an AN/APQ-102 side-looking mapping radar or an AN/AAS-18 infrared reconnaissance set. A small number of

RF-4C-31-MC from the 32nd Tactical Reconnaissance Squadron, 10th Tactical Reconnaissance Wing, at RAF Alconbury, England. *(George Pennick, courtesy of David W Menard)*

RF-5Cs was fitted with AN/ARN-92 LORAN-D (Long Range Navigation) equipment with distinctive 'towel rack' antennae atop the fuselage. The RF-4C carried neither guns nor missiles but, unlike the RF-4B, it retained the provision for carrying a nuclear store on the centreline station. It was powered by two J79-GE-15s as fitted to the F-4C.

In its long service life with the USAF, the RF-4C has had its ECM capabilities steadily improved (notably through the addition of RHAWS and other sensors) and its other systems upgraded. Newer systems include the AN/ALQ-125 TEREC (Tactical Electronic Reconnaissance sensor with data link equipment for transmission in near real-time) which was fitted to 24 RF-4Cs, the AN/ARN-101 navigational unit, the Electronic Wide-Angle Camera System (EWACS), the AN/AVQ-26 *Pave Tack* infrared detecting set and laser target designator, and an upgraded forward-looking radar.

As part of Project *Peace Jack* which was initiated to provide the Israeli Air Force with the capability of photographing deep into Arab countries without intruding into their airspace, an Air Force RF-4C (66-0419) was used by General Dynamics during the autumn of 1971 to flight-test an HIAC-1 LOROP (Long Range Oblique Photography) camera mounted in a large ventral pod. The system worked well but the drag of the pod limited top speed to just under Mach 1.5 and ceiling to about 50,000 ft (15,240 m). As this performance was insufficient for operations over unfriendly territory, *Peace Jack* was redirected to provide for the internal carriage of a LOROP camera in specially modified F-4Es as described under the F-4E(S) and RF-4X headings. The USAF, however, obtained a few HIAC-1 pods for RF-4Cs flying along the North Korean and Eastern European borders.

194

F-4D: After the F-4C had been put into production rather hurriedly in compliance with Secretary MacNamara's policy of encouraging equipment commonality among the Services, Tactical Air Command sought to obtain an F-4 version better suited to its requirements. To that end, McDonnell evaluated several changes to the basic F-4C with proposals ranging from mundane improvements in the fire control and weapons delivery system to drastic upgrading of the aircraft capability.

A LORAN-equipped F-4D-33-MC (66-8812) of the 80th TFS, 8th TFW, at Yokota AB, Japan, on 13 December, 1975. *(Toyokazu Matsuzaki)*

Examples of the latter included the proposed incorporation of a terrain following system, a nose-mounted gun, and/or Pratt & Whitney TF30 turbofans. Although offering substantial improvements, such major modifications were expensive and would have resulted in reduced commonality between Navy and Air Force F-4 variants. Consequently, the F-4D version which was ordered in March 1964 and first flown on 7 December, 1965, was a straightforward development of the F-4C with improved avionics to increase its air-to-air gunnery capability and its air-to-ground weapon delivery accuracy. Major new components included an AN/ASG-22 lead computing sight and an AN/ASQ-91 weapon release computer set, whilst most F-4Ds were fitted with the AN/APA-165 radar set group and the AN/APQ-109A radar system in a larger radome. However, some F-4Ds were fitted with the AN/APA-157 radar set group similar to that installed in all F-4Cs and hence were externally identical to the F-4Cs.

Deliveries began in March 1966. In total, 825 aircraft were built comprising 793 F-4D-24-MC to -33-MCs for the USAF (*see* Appendix C for serials) and 32 F-4D-35-MC to -39-MCs for the Imperial Iranian Air Force (67-14869/67-14884 and 68-6904/68-6919). At least 42 F-4Ds were transferred by the USAF to Korea beginning in August 1969 and as many may be transferred to Greece after being phased-out of service by the Air National Guard between 1989 and 1991.

195

F-4D-31-MC (66-7227) of the 457th TFS, AFRES. *(René J Francillon)*

F-4D-26-MC (65-0583) of the 194th FIS, 144th FIW, California ANG, taxi-ing at Fresno ANGB on 25 August, 1987. *(René J Francillon)*

In service, the electronic suit of the F-4D has been frequently upgraded to meet special operational requirements. Notably, the AN/AVQ-10 and AN/ASQ-153(V)-2 Laser Target Designators were respectively installed in *Pave Knife* F-4Ds and *Pave Spike* F-4Ds and AN/ARN-92 LORAN-D (Long Range Navigation) equipment was fitted to *Pave Phantom* F-4Ds.

EF-4D: This designation was given to at least four F-4Ds modified as prototypes for advanced *Wild Weasel* defence suppression aircraft. Two of these development aircraft (65-0657 and 65-0660) were fitted with AN/APS-107 RHAWS and a target acquisition system for AGM-78 Standard ARM anti-radiation missiles. Two others (66-7635 and 66-7647) served as test beds for the AN/APS-38 warning and attack system developed by McDonnell Douglas and later adopted for the F-4G.

YF-4E: Although the original Model 98 study had called for the installation of four 20-mm cannon and several gun-armed proposals had been made by McDonnell, all Phantom fighters with the exception of the F-4E, F-4EJ, and F-4F have relied on missiles as their primary air-to-air armament. Design studies for an F-4 variant with built-in cannon were

196

undertaken anew in late 1964 to meet Air Force TSF (Tactical Strike Fighter) requirements and led to the development of the F-4E series. As no space could be found within the existing airframe, the first YRF-4C was used to test a new nose section housing an AN/APG-30 radar and into which was faired an external pod enclosing a single six-barrel 20-mm General Electric M-61A1 rotary cannon. Temporarily redesignated YF-4E, the modified aircraft first flew on 7 August, 1965. Two other YF-4E development aircraft were later added by modifying an F-4C (63-7445) and an F-4D (65-0713 which was also used to test a boron fibre rudder).

F-4E: Promising YF-4E test results led to an intial batch of 96 F-4Es being ordered in August 1966 as part of an F-4D contract. The first of these aircraft flew on 30 June, 1967, and deliveries to TAC began in October of that year. As the gun installation beneath the nose precluded the use of a large radar such as that fitted to F-4Cs and F-4Ds, the F-4Es were equipped with a solid-state AN/APQ-120 set with a smaller antenna (24.5 in by 27.4 in/62.2 cm by 69.6 cm). Moreover, to balance the weight of the gun and its 639-round ammunition drum, a 95-gallon (360-litre) tank was added in the rear fuselage (however, internal fuel capacity was reduced from 1,993 to 1,855 gallons/7,544 to 7,022 litres when the

F-4E-31-MC (66-0295) during spin tests at the Air Force Flight Test Center, Edwards AFB. An anti-spin parachute has been fitted in a tail fairing and a recording camera mounted atop the centre fuselage. *(AFFTC)*

fuselage bladders were replaced by self-sealing tanks starting with Block 41 aircraft, 68-0495 and up). The F-4E retained the semi-recessed AIM-7 air-to-air missiles and external stores of earlier variants but were powered by a pair of J79-GE-17 (later -17A, -17C, -17E, -17F, or -17G with low smoke combustors) engines with an afterburning thrust of 17,900 lb (8,119 kg) instead of retaining the J79-GE-15s of the F-4C, RF-4C, and F-4D versions. Other modifications included the use of a slotted stabilator and the removal of the automatic wing folding mechanism. Due to the non-availability of the AN/APQ-120 radar and the unsatisfactory performance of the AN/APS-107 RHAW with which F-4Es were to have been equipped, the first 30 aircraft were delivered without radar and the first 67 had no RHAW. Most, however, were retrofitted with AN/

197

APQ-120 and AN/APR-36/37. Another early retrofit saw a longer blast diffuser and derichment system being installed to eliminate a gun gas ingestion problem leading to engine flame-out.

Remaining in production for 12 years, the F-4E was built for more air forces and in larger number than any other F-4 variant. Serials for the 959

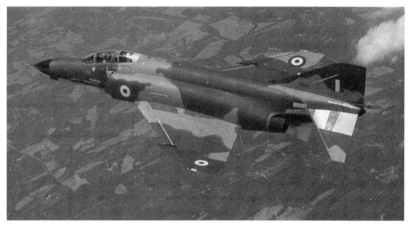

F-4E-55-MC (72-1512) of the Helliniki Aeroporía. *(MCAIR)*

The last F-4E-42-MC (69-0303), in the markings of the 51st TFW at Osan AB, Korea, during the winter of 1982. *(USAF)*

F-4E-31-MCs to -62-MCs built for the USAF[9], including a fair number of aircraft subsequently transferred to foreign air forces, are given in Appendix C. In addition, 428 F-4E-38-MCs to -67-MCs were built for export customers [including 86 aircraft for Israel which were funded by the United States under FMS (Foreign Military Sales) contracts] and

[9] Included in this total are 10 F-4E-63-MCs purchased by the Federal German Government for use in a joint US/German training programme at George AFB, California, and 58 'payback' F-4E-60-MC to -62-MCs acquired as replacement for aircraft transferred by the USAF to the Israeli Air Force.

198

were given USAF serials for contractual purpose. All export F-4Es were delivered without the capability of arming and delivering special weapons; other differences with USAF aircraft varied according to intended customer and period of delivery, as certain weapons and systems were not initially released for export.

Continuous updating of systems and some airframe changes have been made to maintain the combat effectiveness of the F-4E and to correct some structural deficiencies. To extend service life, the wing centre-section of early production F-4Es (as well as that of most other Air Force Phantoms) had to be reinforced with metal straps, while thicker skin panels were used in the manufacture of late production F-4Es. The most significant airframe change, the addition of leading-edge slats to improve manoeuvrability, was first tested in June 1969. However, as the slats required much development work, they were not incorporated during production until 1972 (starting with 71-0238). Using modification kits produced by McDonnell, the Air Force subsequently fitted leading-edge slats to 304 early F-4Es, and the Imperial Iranian Air Force similarly upgraded some of its Phantoms.

New sensors and systems retrofitted or added during production included (1) the AVQ-23A/B *Pave Spike* laser designator and range finder system; (2) the AN/AVQ-26 *Pave Tack* infrared/laser target designator; and (3) the AN/ASX-1 TISEO (Target Identification System, Electro-Optical) mounted in a canister on the port wing leading-edge. Finally, to improve the accuracy of navigation and weapons delivery, some 180 F-4Es were retrofitted with the Lear Siegler AN/ARN-101(V) system starting in the autumn of 1977.

F-4EJ: Developed to meet the requirements of the Nihon Koku Jieitai (Japanese Air Self-Defence Force), F-4EJs differed from F-4Es in

A Mitsubishi F-4EJ (47-8327) of the 305 Hikotai. *(Dr Masahiro Yamasaki)*

being optimized for the air defence role and in dispensing both with the AN/AJB-7 bombing system and with the provision for carrying air-to-ground conventional and special weapons. These aircraft were fitted with a data link system with the Japanese BADGE (Base Air Defence Ground

199

Environment) system and the Japanese J/APR-2 tail warning radar, but plans to arm them with Mitsubishi AAM-2 air-to-air missiles did not materialize. Ordered on 1 November, 1968, two F-4EJs (Japanese serials 17-8301 and 17-8302) were built in St Louis and were tested by McDonnell beginning on 14 January, 1971. The next 11 aircraft (27-8303/27-8306, 37-8307/37-8310, and 47-8311/47-8313) were delivered by McDonnell as knockdown kits and were assembled in Japan by Mitsubishi Jukogyo KK (Mitsubishi Heavy Industries Ltd) which then built 127 F-4EJs under licence. The last Japanese-built F-4EJ, which was also the very last Phantom II, was delivered on 20 May, 1981.

As built, the Japanese F-4EJs were not fitted with an inflight refuelling receptacle, but this was retrofitted. Whereas the retrofit of leading-edge slats was considered but not implemented, the Japanese Diet later approved the replacement of the AN/APQ-120 radar with an AN/APG-66J.

F-4EJ(KAI): This designation identified F-4EJs retrofitted with the AN/APG-66J radar, Litton inertial navigation system, a HUD (head-up display), and updated RHAW system. Serial 07-8431, the first of 96 aircraft brought up to the F-4EJ(KAI) standard, flew on 12 December, 1984. The upgraded aircraft are cleared to carry AIM-7F Sparrow and AIM-9L Sidewinder air-to-air missiles, as well as Mitsubishi ASM-1 anti-ship missiles.

F-4E(S): After development of the high-performance RF-4X had to be abandoned, General Dynamics modified three Israeli Air Force F-4Es

The first of three F-4E(S) reconnaissance aircraft, with HIAC-1 LOROP camera installation in the nose, before its delivery to the Israeli Air Force. *(General Dynamics, courtesy of Jay Miller)*

to a special reconnaissance configuration by replacing the F-4E radar and gun installation with a new nose housing a 66-in (1.68-m) focal length

HIAC-1 LOROP (Long Range Oblique Photography) camera. The modified aircraft were redelivered to the Israeli Air Force in 1976-77.

RF-4E: Combining the photographic and electronic reconnaissance system and modified nose of the RF-4C with J79-GE-17 engines and much of the airframe of the F-4E, the unarmed RF-4E version was produced for the export market. The first RF-4Es were ordered for the Luftwaffe in January 1969 and the last were delivered to the Greek and Turkish Air Forces in 1978. Serials for the 132 built by McDonnell for five foreign customers are given in Appendix C.

RF-4E from Aufkl G 51 at Bremgarten. *(Bundesministerium der Verteidigung)*

Under the *Peace Trout* programme, a German RF-4E was fitted by E-Systems with an ELINT (electronic intelligence) system in place of nose-mounted cameras. In a programme completed in 1982, all other German RF-4Es were equipped by Messerschmitt-Bölkow-Blohm (MBB) with a weapons delivery system to endow them with a secondary attack capability.

RF-4EJ: This was the unarmed reconnaissance version of the F-4EJ of which 14 (Japanese serials 47-6901/47-6905 and 57-6906/57-6914) were built by McDonnell and delivered to the JASDF between November 1974 and June 1975.

RF-4EJ(KAI): This designation will identify 14 F-4EJ fighters which will be modified as reconnaissance platforms and fitted with Thomson-CSF Raphaël sideways-looking radar (SLAR).

F-4F: After contemplating the acquisition of a proposed single-seat fighter version of the Phantom or that of the Lockheed CL-1200 Lancer or the Dassault Mirage F.1, the Luftwaffe finally decided to order 175 two-seat F-4Fs (German serials 3701/3875 which, for contract management purposes, also received USAF serials 72-1111/72-1285). Major assemblies were produced in Germany by MBB and VFW-Fokker, and the J79-MTU-17A engines were built under licence from General

F-4F of Jagdbombergeschwader 36, Luftwaffe, based at Hopsten. *(Dirk Lamarque)*

Electric by Motoren-und-Turbinen-Union München GmbH. As delivered between June 1973 and April 1976, the F-4Fs differed from late production F-4Es with leading-edge slats in not being provided with an inflight refuelling receptacle, in having the slotted stabilator replaced by a standard unit, and in lacking provisions for carrying special weapons and some air-to-ground (Maverick, Shrike, and Walleye) and air-to-air (Falcon and Sparrow) missiles. Under the *Peace Rhine* programme, however, the F-4Fs were later retrofitted with inflight refuelling receptacles and armed with Sparrow air-to-air missiles.

Under the ICE (Improved Combat Efficiency) programme, 75 F-4Fs assigned to two fighter wings (JG 71 and JG 74) are to be upgraded by MBB before the end of 1992 through (1) the replacement of the AN/APQ-120 radar by a licence-built AN/APG-65; (2) the provision for AIM-120 AMRAAM air-to-air missiles; and (3) the installation of a laser

F-4F-55-MC (3756) of JG 74. *(Jean-Michel Guhl)*

gyro inertial navigation system, digital central air data computers, and a new data bus. Under a less ambitious upgrade programme, MBB is also to install the new INS, air data computers, and data bus in 75 F-4Fs assigned to two fighter-bomber wings (JBG 35 and JBG 36).

TF-4F: This unofficial designation was given to 12 F-4Fs used to train Luftwaffe crews in the United States. These aircraft were later flown to Germany and restored to the F-4F operational configuration.

F-4G (USN version): This designation was first used by the US Navy for 12 F-4Bs fitted with the AN/ASW-21 two-way data link communications system and approach power compensator for operational evaluation of an automatic carrier landing system. The first F-4G flew on 20 March, 1963, and these 12 aircraft[10] were flown by VF-213 from the USS *Kitty Hawk* (CVA-63) during deployment in the Gulf of Tonkin from November 1965 until June 1966. One was shot down by North Vietnamese AAA and the others were later brought back to F-4B standard (with six later modified as F-4Ns).

F-4G from VF-213 after engaging a cross-deck pendant on the USS *Kitty Hawk* (CVA-63) in the winter of 1965. *(Lionel Paul)*

F-4G (USAF version): The F-4G designation was used next by the USAF to identify 116 F-4E-42-MCs to -45-MCs[11] which were brought up

[10] BuNos 150481, 150484, 150487, 150489, 150492, 150625, 150629, 150633, 150636, 150639, 150644, and 150645.

[11] Serials 69-0236/69-0243, 69-0245/69-0248, 69-0250/69-0255, 69-0257/69-0259, 69-0261, 69-0263, 69-0265, 69-0267, 69-0269/69-0275, 69-0277, 69-0279/69-0281, 69-0283/69-0286, 69-0292/69-0293, 69-0297, 69-0304, 69-0306, 69-7201/69-7202, 69-7204/69-7220, 69-7223, 69-7228, 69-7231/69-7236, 69-7251, 69-7253/69-7254, 69-7256/69-7260, 69-7262/69-7263, 69-7270, 69-7272, 69-7286/69-7291, 69-7293, 69-7295, 69-7298, 69-7300/69-7303, 69-7546, 69-7550, 69-7556, 69-7558, 69-7560/69-7561, 69-7566, 69-7571/69-7572, 69-7574, 69-7579/69-7584, and 69-7586/69-7588.

F-4G modified from an F-4E-44-MC (69-7263). *(MCAIR)*

to a new configuration for use in the *Wild Weasel* defence suppression role and fitted with leading-edge manoeuvring slats. The first of these aircraft (69-7254) was modified by McDonnell Aircraft and began flight trials in December 1975; subsequent aircraft were modified by the Air Force at the Ogden Logistics Center, Hill AFB, Utah. The M-61A1 gun and ammunition drum of the F-4E was removed to make room respectively for an under-nose fairing housing forward- and side-looking antennae and line-replaceable units (LRUs) for the AN/APR-38 radar warning and attack system. Rearward-facing antennae were mounted in an enlarged fairing at the top of the vertical tail fin. Primary armament consisted of anti-radiation missiles (AGM-45 Shrike, AGM-78 Standard ARM, and AGM-88 HARM), TV-guided or IIR (imaging infrared) AGM-75

A Wild Weasel F-4G (69-0284) of the 561st TFS, 37th TFW, at Nellis AFB, Nevada, during Red Flag 84-3 in January 1984. *(René J Francillon)*

Maverick air-to-ground missiles, and CBUs (cluster bomb units). For self-protection, F-4Gs retain the capability of carrying AIM-9 Sidewinder air-to-air missiles.

A Performance Update Program (PUP) was undertaken in the late 'eighties to upgrade the APR-38's signal processor and extend the frequency range of the direction receiver, thus enabling F-4Gs to cope with new threats.

F-4H: This model designation was not used to avoid confusion with the pre-1962 basic aircraft designation F4H.

YF-4J and F-4J: Following the testing of three YF-4Js (BuNos 151473, 151496, and 151497) modified from F-4B airframes, the F-4J was adopted as the second and last fighter version to be placed in production for the Navy and Marine Corps. Powered by two J79-GE-10s with an afterburning thrust of 17,900 lb (8,119 kg), the F-4J had 16½-deg drooping ailerons and slotted stabilators to shorten take-off distance and reduce approach speed. It was equipped with the AN/AJB-7 bombing system which provided ground attack capability substantially increased over that of the F-4B and with the AN/AWG-10 fire-control system. The latter was housed in an enlarged radome and incorporated an AN/APG-59 pulse-doppler radar to detect and track aircraft flying at low altitudes in radar sea/ground return. The F-4J was also fitted with the AN/ASW-25 one-way data link which provided automatic carrier landing capability. Other changes from the F-4B included (1) the use of larger mainwheels with 'thick' wings as used on Air Force aircraft; (2) improved RHAW and countermeasure sets; (3) 30-kVA in place of 20-kVA generators; (4) an additional fuel cell in the rear fuselage to bring internal capacity to 1,998 gallons (7,525 litres); and (5) fixed inboard wing leading-edge. The VTAS (Visual Target Acquisition System) helmet

A pair of Phantom IIs from Air Development Squadron Four (VX-4) near NAS Point Magu on 12 June, 1970. The nearest aircraft is an F-4J-39-MC and the other is an F-4B-13-MC. *(USN)*

sight and radar ground cooling fans (AFC-555) were fitted to Blocks 45 and 46 F-4Js, with VTAS being retrofitted to most earlier aircraft. Other items retrofitted at various times included AN/ALQ-126 ECM with antennae on the intakes, improved ejection seats, reduced smoke J79-GE-10B engines, and cockpit optimization (AFC-506).

The first YF-4J flew on 4 June, 1965, and the first production F-4J was airborne on 27 May, 1966. In all, 522 F-4Js (*see* Appendix C for BuNos) were delivered to the USN and USMC between December 1966 and January 1972.

F-4J(UK):   To bring British home-based defence back to strength after the transfer of the Phantom FGR Mk.2s (F-4Ms) of No 23 Squadron

F-4J(UK) of No. 74 Squadron, Strike Command, Royal Air Force. ZE358 had carried the BuNo 155810 while in service with the US Navy.

to RAF Stanley to provide air defence for the Falklands, the Royal Air Force obtained 15 low-time F-4Js which had been stored at the Military Aircraft Storage and Disposal Center at Davis-Monthan AFB. Before their transfer to Britain, these F-4Js surplus-to-USN-requirements were overhauled and modified by the Naval Air Rework Facility at NAS North Island, California. In the process, a number of USN systems (*eg* the AN/ASN-54 Approach Power Compensator System, the AN/ASW-25

206

Data Link System, and the AN/ALQ-126 Countermeasures Set) were removed and British systems and equipment were installed (*eg* Telebrief secure communications system and Skyflash air-to-air missiles). In RAF service, these aircraft have been designated F-4J(UK)s and given serials ZE350/ZE364 [12]. The first three were flown to the United Kingdom in August 1984.

EF-4J: The EF-4J designation was given to a few F-4Js (including BuNos 153076 and 153084) which were modified for use by VAQ-33 in

An EF-4J of VAQ-33 at NAS Key West, Florida. *(Rick Morgan)*

the 'electronic aggressor' role with countermeasures pods and jammers carried beneath their wings.

YF-4K: Design work on the first export model of the Phantom to be put into production was begun in January 1963 and was offered to the Royal Navy as an alternative to the projected Hawker Siddeley P.1154 supersonic V/STOL fighter. A number of major modifications were made to the basic F-4J model to permit its use aboard the smaller British carriers and to enable 40 to 45 per cent of its value to be produced in the United Kingdom. Most important was the substitution of a pair of 12,250 lb (5,557 kg) thrust dry, 20,515 lb (9,305 kg) thrust with reheat, Rolls-Royce RB.168-25R Spey 201 turbofans which necessitated a 20 per cent increase in the air intake area as well as a redesign of the lower portion of the aft fuselage (the latter proving rather unfelicitous as it resulted both in a significantly increased unit cost and in lower performance in spite of the use of more powerful engines). Other changes included the use of a double-extensible nose leg for high angle of attack launches; the adoption of larger flaps to enable the aircraft to operate from the short deck of British carriers; and the use of some British equipment. The AN/AWG-11 fire control system as installed in the British version differed from the AWG-10 of the F-4Js mainly in having a radar dish which could swing sideways to reduce length to 54 ft (16.46 m) to permit

---

[12] These aircraft were respectively ex-BuNos 153768, 153773, 153783, 153785, 153795, 153803, 153850, 153892, 155510, 155529, 155574, 155734, 155755, 155868, and 155894.

the F-4K to fit on the small deck lifts of British carriers. The decision to order F-4Ks for the Royal Navy was announced by the Minister of Defence on 27 February, 1964, and the initial contract for two YF-4Ks (XT595/XT596) and two F-4Ks (XT597/XT598) was received by McDonnell on 30 September, 1964. The YF-4K made its first flight on 27 June, 1966.

F-4K: Forty-eight production F-4Ks (XT857/XT876 and XV565/XV592), which were designated Phantom FG Mk.1s in British service, were ordered for the Royal Navy but only 29 were delivered to the Senior Service, the others being diverted to the Royal Air Force. They differed from the two YF-4Ks and two pre-production F-4Ks in being powered by Spey 202/203s and in being fitted with all specified British equipment.

F-4L: This designation was given to a number of advanced versions proposed to the US Navy in 1963-64 but not ordered into production. One of the configurations, Model 98FOA, called for the aircraft to be powered by Rolls-Royce RB.168-25R turbofans and to carry either six medium-range Sparrow III or two long-range Phoenix air-to-air missiles.

YF-4M and F-4M: In February 1965, the Royal Air Force followed the Royal Navy's lead when it selected the Spey-powered F-4M

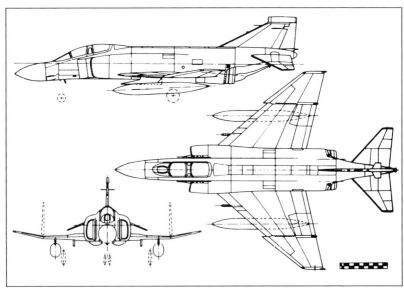

McDonnell Phantom FGR 2.

(Phantom FGR Mk.2) as a replacement for Hawker Hunters operated in the ground attack and fighter reconnaissance roles. Powered by Spey 202/203 turbofans, the RAF aircraft differed from those of the Royal Navy in being fitted with the AN/AWG-12 fire control system and a Ferranti inertial nav/attack system. Furthermore, they lacked the slotted

F-4M-36-MC (XV475).

stabilators, double-extensible nose leg, and the aileron droop of the naval variant. For safer operations on short and wet runways, the F-4M was also fitted with anti-skid brakes. The basic armament of four Sparrow air-to-air missiles (later replaced by British Aerospace Sky Flash missiles) was retained as was provision for a wide variety of external stores. For use in the reconnaissance role, the F-4Ms carried a special pod which, developed by EMI and produced by Hawker Siddeley, housed cameras, infrared linescan and side-looking radar. Retrospectively, the Phantom FG Mk.1s and FGR Mk.2s in service with the Royal Air Force were fitted with ECM in a fin cap fairing. The first of two YF-4Ms (XT852/XT853) flew at St Louis on 17 February, 1967. Delivery of 116 F-4Ms (XT891/XT914, XV393/XV442, and XV460/XV501) began in July 1968 and ended in October 1969.

F-4N: As part of Project *Bee Line*, a SLEP undertaken at NARF San Diego, 228 F-4Bs[13] were rebuilt and fitted with updated equipment. changes and new equipment included: (1) structural strengthening to extend fatigue life; (2) complete rewiring; (3) AN/ASW-25 one-way data link; (4) Sidewinder Expanded Acquisition Mode (SEAM); (5) VTAS helmet sight; (6) air-to-air IFF; (7) dogfight computer; (8) engine smoke abatement (often removed in service); (9) Automatic Altitude Reporting System (AIMS); and (10) upgraded ECM systems. The first F-4N flew on 4 June, 1972.

QF-4N: This designation identified at least 35 F-4Ns[14] which were modified as drones by the Navy.

F-4P, F-4Q, and F-4R: These designations were not used.

F-4S: In a programme similar to that which had seen F-4Bs upgraded as F-4Ns, 265 F-4Js[15] underwent a SLEP at NARF San Diego. Desig-nated F-4S, the first modified aircraft was completed in June 1975. Major changes and new equipment included: (1) airframe and undercarriage strengthening; (2) complete rewiring; (3) manoeuvring slats (not initially

209

Footnotes for page 209

13   BuNos of the 228 F-4Bs upgraded as F-4Ns were: 150407, 150411/150412, 150415, 150419, 150422/150423, 150425/150426, 150430, 150432, 150435/150436, 150438, 150440/150442, 150444/150445, 150448, 150450, 150452, 150456, 150460, 150464/150466, 150468, 150472, 150475/150476, 150478/150482, 150484/150485, 150488/150492, 150625, 150627/150628, 150630, 150632, 150634/150635, 150638/150640, 150642/150643, 150648, 150651/150652, 150993, 150996, 151000, 151002/151004, 151006/151008, 151011, 151015/151016, 151397/151398, 151400/151401, 151406, 151413, 151415, 151417, 151422, 151424, 151430/151431, 151433/151436, 151439/151440, 151442, 151444, 151446, 151448/151449, 151451/151452, 151455/1514556, 151461, 151463/151465, 151468/151469, 151471, 151475/151477, 151480, 151482, 151484, 151487, 151489, 151491, 151498, 151502/151504, 151510/151511, 151513/151514, 151519, 152208, 152210, 152212, 152214, 152217, 152221/152223, 152225/152228, 152229/152230, 152235/152237, 152241, 152243/152244, 152246, 152250, 152252/152254, 152258/152259, 152263, 152267, 152269/152270, 152272, 152275, 152277/152282, 152284, 152288, 152290/152291, 152293/152295, 152298, 152300, 152302/152303, 152306/152307, 152310, 152313, 152317/152318, 152321, 152323, 152326/152327, 152965, 152967/152971, 152975, 152977, 152981/152983, 152986, 152990/152992, 152996, 153006, 153008, 153010/153012, 153016/153017, 153019, 153023/153024, 153027, 153030, 153034, 153036, 153039, 153045, 153047, 153050, 153053, 153056/153060, 153062, 153064/153065, 153067, and 153914/153915.

14   Known QF-4N BuNos include 150412, 150415, 150419, 150432, 150464, 150489, 150630, 150993, 151002, 151004, 151440, 151449, 151455, 151461, 151471, 152217, 152222/152223, 152229/152230, 152235, 152243, 152253, 152258, 152272, 152279, 152281, 152303, 152321, 152323, 152326, 153011, 153030, 153053, and 153064.

15   BuNos of the 265 F-4Js upgraded as F-4Ss were: 153779/153780, 153784, 153787, 153791/153792, 153798, 153800, 153805, 153807/153810, 153814, 153818/153821, 153823/153828, 153832/153833, 153835, 153840, 153842/153843, 153845, 153847/153848, 153851, 153853, 153855/153862, 153864, 153866, 153868/153869, 153872/153874, 153877, 153879/153882, 153884, 153887, 153889/153891, 153893, 153896, 153898/153900, 153902/153904, 153907/153911, 154781/154782, 154786, 154788, 155504, 155510/155511, 155515, 155517/155519, 155521/155522, 155524/155525, 155527/155528, 155530/155532, 155539, 155541/155545, 155549/155550, 155552, 155555, 155558/155562, 155565/155570, 155572/155575, 155579/155580, 155731/155736, 155743, 155745/155747, 155749, 155753/155755, 155757, 155759, 155761, 155764/155767, 155769, 155772/155773, 155779, 155781, 155783/155784, 155786/155787, 155792, 155794, 155799, 155801, 155805/155808, 155810, 155812/155813, 155818, 155820/155822, 155825, 155827/155829, 155832/155834, 155836, 155838/155841, 155844/155845, 155847/155849, 155851/155852, 155854/155855, 155858/155859, 155861/155865, 155868/155869, 155871/155872, 155874, 155876, 155878/155883, 155885, 155887/155888, 155890/155894, 155896/155901, 157242/157243, 157245/157246, 157248/157251, 157254/157255, 157257, 157259/157261, 157267, 157269, 157274, 157276, 157278/157279, 157283, 157287, 157290/157291, 157293, 157297/157298, 157305, 157307/157309, 158346, 158348, 158350/158354, 158360, 158362, 158370, 158373/158374, and 158376/158378.

F-4N (BuNo 150634) of VF-151 at NAF Atsugi, Japan, in 1977. *Toyokazu Matsuzaki)*

F-4S from VMFAT-101 coming behind a KC-10A of the 452nd Air Refueling Wing (Associate) on 8 August, 1986. *(René J Francillon)*

fitted to the first 43 F-4Ss); (4) digital AWG-10B weapon control system; (5) new radio and TACAN (but not to all F-4Ss); (6) smokeless engines; (7) formation lights; and (8) staggered cooling ports near the nosewheel well.

F-4(FV)S: This unofficial designation was used to identify a variable-geometry version (Model 98FVS) proposed in 1966-67 as an alternative to the Grumman/General Dynamics F-111B. As detailed in Appendix A, the Navy did not find this proposal of sufficient interest to order a prototype.

F-4X and RF-4X: When it became evident in 1972 that the carriage of the HIAC-1 LOROP (Long Range Oblique Photography) camera pod being developed as part of the *Peace Jack* programme would result in unacceptable performance penalties, General Dynamics proposed a very high performance derivative of the Phantom with a long range camera mounted in a modified nose and engine thrust markedly boosted at high

The Israeli F-4E (69-7676) modified by General Dynamics to serve as a mock-up of the proposed RF-4X. In this December 1974 photograph, the aircraft is seen fitted with dummy PCC water tank on the upper fuselage side and a mock-up of the LOROP installation in the nose. *(General Dynamics, courtesy of Jay Miller)*

altitude through the use of PCC (pre-compressor cooling). With this PCC system, the aircraft was expected to have a top speed of Mach 3.2 and to cruise for 10 minutes at Mach 2.7 and at an altitude of 78,000 ft (23,775 m). Impressed with this performance estimate, the Israeli Air Force provided one of its F-4Es (69-7576) for modification by General Dynamics first as an RF-4X mock-up and then as a prototype. The mock-up was completed in December 1974 with enlarged intakes, revised variable ramps, dorsally-mounted water tank for the PCC system, and nose-mounted HIAC-1 camera. However, without a USAF requirement for the RF-4X or its proposed F-4X fighter variant, development costs for these promising aircraft were soon found too high to justify either the manufacture of a few aircraft for the Israeli Air Force or even the completion of a prototype. Accordingly, 69-7576 was modified to the less ambitious F-4E(S) configuration described on page 200.

Phantom II in US service

Including prototypes and development aircraft, 1,264 Phantoms were built for the USN and USMC and 2,840 were produced for the USAF. By the late 'eighties, with the exception of a small number of reconnaissance aircraft with a Marine squadron and a fast dwindling number of development aircraft and drones with Navy experimental units, all naval F-4s and RF-4s had been withdrawn from service. With active USAF units, Phantoms were then soon to be limited to RF-4C reconnaissance aircraft, F-4G defence suppression aircraft, and various test models while the type was expected to be withdrawn from Air Force Reserve service

An F-4B fitted with an experimental buddy refuelling pod during evaluation at the Naval Test Center, NAS Patuxent River, in the autumn of 1964. *(USN)*

before the end of 1991. In Air National Guard service, the last F-4Es will be phased out in 1992, but the RF-4Cs will be retained well into the last decade of the 20th Century. The operational career of US Phantoms is summarized hereafter by branches of service.

USN: Before and shortly after entering naval service, the Phantom II demonstrated its superior performance by establishing numerous National Aeronautic Association (NAA) and Fédération Aéronautique Internationale (FAI) world and class records as follows:

● 6 December, 1959: Flying the specially modified second YF4H-1 (BuNo 142260) from Edwards AFB, California, as part of Project *Top Flight*, Cdr L E Flint, USN, climbed to 50,000 ft (15,240 m) where he levelled off to accelerate before zooming to set a new absolute altitude record of 30,040 m (98,556 ft).

● 5 September, 1960: Lt Col T H Miller, USMC, flew his F4H-1F over a 500-km (310.7-mile) triangular course in 15 min 19.2 sec, at an average speed of 1,958.16 km/h (1,216.74 mph).

• 25 September, 1960: Cdr J F Davis, USN, set a new record over the 100-km (62.1-mile) course at an average speed of 2,237.41 km/h (1,390.26 mph).

• 24 May, 1961: As part of Project LANA (L for the roman numeral 50 and ANA for Anniversary of Naval Aviation) to mark the 50th Anniversary of US Naval Aviation, five F4H-1Fs competing for the Bendix Trophy took off at timed intervals from Ontario, California, and set out for NAS Brooklyn (Floyd Bennett Field), New York. In four supersonic dashes at an altitude of 50,000 ft (15,240 m) separated by three subsonic flight refuellings at 35,000 ft (10,670 m) from tanker-configured Douglas A3D-2s, three Phantoms flown by USN crews reached their destination after shattering the record of 3 hr 8 min set in November 1957 by an Air Force McDonnell RF-101C. The best time—for which the team of Lt R F Gordon, pilot, and Lt (jg) B R Young, RIO, received the Bendix Trophy—was 2 hr 47 min and represented an average speed of 870 mph (1,400 km/h) over the 2,446-mile (3,936-km) flight.

• 28 August, 1961: Project *Sageburner* saw Lt H Hardisty, pilot, and Lt E H DeEsch, RIO, both USN, set a new low-altitude record over the 3-km (1.86-mile) course. Taking off from Holloman AFB, New Mexico, this crew flew twice in each direction at a maximum altitude of 125 ft (38 m) over rough terrain to average 1,452.869 km/h (902.769 mph).

The *Sageburner* (BuNo 145307) and *Skyburner* (BuNo 142260) record-breaking aircraft. *(MCAIR)*

• 22 November, 1961: The true Mach 2 capability of the Phantom was demonstrated during Operation *Skyburner* when Lt Col R B Robinson, USMC, flew twice over a 15/25-km

(9.3/15.5-mile) course at Edwards AFB at an average speed of 2,585.1 km/h (1,606.3 mph) at an altitude of 45,000 ft (13,715 m). To set the world's first record at more than Mach 2, the second YF4H-1 (BuNo 142260) had been specially fitted with a water/alcohol spray in the engine inlet ducts to cool the air ahead of the compressors and thus increase engine thrust.

• 5 December, 1961: Flying the previously modified second YF4H-1 from Edwards AFB, Cdr G W Ellis, USN, established a new sustained altitude record of 20,252.1 m (66,443.8 ft).

• 21 February, 1962: Two time-to-height records were broken at NAS Brunswick, Maine: LCdr J W Young, USN, climbed to 3,000 m (9,843 ft) in 34.52 sec and Cdr D M Longton, USN, climbed to 6,000 m (19,685 ft) in 48.78 sec.

• 1 March, 1962: Three more time-to-height records were broken at NAS Brunswick: 9,000 m (29,528 ft) in 61.62 sec and 12,000 m (39,370 ft) in 77.15 sec by Lt Col W C McGraw, USMC, and 15,000 m (49,213 ft) in 114.54 sec by LCdr D W Nordberg, USN.

• 31 March, 1962: Flying from NAS Point Mugu, California, LCdr F T Brown, USN, climbed to 20,000 m (65,617 ft) in 178.50 sec.

• 3 April, 1962: LCdr J W Young, USN, climbed to 25,000 m (82,021 ft) in 230.44 sec. over NAS Point Mugu.

• 4 April, 1962: The Phantom's clean sweep of time-to-height records was completed by LCdr D W Nordberg, USN, who climbed to 30,000 m (98,425 ft) in 371.43 sec. In setting the time to 30,000 m record, LCdr Nordberg zoomed over the 100,000 ft (30,480 m) mark and thus surpassed the record which had been set by Cdr Flint on 6 December, 1959. This mark, however, was not officially recorded by the FÁI.

BuNo 152980, an F-4B-23-MC of VF-11. *(USN)*

When entering service, just short of 31 months after its first flight and one year after setting its first world's record, the Phantom II was not only the fastest fighter of the US Navy but also the highest flying and longest ranged. The service life of this remarkable aircraft began in December 1960 when F4H-1Fs were delivered to Fighter Squadron One Twenty-One (VF-121), the Pacific Fleet RAG (Replacement Air Group) at NAS Miramar, California. Shortly after, Detachment A of VF-101, the Atlantic Fleet's RAG, also received F4H-1Fs. The first fully operational Phantom squadrons, VF-74 and VF-114, were equipped with F4H-1s in mid-1961 and in October of that year VF-74 became the first F4H-1 squadron to complete carrier qualifications. The next significant events in the Phantom's operational career were the first short cruise, which was made in August-October 1962 by the *Diamondbacks* of VF-102 aboard the USS *Enterprise* (CVAN-65), and the first full deployment, when from August 1962 until March 1963 the *Be-Devilers* of VF-74 went to the Mediterranean aboard the USS *Forrestal* (CVA-59). While VF-74 was in the Mediterranean, Soviet missiles were discovered on Cuba and during the resulting Cuban Missile Crisis in October 1962, VF-41 and its F-4Bs were transferred from NAS Oceana, Virginia, to NAS Key West, Florida, for temporary duty with the North American Air Defense Command. At the same time, other F-4Bs operating from the USS *Enterprise* (CVAN-65) and USS *Independence* (CVA-62) helped impose the blockade of Cuba.

F-4B (BuNo 151413) of VF-161, CVW-15, aboard the USS *Coral Sea* (CVA-43) in February 1970. *(Jerry Edwards)*

At the time of the Gulf of Tonkin Incident in August 1964, 13 of the 31 Navy deployable fighter squadrons were equipped with F-4Bs, one had a mix of F-4Bs and F-4Gs, and one was converting from F-3Bs to F-4Bs. In addition, two RAG squadrons flew a mix of F-4As and F-4Bs. The first Phantom combat sorties were flown during Operation *Pierce Arrow* on 5 August, 1964, when F-4Bs from VF-142 and VF-143 flew from the USS *Constellation* (CVA-64) in the Gulf of Tonkin to provide cover for retaliatory air strikes against North Vietnamese gunboats and shore facilities. Next to see action during the drawn out Southeast Asia War were F-4Bs from VF-92, VF-96, and VF-151 which flew combat air patrols during retaliatory strikes in February 1965 (*Flaming Dart*) and early *Rolling Thunder* raids in the spring of 1965.

Altogether, between August 1964 and August 1973, 22 Navy squadrons and one Marine squadron made 84 war cruises to the Gulf of Tonkin,

51 with F-4Bs, one with F-4Gs in 1965-66, and 32 with F-4Js beginning with VF-33 and VF-102 aboard USS *America* (CVA-66) in May 1968. They claimed their first air combat victory, which was not confirmed for fear of publicly antagonizing the People's Republic of China, on 9 April, 1965, when Lt (jg) Terence Murphy and Ensign Ron Fegan shot down a MiG-17 from China's Air Force of the People's Liberation Army. Unfortunately, this VF-96 crew did not return to the USS *Ranger* (CVA-61). They were either shot down by a Chinese MiG-17 or downed by another F-4B. The first officially confirmed victory over a North Vietnamese fighter was credited to Cdr Louis C Page, Jr, and Lt John Smith from VF-21 who shot down a MiG-17 on 17 June, 1965, while flying from the USS *Midway* (CVA-41). Before the fighting ended in 1973, Navy F-4 crews were credited with the destruction of 40 other enemy aircraft, including five by Lt Randall H Cunningham and Lt (jg) William P

BuNo 153045, the F-4B of VF-161 in which Lieut Victor T Kowaleski and Lieut(jg) James A Wise shot down the last enemy aircraft of the Vietnam War, a MiG-17, on 12 January, 1973. *(Peter B Lewis)*

Driscoll of VF-96, the only Navy aces of the Southeast Asia War. On the debit side, the war had seen the loss of 71 Navy F-4s (five to enemy aircraft, 13 to surface-to-air missiles, and 53 to AAA and small arms fire) in combat and 54 in operational accidents.

At war's end, the F-4 was already being supplemented by the variable-geometry Grumman F-14 Tomcat and some of these joined the Phantoms in providing air cover during the final evacuation of South Vietnam in April 1975. Afterwards, F-14As progressively replaced F-4Bs and F-4Js in most deployable squadrons, the exception being the six squadrons assigned to the older and smaller USS *Midway* (CVA-41), *Franklin D. Roosevelt* (CVA-42), and *Coral Sea* (CVA-43) which were eventually re-equipped with F-4Ns or F-4Ss. The end of the Phantom's career with active duty carrier-based squadrons finally came on 24 March, 1986, when F-4Ss from VF-151 and VF-161 were last launched from USS *Midway*.

In addition to their long and distinguished career as carrier-based fighters, Navy Phantoms were operated by the Naval Air Test Center (NATC) and the Naval Test Pilot School (NTPS) at NAS Patuxent River between 1958 and 1988. Moreover, F-4s have been used for a great variety of experimental purposes, mainly from NAS Point Mugu, NAS China Lake, and NAF El Centro in California, NASWF/NWEF at Kirtland AFB in New Mexico, and NADC at Johnsville in Pennsylvania. Notably, on 10 May, 1962, an F4H-1 flying from Point Mugu obtained the first successful head-on intercept and kill at supersonic speeds. In this test, a demonstration of the effectiveness of fighter-launched missiles against high-speed aircraft, the Phantom fired a Sparrow III air-to-air missile at a surface-launched KD-2U Regulus II missile while both fighter and target were flying at supersonic speeds towards each other. The F4H-1 also registered an important first in the annals of aerospace when

F-4J-30-MC (BuNo 153812) from the Naval Weapons Center at NAS China Lake, California, carrying three tube-launched AIM-95 Agile air-to-air missiles. These experimental, Navy-developed, short-range missiles were IR-homing and had thrust vector control (TVC) steering. *(USN)*

on 25 July, 1962, Lt A Newman of the Naval Ordnance Test Station (NOTS) China Lake lifted his Phantom loaded with a 3,000-lb (1,361-kg) Caleb rocket carrying a scientific payload of 120 lb (54 kg). After accelerating at an altitude of 26,000 ft (7,925 m), Newman zoomed his F4H-1 to 36,000 ft (10,975 m) to launch the two-stage rocket which reached a top altitude of 725 miles (1,167 km). Designated Project *Hi-Hoe*, this experiment established the feasibility of using a manned aircraft as a recoverable first stage in the orbiting of small satellites.

Seven modified F-4Js were assigned to the *Blue Angels* in January 1969, and this famous Navy flight demonstration squadron flew Phantoms until the end of the 1973 season when the energy crisis forced a switch to Douglas Skyhawks.

Following the retirement of the last two F-4Ss from the Strike Aircraft Test Directorate of the Naval Air Test Center, the only Phantom IIs remaining in USN service after October 1988 were F-4Ss at NAS Point

BuNo 153082, an F-4J flown by the leader of the *Blue Angels*, at NAS Lemoore, California, on 5 October, 1970. *(Peter B Lewis)*

Mugu (with VX-4) and QF-4 drones at PMTC Point Mugu and NWC China Lake.

Naval Air Reserve: Phantoms first reached the Naval Air Reserve in 1969 when F-4Bs were assigned to VF-22L1 at NAS Los Alamitos, California. During the following year, when NAVAIRES was re-organized along more operational lines, four reserve fighter squadrons were established. However, as F-4s were urgently needed by active units, VF-201 and VF-202 with the Atlantic Fleet and VF-301 and VF-302 with the Pacific Fleet were first equipped with LTV F-8 Crusaders. F-4Bs replaced the Crusaders in 1974 and were in turn replaced by F-4Ns and F-4Ss. The last F-4N was flown by VF-201 from NAS Dallas, Texas, to NATTC Memphis, Tennessee, on 29 February, 1984, and the last F-4S was retired by VF-202 from NAS Dallas on 14 May, 1987 (BuNo 155560 becoming the Navy's last tactical Phantom II).

USMC and USMCR: With the Marines, Phantoms were operated by active fighter squadrons between June 1962, when VMF(AW)-314 received its first F4H-1s at MCAS Cherry Point and the spring of 1989, when VMFA-134 exchanged its F-4Ss for F/A-18As at MCAS El Toro, California.

In the summer of 1964, as US forces were being drawn into combat in Vietnam, the Marine Corps had six squadrons equipped with F-4Bs (VMFA-115 and -323 at MCAS Cherry Point, VMFA-513 and -542 at MCAS El Toro and VMFA-314 and -531 at Atsugi, Japan) and others were about to convert from F-8s to F-4s. The first to reach the war zone

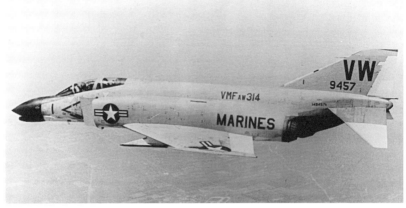

An F4H-1 of VMF(AW)-314, the first Marine squadron to fly Phantom IIs. *(USMC)*

were those of VMFA-531 which landed at Da Nang AB on 11 April, 1965, and flew their first combat sorties in South Vietnam two days later. Thereafter, and until the Marine withdrawal from Vietnam in 1970, eleven squadrons relayed each other to fly Phantoms from Da Nang and Chu Lai Air Bases, mainly in support of Marine ground forces in South Vietnam but also on *Tally Ho* offensive strikes in the North Vietnamese panhandle and *Steel Tiger/Tiger Hound* interdiction sorties in Laos. Following the North Vietnamese offensive in the spring of 1972, Marine F-4 squadrons returned to South Vietnam in April and during the following month moved to Thailand. In Vietnam, they provided much needed support to repell the invaders while from Thailand they flew strikes against targets in Laos and North Vietnam. During the war, the Marines lost 72 F-4s in combat (one to a MiG, 65 to AAA and small arms

F-4N of VMFA-323 in landing configuration. *(Peter B Lewis)*

fire, and six in mortar or sapper attacks on their bases) and 23 in operational accidents. No air combat victories were claimed by Marine F-4 units in Vietnam and Thailand, but USMC pilots on exchange duty with the USAF shot down a MiG-17 and a MiG-21. Another MiG-21 was shot down by a crew from VMFA-333, an F-4J squadron which deployed aboard the USS *America* (CVA-66) from July 1972 until March 1973.

After the war had ended, Phantoms remained the only fighter aircraft in service with the Fleet Marine Force until the arrival of the first F/A-18s in January 1983 and the last F-4Ss were only phased out in early 1989. With the Marine Air Reserve, F-4Bs were first delivered to VMFA-321 at NAF Washington in December 1973 and, more than fifteen years later, F-4Ss were still in use with VMFA-112 and VMFA-321. The last Phantoms in reserve service were expected to be replaced by F/A-18s in 1990-91.

The RF-4B, the Phantom II version which is unique to the Marine Corps, was first delivered to VMCJ-3 at MCAS El Toro in May 1965 and soon after to VMCJ-2 at MCAS Cherry Point and to VMCJ-1 at Iwakuni in Japan. It was the last which took RF-4Bs to Da Nang in October 1966 for operations in Vietnam. During the conflict, three RF-4Bs were lost to AAA and small arms fire and one in an operational accident. In 1975, two years after combat operations had ended, the RF-4Bs were regrouped in a new squadron, VMFP-3, based at MCAS El Toro as part of 3rd Marine Air Wing. In 1989, still attached to 3rd MAW, VMFP-3 was continuing to send RF-4B detachments wherever needed to support not only its parent organization but also the 1st MAW in Japan, the 2nd MAW on the East Coast, and the 1st Marine Brigade in Hawaii. VMFP-3 stood down in August 1990.

USAF: If at first the Air Force had been reluctant to acquire the Navy developed Phantom, it quickly became the largest F-4 operator. Preceded by the pair of F-4Bs which were evaluated at Langley AFB in early 1962, F-4Bs on loan from the Navy and the first F-4Cs entered service with the 4453rd Combat Crew Training Wing at MacDill AFB in November 1963. F-4Cs began being assigned to operational TAC units in January 1964 when they replaced F-84Fs with the 12th TFW at the same Florida base. In the Pacific, the first F-4Cs were those from the 555th Tactical Fighter Squadron which, assigned on temporary duty (TDY) from the 12th TFW to the 51st TFW, arrived at Naha AB, Okinawa, in December 1964. In Europe, the first Phantom fighters were those of the 81st TFW which arrived at RAF Bentwaters in October 1965 (five months after the 10th TRW at RAF Alconbury had received two RF-4Cs, the first reconnaissance Phantoms assigned to a European-based USAF unit).

In a less well-known role, Phantoms were repeatedly used by the Air Force to photograph the early flight phase of space projects as their speed and rate of climb enabled them to follow the launch sequence. Equipped with 16 and 35 mm motion picture cameras, an F-4C was first used during 1965 to photograph the launching of the moon-mapping Ranger capsule.

F-4C-24-MC of the 92nd TFS, 81st TFW, USAFE, at RAF Bentwaters, England.
(George Pennick, courtesy of David W Menard)

Later, several manned space missions were similarly recorded by Phantoms.

In combat, the first Phantoms were the F-4Cs of the 45th TFS, a squadron from TAC's 15th TFW which deployed from MacDill AFB to Ubon RTAFB, Thailand, in April 1965 on TDY assignment to the 2nd Air Division. Crews from this squadron—Capts K E Holcombe and A C Clark and Capts T S Roberts and R C Anderson—shot down two MiG-17s during a mission over North Vietnam on 10 July, 1965, to obtain the first USAF air-to-air combat victory of the war. The 45th TFS was returned to the 15th TFW in August 1965 and the first squadrons sent to Southeast Asia on PCS (permanent change of station) status were those from the 12th TFW (the 557th, 558th, and 559th TFSs) which arrived at Cam Rahn Bay AB in the Republic of Vietnam on 8 November, 1965. From then until 15 August, 1973, when in accordance with a Congressional mandate, the last US combat missions were flown in Southeast Asia, 15 other Tactical Fighter Squadrons were assigned PCS to the war zone with Phantoms. Altogether, five PCS squadrons operated F-4Cs only, six were first equipped with F-4Cs and converted to F-4Ds (first assigned in the theatre to the 555th TFS in May 1967), three were exclusively equipped with F-4Ds, and four had F-4Es only (first assigned in the theatre in November 1968 when the 469th TFS at Korat RTAFB, Thailand, converted from F-105Ds). In addition to these squadrons sent to Southeast Asia on PCS status, 15 squadrons (one with F-4Cs, one with *Wild Weasel-* configured F-4Cs, seven with F-4Ds, and six with F-4Es) deployed TDY to Vietnam and Thailand in 1972 as part of *Constant Guard*, the US reaction to the North Vietnamese invasion of South Vietnam in the spring of 1972.

During the war, F-4C crews claimed the destruction of 22 MiGs with Sidewinders, 14 with Sparrows, four with gunfire, and two by causing them to crash while manoeuvring; F-4D crews scored 26 kills with Sparrows, six and a half with gunfire, five each with Sidewinders and

222

F-4C carrying two camera pods, four AIM-7D Sparrow missiles, and two external tanks, over North Vietnam in 1965. *(USAF)*

Falcons[16]; and two while manoeuvring; and F-4E crews[17] were credited 21 MiGs, 10 with Sparrows, five with gunfire, four with Sidewinders, one with Sidewinder and gunfire, and one while manoeuvring). The last USAF victory, a MiG-21, was claimed on 8 January, 1973, by a crew from the 4th TFS, Capt P D Howman and 1 Lt L K Kullman. Although Phantom crews gained more fame for their air-to-air victories, they mostly flew air-to-ground missions in South and North Vietnam, Cambodia, and Laos. For these missions, primary weapons were conventional and retarded bombs with standard or extended fuses, rocket launchers, CBUs (cluster bomb units), or BLU fire bombs. Newer weapons introduced during the war by Phantom units included (1) AGM-62 Walleye TV-guided missiles, which were first used by the 555th TFS on 24 August, 1967, for a successful attack against a bridge; (2)

[16] Disappointing results with the Air Force-developed Falcon infrared-guided missile led the 8th TFW to modify its F-4Ds so that they would once again be able to launch Navy-developed Sidewinders.

[17] All three USAF aces of the war scored their victories in 1972 while flying F-4Ds and F-4Es with the 432nd TFW at Udorn RTAFB. Capt Charles B DeBellevue, a WSO who was credited with six victories while flying with Capts Ritchie and Madden, and Capt Richard S 'Steve' Ritchie, a pilot with five kills obtained with Capts DeBellevue and Pettit, were with the 555th TFS. Capt Jeffrey S Feinstein, a WSO who flew with four pilots to get five victories, was assigned to the 13th TFS.

223

F-4C-19-MC of the 356th TFS. 475th TFW, at Yokota AB, Japan, on 4 June, 1968. *(Toyokazu Matsuzaki)*

GBU-10 laser-guided bombs, which were first launched on 23 May, 1968, from F-4Ds of the 8th TFW; (3) ADSID-1 acoustical sensors, which were seeded along the Ho Chi Minh Trail by F-4Ds from the 25th TFS; and (4) EOGBs (Electro-Optical Guided Bombs), which were first dropped by Phantoms from the 8th TFW on 6 April, 1972.

Having lost its first Phantoms on 20 June, 1965 (an F-4C from the 45th TFS brought down by flak during a strike against barracks at Son La,

F-4C-20-MC of the 6512th Test Squadron, Air Force Systems Command, flying near Edwards AFB, California. *(AFFTC)*

North Vietnam), the USAF went on to lose a total of 442 F-4s (plus 83 RF-4Cs as detailed further on) during the war. Thirty-three were shot down by MiGs, 30 by SAMs and 307 by AAA and small arms fire. Nine were destroyed on the ground during mortar and sapper attacks and 63 went down as the result of operational accidents.

Fighter versions of the F-4 began being supplemented by F-15s in 1975 and by F-16s in 1979 with the conversion to the newer aircraft accelerating as time passed. The first major command to lose its F-4s was the Alaskan Air Command, which did so in 1982, and by 1989 Phantom fighters were definitely on their way out. With USAFE the last F-4Es were those from the 52nd TFW at Spangdahlem AB which were replaced by F-16C/Ds in 1987, and with PACAF the last two F-4E squadrons were converting to F-16C/Ds in 1989. During that year, Air Force Systems Command continued to operate F-4Es from Eglin AFB, Florida, and Edwards AFB, California, while three TAC wings still flew F-4Es (two squadrons of the 4th TFW were at Seymour Johnson AFB, North Carolina; two squadrons of the 35th TTW, the F-4 conversion unit, and three squadrons of the 37th TFW, which also flew F-4Gs, were at George AFB, California).

In addition to their main use within TAC, F-4Es were operated by that command to equip the USAF Air Demonstration Squadron at Nellis AFB during a five-year period. After converting from F-100Ds, the *Thunderbirds* made their debut in F-4Es at the Air Force Academy in Colorado Springs, Colorado, on 4 June, 1969. Rising fuel costs forced the *Thunderbirds* to convert to T-38As in 1974.

The solo F-4E of the *Thunderbird* demonstration team making a low pass over its home base at Nellis AFB, Nevada. *(Peter J Mancus)*

After its protracted development, the first *Wild Weasel* (defence suppression) version of the Phantom, the EF-4C, entered service with the 66th Fighter Weapons Squadron, an operational conversion and tactic development unit at Nellis AFB, Nevada, in June 1968. EF-4Cs then went to the 67th TFS, which was based at Kadena AB, Okinawa, and deployed TDY to Korat RTAFB, Thailand, in 1972-73 to take part in *Linebacker I* operations. Others went to the 81st TFS at Spangdahlem AB, Germany. In 1979, after being replaced in service with active squadrons by F-4Gs, the remaining EF-4Cs were handed over to squadrons of the Indiana ANG. The definitive *Wild Weasel* version of the Phantom, the F-4G, reached operational units in 1978. Twelve years later, F-4Gs were operated alongside F-4Es by two squadrons of the 35th TFW at George AFB and alongside F-16C/Ds by one squadron of the 3rd TFW at Clark AB, the Philippines, and three squadrons of the 52nd TFW at Spangdahlem AB. Replacement by *Wild Weasel* F-16s is not anticipated to take place until the mid-1990s.

In the reconnaissance role, RF-4Cs were first assigned to a conversion unit, the 33rd Tactical Reconnaissance Training Squadron, at Shaw AFB in September 1964 and soon after were assigned to a first operational unit, the 16th Tactical Reconnaissance Squadron also at this South Carolina base. Subsequently, they equipped 19 Tactical Reconnaissance Squadrons (the 1st, 4th, 7th, 9th through 12th, 14th through 18th, 22nd, 30th, 32nd, 38th, 45th, 62nd, and 91st) with TAC, PACAF, and USAFE.

RF-4C-53-MC of the 15th Tactical Reconnaissance Squadron, 18th Tactical Fighter Wing, at Yokata AB, Japan, on 17 December, 1988. *(Toyokazu Matsuzaki)*

In Southeast Asia, the first RF-4Cs were nine aircraft from the 16th TRS which were deployed on a TDY basis to Tan Son Nhut AB, Republic of South Vietnam, on 30 October, 1965. Combat operations began the next day, and during the next eight years RF-4Cs assigned at various times to the 11th, 12th, 14th, and 16th TRSs served impressively from Tan Son Nhut AB and from Udorn RTAFB. Although flying alone more often than not, no RF-4Cs were lost to MiGs. However, seven fell victim to SAMs, 65 were shot down by AAA or small arms fire, four were destroyed on the ground, and seven were lost in operational accidents.

By early 1989, the number of RF-4C squadrons in service with active Air Force units had been reduced to seven (the16th TRS at Shaw AFB and the 12th TRS, 45th TRTS, 62nd TRS, and 91st TRS at Bergstrom AFB with TAC; the 15th TRS at Kadena AB, Okinawa, with PACAF; and the 38th TRS at Zweibrücken AB, Germany, with USAFE) and plans to deactivate two of these squadrons had been announced. In addition, however, RF-4Cs were still operated by the 6512th Test Squadron and the USAF Test Pilot School at Edwards AFB. Notwithstanding the substantial reduction in the number of operational RF-4Cs and the fact that the youngest airframes were already over 15 years old in 1989, the reconnaissance version of the Phantom was planned to remain in USAF service until around 1997.

AFRES: The Air Force Reserve became a Phantom operator only in October 1978 when the 915th Airborne Early Warning and Control Group at Homestead AFB, Florida, was redesignated the 915th Tactical Fighter Group and F-4Cs were assigned to its 93rd TFS. Over the next four years, F-4Ds were given to four other AFRES squadrons, and by

F-4D-31-MC of the 457th TFS, 301st TFW, AFRES, at Nellis AFB Nevada, in October 1983 during the Gunsmoke '83 competition. *(René J Francillon)*

1984 the 93rd TFS had exchanged its F-4Cs for F-4Ds. The number of F-4D squadrons remained constant at five until 1988 when the 457th TFS at Carswell AFB, Texas, began receiving F-4Es. in 1989 the 93rd TFS became the first AFRES squadron to replace its Phantoms with F-16A/Bs. Conversion of the remaining four F-4 squadrons to F-16s is scheduled to be completed before the end of Fiscal Year 1991 (*ie* by 30 September, 1991).

ANG: The first Phantoms assigned to the Air National Guard were RF-4Cs which were initially delivered to the 106th TRS, Alabama ANG, in February 1971. Afterwards, eight Guard squadrons transitioned into the RF-4C. A training unit was later added in the Idaho ANG, but by early 1989 the number of Guard units flying RF-4Cs had been reduced to five operational squadrons and one training squadron. Most of these squadrons (the 106th TRS, Alabama ANG; 153rd TRS, Mississippi ANG; 173rd TRS, Nebraska ANG; 189th TRTS and 190th TRS, Idaho ANG; 192nd TRS, Nevada ANG; and the 196th TRS, California ANG) were expected to fly RF-4Cs until close to the end of the century.

F-4Cs were first assigned to the 170th TFS, Illinois ANG, in January 1972; F-4Ds first went to the 178th FIS in 1977; EF-4Cs, no longer used in the *Wild Weasel* role, went to the 113th and 163rd TFSs, Indiana ANG, in 1979; and F-4Es joined the Guard in 1985 when the 110th TFS, Missouri ANG, converted from F-4Cs. In early 1989, one Fighter Interceptor Squadron (the 123rd in Oregon) was still flying F-4Cs, six FISs (the 111th in Texas, 136th in New York, 171st in Michigan, 178th in North Dakota, 179th in Minnesota, and 194th in California) and four Tactical Fighter Squadrons (the 121st in the District of Columbia, 127th and 177th in Kansas, and 170th in Illinois) had F-4Ds, and five TFSs (the 110th in Missouri, 113th and 163rd in Indiana, 141st in New Jersey, and 196th in California) operated F-4Es. During that year, however, the last F-4Cs

RF-4C-19-MC of the 160th TRS, 187th TRG, Alabama ANG, at Tyndall AFB, Florida, in November 1978. *(Peter J Mancus)*

were phased out, F-4Ds were being replaced by F-16ADFs, and F-4Es were beginning to be withdrawn from use. By 1992, only RF-4Cs and F-4Es are expected to remain with the Air National Guard and these, the last Phantoms in US service, are expected to remain until the turn of the century.

Phantom II in foreign service

Outside the USA, Phantoms first entered service with the Fleet Air Arm in the spring of 1968 and with the Royal Air Force during the summer of that same year. Since then, F-4s and RF-4s have joined the air forces of ten other nations. Some of these air arms are expected to fly Phantoms until at least the first decade of the 21st Century. Brief summaries of overseas deliveries and foreign service history are given by country in chronological order of date of entry into service.

United Kingdom: Including prototypes, 185 Phantom IIs—52 FG.1s, 118 FGR.2s, and 15 F-4J(UK)s—have been delivered to the Royal Navy and Royal Air Force. The first British unit was a Fleet Air Arm trials squadron, No. 700P at RNAS Yeovilton (HMS *Heron*), which was commissioned on 30 April, 1968. Next was No. 767 Squadron, the FAA's conversion training unit, which was formed in January 1969 and disbanded in August 1972. The only operational unit, No. 892 Squadron, was commissioned on 31 March, 1969[18], became carrier qualified aboard the USS *Saratoga* (CVA-60) in the autumn of 1969, and first embarked

F-4K Phantom FG 1 of No 892 Squadron, Royal Navy, landing on the USS *Saratoga* (CVA-60) during cross-deck operations in 1969. *(Royal Navy)*

aboard HMS *Ark Royal* in June 1970. Eight years later the squadron was decommissioned as HMS *Ark Royal*, the last Royal Navy carrier capable of embarking conventional fixed-wing aircraft was paid off. The last sixteen FG.1s in Royal Navy service were transferred to the Royal Air Force at the end of 1978.

Whereas the three FAA squadrons only flew Phantom FG.1s, RAF units have flown all three British versions. The first FGR.2s were handed to No. 228 OCU at RAF Coningsby in August 1968 and the first operational squadron, No. 6 Squadron, was formed at the same station in

---

[18] Less than six weeks later, on 11 May, the CO of No. 892 Squadron established the fastest time in the *Daily Mail* Transatlantic Race by flying from New York to London in 4hr 46 min 57 sec.

May 1969. Subsequently, FGR.2s were flown by Nos. 6 and 54 Squadrons, Air Support Command; Nos. 23, 29, 56, and 111 Squadrons, Strike Command; and Nos. 14, 17, 19, 31, and 92 Squadrons, RAF Germany, in the ground attack and air defence roles. In the tactical reconnaissance role, FGR.2s were operated by No. 2 Squadron, RAF Germany, and No. 41 Squadron, Air Support Command. In the air defence role, FG.1s were assigned to Nos. 43 and 111 Squadrons and from the end of 1984 were supplemented by the F-4J(UK)s of No. 74 Squadron.

F-4M Phantom FGR 2 of No. 19 Squadron, RAF Germany, landing at Wildenrath. *(MAP)*

Phantoms were first replaced by Jaguars in April 1975 when No.14 Squadron was re-equipped by Tornado F.3s and in April 1987 when No. 29 began its conversion. Thus, at the beginning of 1989, Phantoms equipped only two squadrons in Germany (Nos. 19 and 92) and five squadrons (Nos. 23, 43, 56, 74, and 111) in the United Kingdom, with one of the UK-based squadrons being deployed to RAF Stanley for the air defence of the Falklands (the first to do so was No. 29 Squadron in October 1982).

Iran: As part of the Shah's ambitious design to turn Iran into a major power in Western Asia and the Middle East, the Nirou Havai Shahanshahiye Iran (Imperial Iranian Air Force or IIAF) placed an initial order for 16 F-4Ds in 1967 and then ordered a second batch of 16 F-4Ds as well as 208 F-4Es and 32 RF-4Es. However, following the overthrow of the Shah in 1979, outstanding Irani contracts for military equipment, including those for the last 31 F-4Es and 16 RF-4Es, were cancelled by the US government. Thus, Iran received a total of 225 Phantoms (*see* Appendix C for a list of USAF serials assigned to these aircraft) to equip two F-4D squadrons, eight F-4E squadrons, and one RF-4E squadron.

The first four F-4Ds were ferried to Teheran-Mehrabad in September 1968 and, supplemented by the remaining 12 aircraft from the first batch,

230

served to equip the 306th Fighter Squadron. The second batch of 16 F-4Ds was delivered in 1969 to equip a second squadron. In addition to helping the IIAF form a nucleus of well-trained pilots for the F-4E and RF-4E squadrons which were formed beginning in the spring of 1971 with the arrival of the first F-4Es, F-4Ds were used in unsuccessful attempts at intercepting high-flying Soviet MiG-25s. During 1975, F-4Ds were also deployed to the Sultanate of Oman to assist in the fighting against Dhofari rebels and one of these aircraft was lost to ground fire.

In 1979, numerous pilots and senior maintenance personnel chose to follow the Shah into exile rather than to stay in Iran under the oppressive rule of the Ayatollah Khomeini. Thus, when in September 1980 Iraqi forces invaded Iran, the Islamic Republic Iranian Air Force (IRIAF) was

A McDonnell F-4D of the 306th Fighter Squadron, Nirou Havai Shahanshahiye Iran (IIAF) taxi-ing at Teheran-Mehrabad in August 1969. *(MCAIR)*

but a shadow of the once proud IIAF. At first its Phantoms took part in deep penetration raids against military and industrial targets in and around Baghdad and supported ground operations along the disputed Shaat-al-Arab waterway and in the fighting for Abadan. Later, they were increasingly used in a defensive role to protect oil refineries and loading facilities, as well as Teheran and other major cities, against Iraqi air raids. However, even these relatively modest efforts could not be sustained for long as the combination of lack of skilled maintenance personnel, US embargo, and mounting combat and operational losses (including a pair of F-4Es shot down by F-15As of the Royal Saudi Air Force after they appeared to threaten Saudi oil facilities) resulted in a drastic reduction in the number of Phantoms remaining operational. Thus, the IRIAF saw its F-4 inventory dwindle from its peak strength of over 220 at the start of the war to less than 50 operable aircraft by 1985. Nevertheless, as late as January 1988 Irani Phantoms were still able to mount rocket attacks against tankers in the Gulf. When hostilities ended in 1988, however, the

IRIAF was said to possess barely a dozen, if that many, F-4Es and RF-4Es.

Republic of Korea: Under the *Peace Spectator* programme, the Republic of Korea Air Force (ROKAF) first obtained 18 ex-USAF F-4Ds in 1969 (six aircraft being initially handed over at Taegu AB on 29 August) to replace the North American F-86Ds of its 1st Fighter Wing. In exchange for F-5A/Bs, it transferred to the Vietnamese Air Force in 1972, the ROKAF obtained 18 additional ex-USAF F-4Ds to re-equip another squadron[19]. Six F-4Ds were supplied later by the USAF as attrition replacements and 24 ex-USAF F-4Ds were transferred in 1987-88 to enable the ROKAF to bring its two F-4D squadrons back to strength and to equip a third. Thirty-seven new F-4Es were delivered in 1977-79 and were assigned to the 17th TFW (serials for the 37 F-4Es delivered under *Peace Pheasant II* are given in Appendix C). These new aircraft were supplemented in 1988-89 by some 76 ex-USAF F-4Es, thus enabling the ROKAF to field five F-4E squadrons by the end of 1989. Also transferred in 1989 were 12 ex-USAF RF-4Cs.

Israel: The *Peace Echo* agreement of 1 July, 1968, which provided for the initial delivery of 44 F-4Es and six RF-4Es to the Tsvah Haganah le Israel – Heyl Ha'Avir (Israel Defence Force – Air Force) was followed on 10 March, 1969, by a licensing and technical assistance agreement between MDC and Israel Aircraft Industries. Deliveries began in

One of the 240 F-4Es which have been operated by the Heyl Ha'Avir since 1969.
(Israeli Defense Attaché in Washington DC)

September 1969. Including aircraft ordered under additional FMS contracts, as well as those transferred by the USAF to make good combat losses and those diverted from USAF contracts, the Heyl Ha'Avir received a total of 240 F-4Es. Serials for the 86 Phantoms ordered under

[19] The 36 F-4D-24-MC to -28-MCs transferred to the ROKAF were 64-0931, 64-0933/64-0935, 64-0941, 64-0943/64-0944, 64-0946/64-0948, 64-0950/64-0951, 64-0955, 64-0957/64-0958, 64-0961/64-0962, 64-0966, 64-0978, 65-0582, 65-0589, 65-0591/65-0592, 65-0605, 65-0610, 65-0620, 65-0622/65-0623, 65-0630, 65-0640, 65-0650, 65-0678, 65-0691, 65-0715, 65-0732, and 65-0762.

FMS and delivered new to Israel are given in Appendix C. Those for the F-4Es transferred by the USAF or diverted from USAF contracts are given in the footnote[20].

Within six weeks of entering service, F-4Es went into action during strikes against Egyptian SAM batteries on 22 October, 1969, and they claimed their first victory on 11 November. When the Yom Kippur War started on 6 October, 1973, Phantoms were the second most numerous aircraft in the Heyl Ha'Avir. During the next two and a half weeks, they performed virtually all its long-range strike missions. In the process, 33 of the 140 Israeli F-4Es were lost in combat, mainly to ground fire, and in operational accidents. However, these losses were made up by the hasty transfer of about 36 F-4Es from USAFE and TAC units (Operation *Nickle Grass*). The Israeli F-4Es were again in the news on 3/4 July, 1976, when they escorted Lockheed C-130s and Boeing 707s over the Red Sea on their way to Uganda during the daring rescue of hostages in Entebbe.

Although by then supplemented by more modern fighters, the F-4Es were still the most important strike aircraft of the Heyl Ha'Avir in June 1982 when Israeli forces invaded Lebanon and took part in violent combat against Syrian forces. Using anti-radiation missiles and bombs, the F-4Es were primarily responsible for the destruction of the Syrian SAM batteries in the Bekaa Valley while the F-15s, F-16s, and Kfirs achieved overwhelming superiority over Syrian fighters. At the end of the 'eighties, some 110 F-4Es still equipped five squadrons of the Heyl Ha'Avir. Even though they have been used mostly in the strike role since their debut in 1969, Israeli Phantoms have been credited with over 100 air combat victories.

Among numerous modifications made in Israel to F-4Es of the IDF-AF, either undertaken for experimental purposes or adopted for operational uses, were (1) the fitting of a non-retractable refuelling probe which was attached to the starboard fuselage, connected to the dorsal fuel receptacle of USAF Phantoms, and canted upward and outboard to place the nozzle within easy sight of the pilot; (2) provision for carrying domestically-produced Shafrir and Python air-to-air missiles and Gabriel air-to-surface missiles; (3) the replacement of the 20-mm M-61A1 rotary gun with a pair of 30-mm DEFA cannon; and (4) installation of a forward-looking infrared (FLIR) sensor.

The Heyl Ha'Avir also planned an ambitious modernization and remanufacture programme for its F-4Es involving the replacement of the

[20] Serials for the ex-USAF F-4Es are 66-0313, 66-0327, 66-0352, 67-0326, 67-0340, 67-0346, 67-0362, 67-0368, 67-0383, 68-0331, 68-0333, 68-0380, 69-0294/69-0296, 69-0299/69-0301, 69-7224/69-7227, 69-7229, 69-7238/69-7250, 69-7255, 69-7547/69-7549, 69-7553/69-7554, 69-7567/69-7570, 69-7575/69-7578, 71-0224/71-0236, 71-0246, 71-1071, 71-1074, 71-1078, 71-1080, 71-1082, 71-1090, 71-1093, 71-1393/71-1402, 72-0121, 72-0123, 72-0127, 72-0129/72-0133, 72-0137/72-0138, 72-0157/72-0158, 72-0163/72-0164, 72-1480/72-1481, 72-1487/72-1488, 72-1491/72-1492, 72-1495/72-1499, 73-1157/73-1159, 73-1161/73-1162, 73-1169/73-1170, 73-1178/73-1179, 73-1190/73-1191, and 73-1201/73-1202.

The F-4E re-engined with Pratt & Whitney PW1120 turbofans by the Bedek Aviation Division of Israel Aircraft Industries. *(IAI, courtesy of Christian Jacquet-Francillon)*

J79 engines with 20,600 lb (9,344 kg) thrust Pratt & Whitney PW1120s, the fitting of canard surfaces, the installation of newer systems and equipment, and the strengthening of the airframe to extend service life. The Bedek Aviation Division of Israel Aircraft Industries installed first one and then two PW1120 engines in a test aircraft. Notwithstanding a substantial improvement in performance as demonstrated during flight tests which began in July 1986, the IDF-AF was forced to scale down its F-4E modernization programme and to abandon the fitting of canard surfaces and PW1120 engines due to budgetary considerations. Moreover, the IDF-AF concluded that the fact that most of its Phantoms were high-time aircraft would make the conversion programme not very cost effective.

The Heyl Ha'Avir has operated three different versions of the Phantom in the reconnaissance role. It first obtained the loan of two RF-4Cs from August 1970 until March 1971 pending delivery of its RF-4Es. It then received two batches of RF-4Es totalling 12 aircraft and had three of its fighters modified by General Dynamics to the *Peace Jack* F-4E(S) configuration.

Federal German Republic: Eighty-eight RF-4Es were ordered for the Luftwaffe in January 1969 with deliveries beginning two years later to enable Aufklärungsgeschwader 51 (AG 51) at Bremgarten and AG 52 at Leck to convert from Lockheed RF-104Gs. In 1989, more than 60 RF-4Es, which since 1982 have been given a secondary conventional attack capability, were still operated by the two squadrons of each of these German wings.

Next to enter service with the Luftwaffe were 175 F-4Fs ordered in 1971 as part of the *Peace Rhine* programme and delivered between June 1973 and April 1976 to equip two fighter wings, JG 71 at Wittmundhaffen and JG 74 at Neuburg, and two fighter-bomber wings, JaboG 35 at Pferdsfeld and JaboG 36 at Rheine-Hopsten. Those aircraft serving with the fighter

An F-4F used as a test-bed for VBW anti-armour dispensers developed by Messerschmitt-Bölkow-Blohm GmbH. *(MBB, courtesy of Christian Jacquet-Francillon)*

wings are to be modernized by 1992 under the ICE programme while the fighter-bombers are to receive a less comprehensive refit. The F-4Fs will then remain in service until the end of the century when they will be replaced by European Fighter Aircraft.

Conversion training for Luftwaffe RF-4E and F-4F crews was undertaken from the onset in the United States under a co-operative agreement. Twelve F-4Fs (sometimes designated TF-4Fs) were kept in the USA for assignment to this training programme until replaced by 10 F-4Es paid for by Germany but delivered to the USAF for use by the 20th TFS at George AFB, California.

Australia: McDonnell first attempted to attract the interest of the Royal Australian Air Force by offering in March 1963 an F-4C version,

F-4E-43-MC (69-7213), one of the twenty-four Phantom IIs leased by the Royal Australian Air Force to equip Nos. 1 and 6 Squadrons. *(RAAF)*

the Model 98-DX, powered by a pair of French-built SNECMA Atar 9 engines as fitted to the Dassault Mirage IIIOs of the RAAF. In spite of the benefit of engine commonality, the RAAF decided to order TF30-powered General Dynamics F-111C in preference to the McDonnell Model 98-DX. However, when the delayed delivery of F-111Cs threatened to leave the RAAF without strike aircraft to replace its Australian-built Canberra B.20 bombers, the USAAF agreed to loan 24 of its F-4Es (69-7201/69-7217, 69-7219/69-7220, 69-7304/69-7307, and 69-7324) to equip Nos. 1 and 6 Squadrons at Amberley, Brisbane. The first five F-4Es were delivered to Australia in September 1970 and the F-4Es (less one lost in an accident) were returned to the United States before the end of June 1973.

Spain: The Ejército del Aire Español (Spanish Air Force or EdA) received 36 ex-USAF F-4Cs between October 1971 and September 1972, four more in July and August 1978, and four RF-4Cs in October and November 1978. These fighters and reconnaissance aircraft[21], which were designated respectively C.12s and CR.12s in Spanish service, were reconditioned by Construcciones Aeronauticas SA (CASA which for a number of years had been overhauling USAF Phantoms in its Getafe plant) and were given serials C.12-1 to C.12-40 and CR.12-41 to CR.12-44. The C.12s, which along with the CR.12s equipped the two

F-4C (Spanish designation C.12) of Ala de Caza 12, Ejército del Aire Español, on 16 September, 1971. *(CASA)*

squadrons (Escuadrón 121 and Escuadrón 122) of Ala 12 at Torrejón since 1972, were replaced by C.15s (McDonnell Douglas EF-18s) during

---

[21]   The USAF serials of the F-4Cs transferred to Spain were 64-0813, -0820, -0846, -0850, -0853/-0859, -0861/-0862, -0864, -0866/-0868, -0870/-0872, -0877/-0878, -0880/-0882, -0884, -0886/-0887, -0892, -0894/-0896, -0900, -0903, -0906/-0907, -0909, -0920, and -0924/-0925. Serials for the first four RF-4Cs were 65-0936/-0938 and 65-0943, and serials for the eight RF-4Cs transferred from the Kentucky ANG in 1989 were 64-1068/-1070, 64-1083, 65-0822, -0835, -0841, -0851, and -0873.

the winter of 1988. Unlike the fighters, the reconnaissance aircraft will remain in service well into the 1990s as the four original CR.12s were supplemented in January 1989 by eight ex-Kentucky ANG aircraft, thus enabling the Ejército del Aire to form a specialized tactical reconnaissance squadron.

Japan: Delivery of two McDonnell-built F-4EJs was made to the Nihon Koku Jieitai (Japanese Air Self-Defence Force or JASDF) in July 1971. These were followed by 11 F-4EJs assembled in Japan, 127 licence-built F-4EJs, and 14 McDonnell-built RF-4EJs (serials for all Japanese

Mitsubishi-built F-4EJ (47-8342) of the 304 Hikotai. *(Dr Masahiro Yamasaki)*

Formation take-off byF-4EJs of 301 Hikotai at Hyakuri AB in 1980. *(Toyokazu Matsuzaki)*

Phantoms are listed in Appendix C). After evaluation by the Koku Jikkendan (Air Proving Wing) at Komaki, F-4EJs were first assigned in August 1972 to the Rinji (Provisional) 301 Hikotai at Nyutabaru. In October 1973, this squadron lost its provisional status and subsequently F-4EJs were assigned to five other Hikotais, the 302 at Naha, the 303 and 306 at Komatsu, the 304 at Tsuili, and the 305 at Hyakuri. Upgraded F-4EJ(KAI)s entered service with 306 Hikotai in November 1989. The RF-4EJs have been assigned since November 1974 to the 501 Hikotai of the Teisatsu Kokutai (Reconnaissance Wing) at Hyakuri. The seven Japanese Phantoms will remain operational well into the 'nineties with some F-4EJ(KAI)s and RF-4EJ(KAI)s being retained until after the turn of the century.

Greece: Delivery to the Helliniki Aeroporía (Hellenic Air Force) began in March 1974 with a first batch of 38 F-4Es under *Peace Icarus*. Follow-on contracts added 18 F-4Es and eight RF-4Es. The F-4Es were assigned to 337 Mira (squadron)/110 Ptérix (wing) at Larissa, and 338 and 339 Mire/117 Ptérix at Andravida. The RF-4Es went to the 348 Mira/110 Ptérix at Larissa.

In 1988, the Greek Defence Ministry announced that the United States would provide 69 F-4Cs and F-4Ds being phased out by the Air Force Reserve and the Air National Guard. No further details were available and delivery of these ex-USAF was yet to take place when this was written.

Bearing the Turkish serial I-286 and the USAF serial 77-0286, this F-4E-65-MC was delivered new to the Türk Hava Kuvvetleri. In 1989, new and ex-USAF F4-Es equipped seven Turkish squadrons (111, 112, 113, 131, 132, 171, 172, and 173 Filoler). *(Sergio Bottaro)*

Turkey: Deliveries of new Phantoms (72 F-4Es and eight RF-4Es as listed in Appendix C) to the Türk Hava Kuvvetleri (Turkish Air Force) under *Peace Diamond III* and *IV* began in August 1974. In addition, the Turkish Air Force had obtained some 45 ex-USAF F-4Es[22] by 1988 and was expected to receive additional F-4Es from surplus US stock in the late 'eighties and early 'nineties. The RF-4Es went to the 113 Filo (squadron) at Eskisehir and the F-4Es to the 111, 112, and 113 Filoler (squadrons) at Eskisehir; the 131 and 132 Filoler at Konya; and the 171, 172, and 173 Filoler at Erhac.

Egypt: Under the *Peace Pharaoh* programme, the Al Quwwat al Jawwiya il Misriya (Arab Republic of Egypt Air Force) received 35 ex-USAF F-4Es[23] beginning in September 1979 in partial exchange for MiG-21s and MiG-23s. Phantoms initially proved difficult for Egyptian personnel to maintain and plans were made for transferring these aircraft to Turkey. In the end, however, the Arab Republic of Egypt Air Force decided to keep its Phantoms and at the beginning of 1990 the surviving F-4Es were still equipping two squadrons of the 222nd Fighter Regiment at Cairo West.

	F-4B	F-4J	RF-4C	F-4E	F-4M
Span, ft in	38 4⁷/₈	38 4⁷/₈	38 4⁷/₈	38 4⁷/₈	38 4⁷/₈
(m)	(11.71)	(11.71)	(11.71)	(11.71)	(11.71)
Span (wings folded), ft in	27 7¹/₈	27 7¹/₈	27 7¹/₈	27 7¹/₈	27 7¹/₈
(m)	(8.41)	(8.41)	(8.41)	(8.41)	(8.41)
Length, ft in	58 3³/₄	58 3³/₄	62 10⁷/₈	63 0	57 7
(m)	(17.77)	(17.77)	(19.17)	(19.20)	(17.55)
Height, ft in	16 3	15 8¹/₂	16 6	16 6	16 1
(m)	(4.95)	(4.82)	(5.03)	(5.03)	(4.90)
Wing area, sq ft	530	530	530	530	530
(sq m)	(49.24)	(49.24)	(49.24)	(49.24)	(49.24)
Empty weight, lb	27,897	30,778	28,276	29,535	31,000
(kg)	(12,654)	(13,961)	(12,826)	(13,397)	(14,061)
Loaded weight, lb	43,907	51,268	50,341	55,957	52,400
(kg)	(19,916)	(23,300)	(22,834)	(25,382)	(23,768)
Maximum weight, lb	54,600	56,000	58,000	61,651	56,000
(kg)	(24,766)	(25,401)	(26,308)	(27,965)	(25,401)
Wing loading*, lb/sq ft	82.8	96.7	95.0	105.6	98.9
(kg/sq m)	(404.5)	(473.2)	(463.7)	(515.5)	(482.7)
Power loading*, lb/lb st	1.3	1.4	1.5	1.6	1.3
(kg/kgp)	(1.3)	(1.4)	(1.5)	(1.6)	(1.3)

[22] Known serials include 66-0293, 66-0298, 66-0301, 66-0304, 66-0309, 66-0312, 66-0318, 66-0320, 66-0336, 66-0339, 66-0344/66-0346, 66-0351, 66-0355, 66-0361, 66-0370, 66-0373/66-0374, 66-0379, 67-0210, 67-0215, 67-0226/67-0227, 67-0230, 67-0232, 67-0242, 67-0251, 67-0259, 67-0262, 67-0268, 67-0274, 67-0280, 67-0285, 67-0298, 67-0304, 67-0334, 67-0336, 67-0338, 68-0307, 68-0313, 68-0319, 68-0350, and 68-0448.

[23] The F-4Es transferred to Egypt were 66-0337, 66-0340/66-0341, 66-0343, 66-0349, 66-0353, 66-0358, 66-0360, 66-0362, 66-0364, 66-0366, 66-0375, 67-0211/67-0213, 67-0220, 67-0231, 67-0236, 67-0238/67-0239, 67-0264, 67-0278, 67-0289, 67-0305, 67-0307, 67-0309, 67-0313, 67-0317, 67-0322, 67-0332, 67-0341, 67-0355, 67-0366, 67-0371, and 66-0373.

Maximum speed, mph at ft	1,485/48,000	1,428/36,100	1,459/40,000	1,485/40,000	1,386/40,000
(km/h at m)	(2,389/14,630)	(2,298/11,000)	(2,348/12,190)	(2,389/12,190)	(2,231/12190)
Cruising speed, mph	575	564	587	585	
(km/h)	(925)	(907)	(945)	(941)	
Climb rate, ft/min	40,800	41,250	48,300	61,400	32,000
(m/sec)	(207)	(210)	(245)	(312)	(163)
Service ceiling, ft	62,000	54,700	59,400	62,250	60,800
(m)	(18,900)	(16,675)	(18,105)	(18,975)	(18,530)
Normal range, miles	1,610	1,380	1,375	1,050	1,000
(km)	(2,590)	(2,220)	(2,210)	(1,690)	(1,610)
Maximum range, miles	2,925	1,750	1,750	1,885	1,750
(km)	(4,705)	(2,815)	(2,815)	(3,035)	(2,815)

* wing and power loadings are calculated at normal loaded weight and maximum take-off power.

N119M, the Westinghouse J34-powered Model 119, at Lambert Field, St Louis, on 25 May, 1959. *(MCAIR)*

McDonnell 119 and 220

To meet the UCX (experimental utility transport) requirement of the USAF for a replacement of the venerable Beech C-45, a team led by Engineering Manager Ralph Harmon began the preliminary design of a small turbojet-powered transport in April 1957. Undertaken by McDonnell as a private venture, this aircraft resembled a scaled-down Boeing 707 or Douglas DC-8 as it had a swept wing with four Fairchild J83 turbojets mounted in individual nacelles attached to the wing by pylons. Its mock-up was inspected on 30/31 October, 1957, but completion of a prototype was delayed until January 1959 by the need to find a substitute powerplant because development of the J83 had been abandoned. Accordingly, it was decided that the prototype would be powered by four 2,980 lb (1,352 kg) thrust Westinghouse J34-WE-22s while the proposed production aircraft would have 2,900 lb (1,315 kg) thrust Pratt & Whitney JT12A-3s.

Powered by J34s, the Model 119 (N119M) was first flown at St Louis by G J Mills and F H Rogers on 11 February, 1959. Flight trials were generally satisfactory but, as the engines were close to the ground, foreign object ingestion was considered a potential operational hazard. Partly because of this, the USAF preferred the Lockheed JetStar which had rear-mounted engines and ordered it into limited production as the C-140. Undaunted, McDonnell decided to convert its Model 119 utility transport prototype into that of an executive jet with accommodation for either ten passengers in luxury or up to 29 passengers in a more spartan cabin. Redesignated Model 220[1] and, for demonstration purposes, retaining the J34 installation of the military prototype, the aircraft was offered in its proposed production form with either four 2,900 lb (1,315

[1]   The number 220 was selected as a publicity play on words to mark the fact that in 1959 the company was starting its second 20 years in business (2-20).

kg) thrust Pratt & Whitney JT12A-3s or 4,000 lb (1,814 kg) thrust General Electric CF700-1 turbofans. The Model 220 received its Provisional Type Certificate on 17 October, 1960, and its Provisional Airworthiness Certificate on 13 December, 1960.

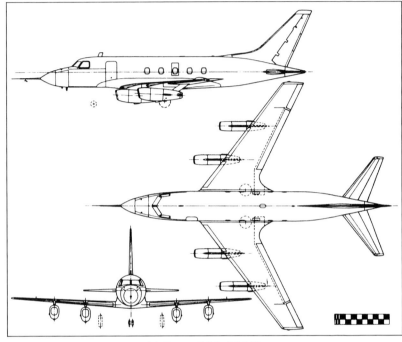

McDonnell Model 119.

A preliminary agreement for the purchase or lease of up to 170 Model 220s by the Business Sales Division of Pan American World Airways was negotiated. Unfortunately, without the benefit of joint production of a military version, the McDonnell 220 was substantially more expensive than the JetStar, the North American Sabreliner, and the Dassault Mystère 20/Falcon and in August 1963 Pan American ordered the Dassault. No other customers could be found for the Model 220. After being operated for several years as a company transport, the Model 220 was sold in March 1965 to Flight Safety Foundation in Phoenix, Arizona. Officially, it was to be used for non-flying research purposes such as crash survival tests. However, unconfirmed rumours placed the Model 220 in various Latin American countries where it was said to have been operated on covert missions. In the early 'seventies, it was reported derelict in Albuquerque, New Mexico, but a few years later its hulk was allegedly seen in Texas.

Span 57 ft 7¹/₄ in (17.55 m); length 66 ft 6 in (20.27 m); height 23 ft 7³/₄ in (7.21 m); wing area 550 sq ft (51.10 sq m).

Empty weight 23,213 lb (10,529 kg); loaded weight 40,928 lb (18,565 kg); maximum weight 45,328 lb (20,560 kg); wing loading 74.4 lb/sq ft (363.3 kg/sq m); power loading 3.4 lb/lb st (3.4 kg/kgp).

Maximum speed 560 mph at 38,000 ft (901 km/h at 11,580 m); cruising speed 520 mph (837 km/h); service ceiling 44,900 ft (13,685 m); normal range 2,340 miles (3,765 km).

A McDonnell Douglas MD 530F of the Las Vegas Metropolitan Police. *(MDHC)*

Hughes 369 (OH-6 Cayuse)
and
McDonnell Douglas 500, 520, and 530

In March 1960, the US Army announced a design competition for a lightweight observation helicopter (LOH) to replace two rotary-wing aircraft, the Bell H-13 Sioux and the Hiller H-23 Raven, and a fixed-wing aircraft, the Cessna L-19 Bird Dog. Missions specified for this LOH were visual observation and target acquisition, reconnaissance, command control, and utility tasks at company level. In addition, the Request for Proposals for the LOH stated the following qualitative needs: 'Attention is specifically drawn to the paramount desires of the US Army for a Small, Light Weight, Inexpensive, Reliable, and Easily Maintainable vehicle most nearly capable of fulfilling the technical requirements of Type Specification TS-153.' Notably, TS-153 called for a payload of at least 400 lb (181 kg) in addition to the pilot, a cruising speed of 110 kt (204 km/h), an endurance of 3 hours, a hover ceiling out-of-ground effect of 6,000 ft (1,830 m) with ambient temperature of 95°F (35°C), and a dynamic component minimum life of 1,200 hr. Although these requirements were demanding, 12 firms submitted no fewer than 22 proposals as potential orders were expected to be quite substantial.

Among manufacturers expressing the greatest interest in this competition was Hughes Tool Company which assigned responsibility for the design and development of the Model 369 to a team led by Malcolm Harned. Convinced that minimum size was all important for the LOH success, the Hughes team aimed its preliminary design studies at determining the minimum possible rotor diameter which could accomplish the mission. They concluded that by minimizing the empty weight and using a four-bladed configuration it would be feasible to use the 25-ft

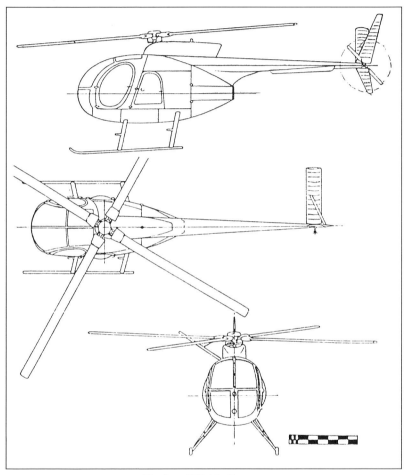

Hughes OH-6A Cayuse.

(7.62-m) diameter rotor blades of the Model 269A which were in production at a very low cost. Later on, the diameter of the main rotor was increased to 26 ft 4 in (8.03 m) and Hughes adopted a novel strap retention system for the blades to eliminate the conventional flapping and feathering bearings. The team then endeavoured to select a fuselage

245

configuration offering an absolute minimum of parasite drag while providing accommodation for a pilot and five fully-armed troops (four of whom sat on the floor in a cramped compartment between the pilot and the diagonally-mounted Allison T63 turboshaft) and adopted the characteristic teardrop-shaped fuselage of the Model 369. Finally, project engineers minimized structural weight by selecting a one-piece tail rotor drive shaft and adopting a simple manual flight control system.

Lacking engineering and flight test personnel experienced in aircraft evaluation procedures, the Army requested assistance from the Navy in running the LOH competition. Thus, it was a joint Army-Navy team which selected Bell and Hiller as winners of the design competition in May 1961. Fortunately for Hughes, the Army and Navy evaluators almost immediately added the Culver City firm to the list of those manufacturers requested to build five prototypes each for competitive evaluation. Initially given HO designations, the new observation helicopters received OH designators before being flown, as the Department of Defense established a new system of aircraft designation in September 1962. The Bell YOH-4A first flew on 8 December, 1962, the Hiller YOH-5A on 26 January, 1963, and the Hughes YOH-6A on 27 February, 1963.

When first flown by James Vittitoe at Culver City, the YOH-6A was temporarily registered N9696F. It then had a broad, upward-canted stabilizer on the starboard side and a fairly large tail boom of flapped aerofoil cross section. However, with this boom design, sideward flight was only feasible at speeds of not more than 5 mph (8 km/h) while the

The first YOH-6A (62-4212) with temporary civil registration. *(Hughes, courtesy of Ray W Prouty)*

stabilizer created both dynamic and static stability problems. Accordingly, before the YOH-6As could be turned over for evaluation by the Army-Navy team, Hughes tested a large number of tail configurations before adopting one characterized by a slimmer tail boom of circular cross section and narrower stabilizer braced to a vertical fin. With this new boom and stabilizer, the YOH-6A exceeded the control margin required by military specifications under all flying conditions.

At the end of the seven-month evaluation, during which prototypes from the three competitors were put through comprehensive field and performance tests at Fort Rucker, Alabama, Fort Benning, Georgia, and Fort Ord and Edwards AFB, California, the Design Selection Board determined that the Bell YOH-4A did not meet the specified requirements, that the Hiller YOH-5A met the requirements on the basis of minimum acceptability, and that the Hughes YOH-6A exceeded the minimum requirements in mission capability, speed, economy of operation, and ease of maintenance. As the bid submitted by Hughes was also lower than that by Hiller, the YOH-6A was declared the winner on 26 May, 1965[1]. Soon thereafter, Hughes received a multi-year production contract for 1,071 OH-6As and, in keeping with the Army's tradition of naming its aircraft after Indian tribes, the new helicopter was named Cayuse after a tribe from Oregon.

Fully satisfied with the performance, handling characteristics, and maintainability of the OH-6A, the Army intended to continue ordering the Hughes light observation helicopter to meet its entire LOH requirements. However, either as the result of a deliberate under pricing of the initial batch of Cayuses or of the rapid manufacturing cost escalation experienced by all contractors during the Vietnam War industrial build-up, Hughes increased substantially the OH-6 unit cost thus prompting the Army to reopen the LOH competition in 1967. By then Hiller was no longer in business, but Bell entered a much redesigned version of its original entry and succeeded in displacing Hughes as the main supplier of LOHs[2]. Only 349 additional OH-6As were ordered from Hughes, while

---

[1] Hiller protested the award and charged that Hughes had bid below cost. The recommendation of the Design Selection Board was reviewed but no irregularities were found.

[2] The selection of Bell as the supplier of LOHs ordered beginning in Fiscal Year 1969 is likely to have been motivated for the most part by the Army's displeasure with the increase in OH-6A's unit price and lagging production schedule. However, the fact that the OH-58As were going to be built in the home state of President Lyndon B. Johnson was quite possibly more than a coincidental factor in the selection of Bell as the winner of the second LOH competition.
    In service, the OH-58As proved less satisfactory than the OH-6As as they were heavier, were markedly noisier on account of their two-bladed rotor (thus rendering the approach of an OH-58A more easily detected by enemy ground forces), and had poorer performance in hot weather. This latter factor later led to a more powerful T63-A-720 being retrofitted (the re-engined Kiowas being designated OH-58Cs) whereas the derated T63-A-5A of the OH-6A did not have to be replaced as it provided an ample reserve of power during hot weather operation.

An MD 500E on an acceptance flight before delivery to Pacific Helicopters in Papua New Guinea. *(MDHC)*

contracts for 2,200 OH-58As were awarded to Bell. Fortunately for the California manufacturer, the civil version of its light turboshaft-powered helicopter, the Model 500 which had been announced on 21 April, 1965, 35 days before the YOH-6A was chosen as the winner of the original LOH competion, had become a popular seller. It was to put Hughes among the world's leading manufacturers of helicopters and, as the MD 520 and MD 530 series, was destined to remain in production during most of the 'nineties and possibly into the next millenium.

Production history
The following versions have been built for the US Army:

YOH-6A (YHO-6):   Five YHO-6s (62-4212/62-4216) were ordered in 1961 for competitive evaluation as part of the Army LOH programme and a sixth (62-12624) was acquired shortly afterwards. Redesignated YOH-6As before the first flight on 27 February, 1963, these pre-production vehicles were each powered by a 317 shp Allison T63-A-5A turboshaft engine derated to 252.5 shp for take-off and 214.5 shp maximum continuous rating and driving a four-bladed main rotor and two-bladed tail rotor. Side-by-side accommodation was provided in the front cabin for a crew of two and space was provided in the rear compartment for two folding seats or cargo. With the rear seats folded, four fully-armed troops could sit on the floor. The first YOH-6A (62-4212) was transferred to the USAF in March 1969.

OH-6A: In all, 1,420 OH-6As were built by Hughes, including 1,417 ordered under the main contracts (65-12916/65-13003, 66-7775/66-7942, 66-14376/66-14419, 66-17750/66-17833, 67-16000/67-16686, 68-17140/68-17369, and 69-15960/69-16075) and three ordered as replacements (66-17905, 66-17918, and one unidentified). Essentially similar to the fully modified YOH-6A with the smaller tail boom and revised stabilizer, the OH-6A was built in three configurations: 505 were completed in

The 16th production OH-6A Cayuse light observation helicopter in standard US Army markings. *(MDHC)*

Series I, 569 in Series II, and 340 in Series III with the use of slightly different parts (including the addition of an air inlet filter), electronics, and avionics (including the notable addition of the LOHAP Light Observation Helicopter Avionics Package) differentiating the series. The Cayuse, when armed, normally carried either a XM27E1 7.62-mm machine-gun kit or a XM75 40-mm grenade launcher on the port side of the fuselage. A flexible gun could be mounted on the aft door on the starboard side.

Over the years, OH-6As have been bailed back to the manufacturer for use in a variety of experimental programmes including one to achieve significant reduction in noise level, one to evaluate a higher harmonic control (HHC) system for helicopter vibration suppression, and one to develop a No Tail Rotor (NOTAR) system. For the noise reduction programme funded in 1969 by the Army and the Advanced Research Projects Agency, aircraft 65-12968 was fitted with a five-bladed main rotor, a four-bladed tail rotor, a shrouded engine inlet, and an engine exhaust muffler. By operating at reduced rotor-tip speeds, as much as 20 decibels in noise reduction was achieved, thus leading to the nickname 'The Quiet One' to be painted on the rear fuselage sides for publicity purposes.

For the HHC research programme funded by Hughes, the Army, and NASA, an OH-6A (68-17230) was fitted with a computer-controlled vibration suppression system and high frequency hydraulic actuators to superimpose high frequency feathering on the normal rotor blade feathering motion. The modified aircraft was first flown at the US Army Proving Ground in Yuma, Arizona, on 25 August, 1982, and was evaluated by the manufacturer, the Army's Research and Technology Laboratories, and the NASA Langley Research Center.

249

68-17230, the OH-6A modified for the Higher Harmonic Control research programme. *(MDHC)*

The NOTAR demonstrator in 1987. *(MDHC)*

In the mid-seventies, company-funded efforts were initiated by Hughes to develop an anti-torque tail boom to dispense of the use of a conventional tail rotor. Flight testing of an externally mounted fan to provide circulation control air and measure the reduction in conventional tail rotor thrust requirement was undertaken in 1977-78 and led to the award in September 1980 of a NOTAR research contract funded by the US Army Applied Technology Laboratory and the Defense Advanced Research Projects Agency. The NOTAR prototype (65-12917) was first flown on 17 December, 1981. It has been modified several times since then, notably in being fitted with an MD 500E forward fuselage and re-engined with a 420 shp Allison 250-C20B turboshaft in 1985, and has enabled McDonnell Douglas Helicopters to develop an advanced NOTAR system for use in the MD 520N, MD 530N, the new MDX for the civil market, and the LHX scout for the Army.

EH-6B: This designation identifies four OH-6As (68-17301, 68-17538, 69-15977, and 69-16018) which were modifed in 1982 for SIGINT (Signal Intelligence) and other electronic surveillance activities in support of Special Forces. At that time, they were re-engined with a military version of the 400 shp Allison 250-C20 turboshaft and fitted with the 'Black Hole' infrared suppression system on the engine exhaust. Two were later brought up to MH-6B standards and one became an AH-6C.

MH-6B: Twenty-three OH-6As (68-17140, 68-17155, 68-17167/68-17168, 68-17175, 68-17193, 68-17225, 68-17256, 68-17290, 68-17316, 68-17320, 68-17332, 68-17334, 68-17341, 68-17346, 68-17348, 69-16015,

Rarely illustrated, one of Task Force 160's MH-6 helicopters. *(Avia Press Associates)*

69-16052/69-16054, 69-16057, 69-16062, and 69-16072) and two EH-6Bs (68-17358 and 69-15977) were modified as multi-mission (scout and light attack) helicopters for assignment to the Army's Special Forces. Modifications included (1) re-engining with 400 shp engine with 'Black Hole' infrared suppression exhaust system; (2) revising the cockpit lighting for operations with night vision goggles (NVGs); (3) fitting a turret-mounted FLIR sensor; and (4) installing a tubular mount through the lower aft fuselage to carry externally either two 7.62-mm miniguns or four troop seats. Three were later modified as AH-6Cs.

OH-6B: First used in the mid-sixties to identify a proposed development which remained on the drawing board, the OH-6B designation was given in 1988 to OH-6As which were to be rebuilt and modernized in the Mississippi Army National Guard's Aviation Classification and Repair Activity Depot (AVCRAD) at Gulfport, Mississippi. As part of the modernization programme, 250 OH-6Bs are being (1) brought to a common Series IV standard to improve their maintainability and increase

An OH-6B (67-16041) of the Mississippi Army National Guard at the Western ARNG Aviation Training Site in Marana, Arizona, in October 1989. This 'Super Cayuse' is fitted with a FLIR sensor beneath the nose and 'Black Hole' infrared suppression system. *(Charles T Robbins)*

their capability; (2) re-engined with the 420 shp Allison T63-A-720 engine with the 'Black Hole' system on the engine exhaust; and (3) fitted with wire strike protection, adjustable landing light, and modernized avionics (including FLIR sensor). The first of three OH-6B prototypes was flown at Gulfport in May 1988 and was assigned to the Maryland ArNG for operational evaluation.

AH-6C: A total of fifteen light attack helicopters is believed to have been obtained for the Special Forces by modifying eleven OH-6As (68-17191, 68-17228, 68-17242, 68-17249, 68-17258, 68-17276, 68-17298, 68-17307, 69-15973, 69-16031, and 69-16058), one EH-6B (69-160180), and three MH-6Bs (69-16052/69-16054) to a common standard with NVG-compatible cockpit, 400-shp engine with 'Black Hole' exhaust system, and provision for carrying either two minigun pods, two or four rocket pods (each with 19 Hydra-70 2.75-in FFARs), or four Hughes BGM-71 TOW (Tube-launched, Optically-tracked, Wire-guided) anti-tank missiles.

OH-6D: This designation was given to the improved Cayuse version which Hughes entered in the Army's Advanced Scout Helicopter (ASH) competition. The ASH programme was not funded and, in its place, the Army decided to have Bell OH-58As brought up to the OH-58D AHIP (Army Helicopter Improvement Program) configuration.

The OH-6D designation was next used to identify Kawasaki-built Model 500Ds in service with the Japanese Ground Self-Defence Force and Japanese Maritime Self-Defence Force.

EH-6E: This designation identifies three Model 500Ds (81-23654/81-23656) procured by the US Army under a covert budget (a so-called 'black program') for electronic surveillance operations with the Special Forces. Like subsequent versions ordered for the Special Forces, this version is characterized by its five-blade main rotor, quiet four-blade tail rotor, mufflers, infrared suppression exhaust system, and advanced avionics.

MH-6E: Based on the 500MD Quiet Advanced Scout Defender developed by Hughes from the civil Model 500D, this multi-mission version was procured for the Special Forces under a covert budget. Fifteen MH-6Es (81-23629/81-23637 and 81-23648/81-23653) were built by Hughes and another was obtained by modifying an EH-6E (81-23655).

AH-6F: This designation identifies nine light attack helicopters (84-24319, 84-24677, 84-24681, 84-24683/84-24684, and 85-25347/ 85-25250) built for the Army's Special Forces and a similar machine (86-0141) acquired by the Air Force for evaluation by its Special Forces at Hurlburt Field, Florida. The AH-6F combines the airframe, engine, and rotor configuration of the MH-6E with the armament of the AH-6C and is fitted with a mast-mounted sight. As an alternative to miniguns, rocket pods, and TOW missiles, the AH-6Fs can carry a 30-mm M230 Chain Gun (the Hughes-developed anti-armour cannon carried under the fuselage of AH-64s) or two Stinger air-to-air missiles on each side of the fuselage.

AH-6G: This version corresponds to the civil Model 530 and differs from the preceding model in being powered by an uprated engine. Five AH-6Gs were built by Hughes/MDHC (84-24678/84-24680, 84-24682, and 85-25346) and seven were obtained by re-engining AH-6Fs

(84-24319, 84-24677, 84-24681, 84-24683/84-24684, and 85-25347/85-25248).

MH-6H: Twelve MH-6Es (81-23629/81-23634 and 81-23648/81-23653) and two EH-6Es (81-23654 and 81-23656) have been retrofitted with uprated engine and redesignated MH-6Hs.

OH-6J: This designation is used to identify the Kawasaki-built Model 500Ms of the Japanese Ground Self-Defence Force and Japanese Maritime Self-Defence Force.

The following versions have been built or remain in production for civil customers and foreign military operators:

Model 500: Powered by a 317 shp Allison 250-C18A turboshaft (civil version of the T63-A-5A) derated to 278 shp for take-off, the commercial counterpart of the OH-6A was developed under the engineering designation of Model 369A and marketed as the Model 500. First flown on 13 September, 1966, it differed from the military variant in having non self-sealing fuel tanks with capacity increased from 61 to 63.4 US gallons

An Australian-registered (VH-BLO) Hughes 500 belonging to Jayrow Helicopters. *(MAP)*

(231 to 240 litres) and in being fitted with commercial avionics. Accommodation was provided for a pilot and four passengers in the executive configuration and for a pilot and six passengers or loads of up to 1,710 lb (776 kg) in the Model 500U utility version. Intended for single-pilot operations, the Model 500 could be fitted with dual controls as an option. The standard skids could either be supplemented by inflatable floats for use during extended overwater operations from shore bases or by inflated floats for occasional use from water. Taller skids were available to provide added clearance when carrying external loads. In addition to being built by Hughes, Model 500s and 500Us were produced under licence by BredaNardi in Italy, Kawasaki in Japan, and RACA (Representaciones Aero Commerciales Argentinas SA) in Argentina.

Hughes also produced two Model 500 versions for foreign military customers, the Model 500M for use in the observation, training, and utility roles, and the Model 500M/ASW for anti-submarine operations with the Spanish Navy. The Model 500M/ASW was fitted with an AN/ASQ-81 towed magnetic anomaly detector (MAD bird) on the starboard fuselage side and taller skids providing clearance for the carriage of one or two Mk.44 or Mk.46 lightweight torpedoes beneath the fuselage.

Model 500C: First flown on 23 February, 1970, this civil version differed from the Model 500 in being powered by a 400 shp Allison 250-C20 turboshaft derated to 278 shp for take-off and offering an ample reserve of power for improved hot-day/high-altitude performance. The Model 500C could be fitted with Chadwick fire suppression equipment consisting of a water/chemical tank in the fuselage aft of the pilot, spray

TF-GRO, a float-equipped Hughes 500C in Iceland. *(MAP)*

booms on the fuselage sides, and nozzles on forward projecting booms. For medical evacuation, two stretchers could be accommodated crosswise in the aft compartment with bubble windows being fitted in place of the aft doors. An aft-facing seat for a medical attendant replaced the forward-facing passenger/co-pilot seat.

Model 500D: This version was preceded by a modified Model 500 which, fitted with a five-bladed main rotor of slightly increased diameter (26 ft 6 in versus 26 ft 4 in, 8.08 versus 8.03 m) and a T-tail with small end plates to improve stability, was tested beginning in August 1974. The first Model 500D was flown on 9 October, 1975, and deliveries started at the end of 1976. Power was provided by a 420 shp Allison 250-C20B engine derated to 375 shp for take-off and fitted with an exhaust muffler. A small 'coolie hat' fairing was added above the rotor to smooth airflow over the tail surfaces. In addition to being produced by Hughes as the Model 500D and by MDHC as the MD 500D, this version has been licence-built by

BredaNardi in Italy, Kawasaki in Japan, Korean Air in Korea, and RACA in Argentina.

The Model 500MD Defender was developed for foreign customers and was offered with different armament and electronic equipment for operations in a variety of military roles. The basic Model 500MD Defender was an unarmed version for use in the observation, utility, and/or training roles. The 500MD Scout Defender and 500MD Quiet Advanced Scout Defender (with the latter differing from the Scout

A Hughes 500D of the Finnish Air Force's Helikopterilentue. *(MAP)*

Defender in having a Hughes MMS mast-mounted sight, a four-bladed tail rotor, and sound reduction modifications) were armed with either a 7.62-mm gun pod, a 30-mm Chain Gun cannon, a 40-mm grenade launcher, or 70-mm rocket pods. The 500MD/TOW Defender (with a stabilised telescopic sight protruding on the port side of the nose) and the 500MD/MMS-TOW Defender (with mast-mounted sight in lieu of the nose-mounted sight) were optimized for the anti-armour role for which they were armed with four TOW missiles in pods on both sides of the fuselage. The 500MD/ASW Defender was developed as an anti-submarine warfare version with features from the earlier Model 500M/ASW supplemented by the installation of a radar on the port side of the nose. Finally, the 500MD Defender II, which was offered as a multi-mission version combining features of the Advanced Scout and MMS-TOW Defender versions, was fitted with a FLIR night vision system. As an alternative to TOW missiles, the Defender II could carry a 30-mm Chain Gun cannon or two Stinger air-to-air missiles on each side of the fuselage. Optionally, all Defender versions could be fitted with an infrared suppression system.

MD 500E (Model 500E): First flown on 28 January, 1982, the Model 500E differed from the 500D in having a longer and more streamlined nose and enlarged endplate fins. Powerplant installation and accommodation remained unchanged but passenger comfort was increased as the

A 500MMS-TOW Defender with mast-mounted sight and four TOW missiles.
(MDHC)

revised cabin offered more legroom and headroom. Standard MD 500Es retained the five-bladed, fully articulated main rotor of MD 500Ds, but an experimental MD 500E became the first MDHC helicopter fitted with an all-composite hingeless rotor. It was first flown at Mesa, Arizona, on 23 April, 1985. MD 500E licence production has been undertaken by BredaNardi and Korean Air.

During the summer of 1989, NASA Langley Research Center's Acoustics Division flew a specially instrumented MD 500E for measuring engine and rotor noise. Preliminary test results indicated that a 5 dB noise reduction could be achieved through the use of variable-speed main and tail rotors.

In addition to MD 500MG Defender versions using MD 500E airframes and corresponding to Defender versions of the MD 500D, MDHC has developed the Paramilitary MG Defender and the FLIR-equipped Nightfox for police, border patrol, and anti-drug smuggling operations. The Nightfox, Paramilitary MG Defender, and all MD 500MG Defender versions can be powered by either the 250-C20B turboshaft of the MD 500E or the 250-C30 of the MD 530F.

MD 520L: This version, which was introduced in 1989, differed from the MD 520E in being fitted with a five-bladed main rotor with a diameter of 28 ft 5 in (8.66 m), a four-bladed tail rotor of 4 ft 9 in (1.45 m) diameter, and a 5.5-in (14-cm) longer tail boom. Power is provided by the Allison 250-C20R turboshaft derated to 375 shp.

MD 520N: This version, which had not flown by the end of 1989, will differ from the NOTAR-equipped MD 530N in being powered by the Allison 250-C20R derated to 375 shp. Customer deliveries are to start in 1991-92.

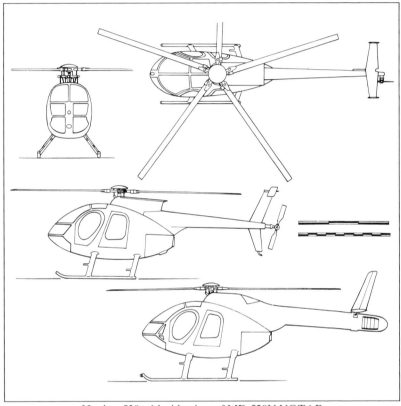

Hughes 530 with side view of MD 520N NOTAR

MD 530F (Model 530F):   Intended for hot-and-high operations and powered by a 650 shp Allison 250-C30 derated to 425 shp for take-off, the Model 530F was first flown on 22 October, 1982. The diameter of the main rotor was increased by 1 ft (30.5 cm) and that of the tail rotor by 2 in (5 cm). Loads of up to 2,000 lb (907 kg) can be carried externally.

On 30 August, 1984, an MD 530F flown by Steve Hanvey, MDHC manager of engineering flight test, set records for time to climb to 3,000 metres (9,843 ft) of 3 min 15 sec and time-to-climb to 6,000 metres (19,685 ft) of 6 min 34 sec in Class E1b (helicopters weighing between 500 and 1,000 kg/1,102 and 2,205 lb) at Thermal, California.

An MD 530F during a simulated rescue operation. *(MDHC)*

MD 530K: This version, which was certificated in August 1988, differed from the MD 530F in being fitted with the longer tail boom and larger main and tail rotors of the MD 520L.

MD 530N: The MD 530N, the first production helicopter to be fitted with the NOTAR anti-torque system, uses the MD 530K airframe, is powered by the Allison 250-C30 derated to 425 shp, and has twin vertical tail surfaces. A prototype (N530NT) was first flown on 29 December, 1989, and customer deliveries are to begin in 1991.

Service history

Before entering service, the Cayuse demonstrated its performance and reliability when, without the need for a change of engine or major component, a single YOH-6A was used by five Army and two civil pilots to break or set 22 world records during flights from Edwards AFB in March and April 1966. Three of these records—distance in a closed circuit (1,740 miles/2,800 km), sustained altitude (26,448 ft/8,061 m); and speed over a 2,000-km/1,243-mile closed circuit (141.51 mph/227.69 km/h)—were for all classes of helicopters. Eight distance, speed, and time-to-height records were set in Class E1b (helicopters weighing between 500 and 1,000 kg/1,102 and 2,205 lb) and 11 altitude, speed, and time-to-height records were established in Class E1c (helicopters weighing between 1,000 and 1,750 kg/2,205 and 3,858 lb). A fourth all-class helicopter record was set on 7 April, 1966, when the same YOH-6A was flown solo by Hughes' test pilot Robert Ferry from Culver City, California, to Ormond Beach, Florida, a distance of 2,213-mile (3,561-km), nonstop in 15 hr 8 min.

Entering service in September 1966, the OH-6A was quickly nick-named "Loach", from its LOH role, and "egg", because of its fuselage shape. After a quick work up in the United States, OH-6As were rushed to Vietnam where in the summer of 1967 they replaced obsolete Bell OH-13s and Hiller OH-23s as the US Army's main type of scout helicopter. Flying in the observation role, acting as pathfinders for troop-carrying Hueys, and seeking targets for Cobra gunships, Loaches were more often than not fitted with a pilot-fired 7.62-mm XM27E1 armament kit on the port side. Typically, two OH-6As were assigned to supplement UH-1s in Airmobile/Assault Helicopter Companies and CH-47s in Medium Helicopter/Assault Support Helicopter Companies while Armored Cavalry Squadrons had nine OH-6A scouts and nine AH-1G gunships.

During the design phase close attention had been paid to combat survivability and occupant safety requirements. Hence, the Cayuse

OH-6A Cayuse with a gun pod on the port side of the fuselage. *(Army Aviation Museum)*

notably incorporated redundant, damage-tolerant components, and had ample power in reserve through the use of a derated engine. Neverthe-less, combat and operational losses where high due to the type of missions flown. More than one out of five US helicopters lost during the Southeast Asia War was an OH-6A. Altogether, 635 Cayuses were shot down by AAA or small arms fire, 23 were destroyed on the ground during enemy attacks against their bases, and 297 were lost in operational accidents. Thus, as others were lost in accidents outside the war zone, fewer than 430 of the 1,420 production OH-6As remained in service when the Cayuses were withdrawn from Vietnam in March 1973.

During the war, the OH-6A earned praise from flight crews and maintenance personnel alike as it was the most manoeuvrable and most easily maintained helicopter in the inventory. Nevertheless, as by the mid-seventies the Army had more OH-58As than OH-6As[3], the decision was made to withdraw OH-6As from active units and transfer them to Army National Guard units in 18 states and Puerto Rico. Fully satisfied with the operational record of its OH-6As, the Army National Guard will have 250 of its Cayuses brought up to OH-6B standard in the early 'nineties and plans to retain them in front line service well past the year 2000.

Since withdrawn from service with active duty Army units, small numbers of OH-6As have been on loan to other government agencies such as the US Border Patrol, the Federal Bureau of Investigation, and

An OH-6A (65-12976) of the Colorado Army National Guard during annual training at Camp McCoy, Wisconsin, in May 1986. *(Charles T Robbins)*

NASA's Ames Research Center at Moffett Field, California, and Langley Research Center at Hampton, Virginia.

With regular Army units, high-performance Hughes helicopters made a comeback in 1982 when MH-6B scouts and EH-6B SIGINT helicopters were delivered to the 160th Special Operations Aviation Group at Fort Campbell, Kentucky. Later supplemented by AH-6C/F/G light attack helicopters, MH-6E/F scouts, and EH-6E SIGINT platforms, these nimble and quiet helicopters have been used discreetly, but most effectively, in support of Special Forces and took part in operations in Grenada in 1983, the Persian Gulf in 1987-88, and Panama in 1989.

---

[3] More Bell Kiowas had been ordered and fewer lost in combat due mainly to their combat debut being made three years later than that of the Cayuse and after the withdrawal of US combat troops had begun.

Abroad, Hughes turbine-engined helicopters have been operated and in most instances continue to be operated by the air arms of the following nations: Argentina (RACA-assembled 500Ms and 500Ds, most now fitted with FLIR and night vision equipment, with I Escuadrón de Exploración y Ataque, Fuerza Aérea Argentina, at Morón and RACA-assembled 500Ms on coast guard duty with the Prefectura Naval Argentina); Bahrain (500Ds with the Bahrain Public Security); Bolivia (500Ms with the Grupo de Operaciones Aéreas Especiales, Fuerza Aérea Boliviana, at BAM Remoré); Brazil (ex-USA OH-6As with the Centro de Instruçao de Helicópteros of the Forçe Aérea Brasileira at Santos, Sao Paulo); Colombia (500Fs, 500Ms and 500MD Defenders with the Grupo Aéreo de Helicópteros and the Escuela de Helicópteros, Fuerza Aérea Colombiana, at BAM Melgar); Costa Rica (369s and 500Es with the Sección Aérea, Ministerio de la Seguridad Pública); Denmark (500Ms with the Haerens Flyvetjaeneste/Army Air Service at Vandel); Dominican Republic (ex-USA OH-6As with the Escuadrón de Helicópteros, Fuerza Aérea Dominicana); Finland (500Cs and 500Ds with the Helikopterilentue/Helicopter Flight, Ilmavoimat, at Hutti); Greece (BredaNardi 500s with the Hellinikí Aeroporía at Dekélia); Haiti (500Cs with the Corps d'Aviation d'Haïti); Honduras (369Ds with the Fuerza Aérea Hondureña at BA Hernán Acosta Mejía in Tegucigalpa); Indonesia (500Cs with the Tentara Nasional Indonesia-Angkatan Udara); Iraq (500Ds and 500Fs sold for civil duties but believed taken over by Al Quwwat al Jawwiya al 'Iraqiya); Israel (500MD/TOW Defenders with the Heyl Ha'Avir); Italy (BredaNardi-built MD 500Es with the Scuola Volo Elicotteri, Aeronautica Militare Italiana, at Frosinone, and BredaNardi-built 500Ms, 500MCs, and 500MDs with the Servicio Aereo della Guardia di Finanze); Japan (Kawasaki-built OH-6Js

Kawasaki-built OH-6J of the Nihon Rikujyo Jietai (Japanese Ground Self-Defence Force). *(MAP)*

262

and OH-6Ds with the Koki Gakko training center and 13 squadrons of the Nihon Rikujyo Jieitai/Japanese Ground Self-Defence Force, and Kawasaki-built OH-6Js and OH-6Ds with a training squadron of the Nihon Kaijyo Jieitai/Japanese Maritime Self-Defence Force); Jordan (500Ds with No 7 Squadron, Al Quwwat al Jawwiya al Malakiya al Urduniya, at Amman-King Abdullah); Kenya (500Ds, 500Ms, 500MD/TOWs, and 500MEs with the Kenya Air Force at Moi); Korea (Hughes-built and Korean Air-assembled 500MD Scout Defenders and MD-TOW

A 500MD-TOW Defender for the Kenya Air Force. *(MDHC)*

Defenders with the ROKAF, the Republic of Korea Army, and the Republic of Korea Navy); Mauritania (500Ms with the Force Aérienne Islamique de Mauritanie); Morocco (500MD Defenders and MD/TOW Defenders with the Force Aérienne Royale Marocaine); Nicaragua (ex-USA OH-6As first with the Fuerza Aérea de Nicaragua and then the Fuerza Aérea Sandinista); Philippines (500Ds operated by the Philippine Air Force for the Philippine Army); El Salvador (500Ms with the Fuerza Aérea Salvadorea); Spain (369Ms, designated Z.13s, with Escuadrilla 006, Arma Aérea de la Armada Espanola, at El Ferrol and aboard destroyers and frigates); and Taiwan (500MD/ASWs with the Chinese Nationalist Navy and 500Ms with the Chinese Nationalist Marine Corps).

Since first delivered to civil operators in 1966, over 2,500 Model 500s and MD 500s of various models built by Hughes, MDHC, and their

HS.13-6, a Hughes 369M equipped for anti-submarine warfare, in the markings of the Sexta Escuadrilla, Arma Aérea de la Armada Española at El Ferrol. *(MAP)*

licensees have operated on all continents. In addition to their more common use as executive transports, these helicopters have been

Hughes 500 (N5141Y) of the California Highway Patrol at the Mojave Airport in January 1984. *(René J Francillon)*

employed frequently for law enforcement, training, geological survey, transport of precious metals, oil drilling and other mineral exploration projects, rescue (notably in 1987 when recently delivered MD 530Fs were used in Colombia to help victims of the eruption of the Nevado del Ruiz volcano), support for civil engineering and construction projects, crop spraying (with a market breakthrough being achieved in 1988 when MD 500Es replaced Soviet-built Kamov Ka-26s operated by the Hungarian Ministry of Agriculture), and battle against pests (such as during attempts by the World Health Organization, WHO, to control the African River Blindness in eleven West African nations).

264

A Hungarian-registered MD 500E equipped for agricultural spraying. *(MDHC)*

	OH-6A	MD 500E	MD 530F
Rotor diameter, ft in	26 4	26 6	27 4
(m)	(8.03)	(8.08)	(8.33)
Overall length, ft in	30 3³/₄	30 10	32 1
(m)	(9.24)	(9.40)	(9.78)
Fuselage length, ft in	23 0	23 11	23 11
(m)	(7.01)	(7.29)	(7.29)
Height, ft in	8 1¹/₂	8 2	8 0
(m)	(2.48)	(2.49)	(2.44)
Rotor diameter, sq ft	544.6	551.5	586.8
(sq m)	(50.64)	(51.28)	(54.51)
Empty weight, lb	1,156	1,441	1,564
(kg)	(524)	(654)	(709)
Maximum gross weight, lb	2,700	3,550	3,750
(kg)	(1,225)	(1,610)	(1,701)
Rotor loading*, lb/sq ft	5.0	6.4	6.4
(kg/sq m)	(24.2)	(31.4)	(31.2)
Power loading*, lb/hp	10.7	9.5	8.8
(kg/hp)	(4.9)	(4.3)	(4.0)
Maximum speed, mph/s.l.	147	160	160
(km/h at s.l.)	(237)	(257)	(257)
Cruising speed, mph	115	148	150
(km/h)	(185)	(238)	(241)
Initial climb rate, ft/min	1,560	1,875	2,100
(m/sec)	(7.9)	(9.5)	(10.7)
Hover ceiling in ground effect, ft	9,150	8,500	14,200
(m)	(2,790)	(2,590)	(4,330)
Hover ceiling out of ground effect, ft	7,600	6,100	12,000
(m)	(2,315)	(1,860)	(3,660)
Normal range, miles	413	320	275
(km)	(665)	(515)	(440)
Maximum range, miles	1,560	---	---
(km)	(2,510)		

* rotor and power loadings are calculated at maximum gross weight and take-off power.

The XV-9 hot-cycle research helicopter during trials in early 1965. *(MDHC)*

Hughes XV-9

Convinced that the use of gas pressure to drive rotors, as used in the XH-17 and proposed for the XH-28, was superior to conventional methods as the elimination of the transmission drive system resulted in a lighter, less complex, and more easily maintained system, Hughes engineers sought ways to improve the propulsive efficiency of pressure-jet rotors. Eventually concluding that much improvement would result from ducting the hot efflux of gas generators directly to cascade vanes at each blade-tip instead of piping cold air to tip-burning nozzles, they succeeded in attracting the interest of the US Army.

Funded by the Army beginning in 1962, the multi-phase development programme for the Model 385 began with 60 hours of test running of a prototype hot-cycle rotor mounted on a ground rig. As results were encouraging, Hughes proceeded to the next phase, 15 hours of bench testing of the Model 385 propulsion module consisting of two General Electric YT64-GE-6 gas generators mounted at the tips of stub wings and driving a three-bladed rotor. Each blade was of two-spar construction with the hot efflux of the gas generators being taken to vanes at their tips by means of a Rene 41 high-temperature steel duct passing between the spars. Cooling air was forced through the leading and trailing edges of the constant-chord blades and was exhausted at the tip, fore and aft of the hot efflux. Results remaining promising, Hughes was authorized to proceed with the manufacture and testing of a research vehicle, the XV-9A (serial 64-15107), which was given a VTOL mission designator instead of the more traditional H helicopter designator.

As the XV-9A was only intended as a demonstrator for the hot-cycle system, the Army requested that manufacturing costs be kept to a minimum by using components from other aircraft. Thus, the cockpit of a Hughes OH-6A (with side-by-side accommodation for a pilot and a co-pilot/flight test engineer) and the undercarriage of a Sikorsky H-34 were mated to a specially-built fuselage and V-tail. The hot efflux from two General Electric YT64-GE-6 gas generators, which were loaned by the Navy and mounted at the tips of a stub wing, drove the three-bladed rotor. Bleed air from these generators was ducted to a yaw control system at the tail.

First flown by Robert G Ferry at Culver City on 5 November, 1964, the XV-9A remained at the manufacturer's facility until it had completed an initial 15-hour flight test programme. It was then transferred to Edwards AFB, where an additional 23 hours were flown. From an engineering point of view, tests proved highly satisfactory and in 1965 Hughes confidently predicted that the hot-cycle system would be used for heavy-lift military helicopters and for compound civil helicopters. The latter, which were to have been fitted with short wings and forward thrust fans, were expected to fly at speeds of up to 300 mph (480 km/h). From the environmental and economic points of view, however, the XV-9A was

Test pilot Robert G Ferry in front of the XV-9 at the Hughes Airfield in Culver City. *(MDHC)*

268

less successful as the exhaust of hot efflux through cascade vanes at the tips of the rotor was noisy and unacceptable in urban areas and as fuel consumption rate was high. To mitigate these deficiencies, Hughes proposed a refinement of the pressure-jet concept based on the use of turbofans in lieu of gas generators. This warm-cycle system was tested in a wind tunnel and on a whirling stand but improvements were insufficient to warrant the manufacture and testing of a flying prototype, thus bringing to an end the development by Hughes of pressure-jet systems successively based on the cold-cycle principle, as used for the XH-17 and XH-28, the hot-cycle principle, as featured by the XV-9A, and the warm-cycle principle, as evaluated during whirling stand tests.

Rotor diameter 55 ft (16.76 m); fuselage length 45 ft (13.72 m); height 12 ft (3.66 m).
Empty weight 8,500 lb (3,856 kg); loaded weight 15,300 lb (6,940 kg); maximum weight 25,500 lb (11,567 kg); rotor loading 6.4 lb/sq ft (31.5 kg/sq m).
Maximum cruising speed 138 mph (222 km/h); range 150 miles (240 km).

The McDonnell 188 on approach to the New York STOLport during its evaluation by American Airlines. *(MDC)*

McDonnell Douglas 188

On 1 June, 1961, the French aircraft manufacturer Breguet Aviation first flew the prototype of its 941 STOL transport. Powered by four 1,250 shp Turboméca Turmo IIID propeller-turbines interconnected through a flexible transmission shaft so that all propellers would remain operative after an engine failure, the Breguet 941 used the deflected-slipstream technique to achieve impressive STOL performance. It thus attracted the interest of McDonnell Aircraft Corporation, which sponsored its demonstration in the United States in June 1964 (at which time the aircraft was damaged when a pilot accidentally reversed the propellers while the aircraft was still 25 ft/8 m off the ground) and in March 1965 (after it had been rebuilt and re-engined with Turmo IIID3s). The St Louis firm also acquired licence rights for the Breguet-patented deflected-slipstream system and proposed to develop minimum change versions of the Breguet 941, as the Model 188 series, and larger, more capable variants, as the Model 210 series.

The Model 188E, the proposed development of the basic Breguet design most seriously marketed by McDonnell Douglas, was to be powered by four 1,600 shp General Electric CT58-16s and to carry up to 76 passengers in a new pressurized fuselage of circular cross-section (that of the Breguet 941 being unpressurized and of square cross-section). The main undercarriage was to have had two twin-wheel trucks instead of the four separate wheels of the 941 and to have been housed in fairings at the end of small stubs.

In support of its marketing activities for the Models 188E and 210 (the latter being described in Appendix A), McDonnell Douglas sponsored the demonstration in the United States of the second Breguet 941S pre-production military STOL transport. Renamed McDonnell Douglas 188

The McDonnell 188 (Breguet 941S) in Eastern Air Lines markings on 31 July, 1968. *(MDC)*

and fitted with limited passenger accommodation and specialized avionics, the aircraft was operated by Eastern Air Lines in the autumn of 1968 for a two-month demonstration programme to evaluate the advantages of STOL aircraft on the high-traffic Northeast Corridor between Boston, New York, and Washington. A similar evaluation was undertaken by American Airlines early the following year. In 1969, the aircraft was also tested briefly by the Federal Aviation Administration at its National Aviation Facilities Experimental Center, Atlantic City, New Jersey, in connection with an FAA definition of STOL-port criteria.

No customers could be found for either the 188 or 210, and McDonnell Douglas did not proceed with the design and construction of either.

Data for the proposed Model 188E:
Span 78 ft 6 in (23.93 m); length 80 ft 8 in (24.59 m); height 33 ft 2 in (10.11 m); wing area 926.7 sq ft (86.1 sq m).

Empty weight 37,695 lb (17,098 kg); loaded weight 56,000 lb (25,401 kg); maximum weight 58,420 lb (26,500 kg); wing loading 60.4 lb/sq ft (295 kg/sq m); power loading 8.75 lb/hp (4.0 kg/hp).

Maximum speed 359 mph at 20,000 ft (578 km/h at 6,095 m); cruising speed 288 mph (463 km/h); normal range 635 miles (1,020 km); ferry range 1,550 miles (2,495 km).

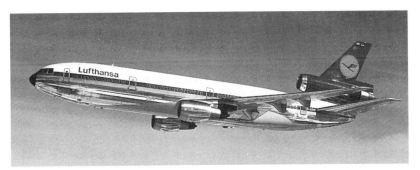

DC-10-30 D-ADHO (s/n 47927) of Lufthansa *(Lufthansa)*

McDonnell Douglas DC-10

In late 1964, when Air Force-funded preliminary studies for the CX-HLS (Experimental Cargo-Heavy Logistics Support) led to the award to Boeing, Douglas, and Lockheed of competitive design studies for the military cargo C-5, Douglas made a determined effort to win this major contract and organized a separate C-5 Division at Long Beach. Unduly confident in its ability to win the competition, Douglas only made desultory efforts to study commercial alternatives whereas Boeing hedged its bet by starting the 747 project immediately after C-5 proposals had been submitted to the USAF in April 1965. Douglas's excessive confidence and lack of foresight were shattered in the autumn of 1965 when Lockheed was declared the winner of the C-5 competition. After the initial shock, Douglas set out to capitalize on the significant advance in engine technology resulting from the high bypass ratio turbofans developed by General Electric and Pratt & Whitney during the C-5 competition and matched by similar progress achieved independently by Rolls-Royce. Initial concepts then studied in Long Beach were for a four-engined long-range aircraft which was tentatively designated DC-10.

S/n 46555, PH-DTF, a DC-10-30 of KLM at Guayaquil's Simón Bolivar Airport in August 1974. *(René J Francillon)*

273

(This designation had been earlier assigned to a proposed STOL transport powered by four propeller-turbines and derived from a proposal to the USMC as described on page 612 of Volume I). However, Douglas set its planning goals too high and proposed to the airlines a double-deck, wide-body aircraft[1] with maximum accommodation for up to 650 passengers. Although promising to offer substantial reduction in seat-mile costs, this aircraft was much too large to replace 707s and DC-8s (with their maximum accommodation ranging from 190 to 250 seats), and the airlines showed little or no interest in the project. Conversely, as the airlines were experiencing a traffic boom, they were attracted by the potential of wide-body aircraft and, led by Pan American World Airways, in April 1966 they began ordering the less ambitious Boeing 747 which offered to provide two-thirds of the capacity of the proposed four-engined, double-deck DC-10.

At that time the Long Beach production line was working at peak load producing DC-8s, Super DC-8s, and DC-9s, while the company was starting to experience cash flow problems due to the unexpected strength of the market which necessitated heavy investment in additional tooling

DC-10-10 (N103AA) of American Airlines after take-off with undercarriage almost retracted and flaps and slats deployed. *(American Airlines)*

[1] Notwithstanding the widely-circulated claim that wide-body aircraft were to provide much improved passenger comfort as the width of economy class seats was being increased by 1.5 in (3.8 cm) over that of seats in 707s and DC-8s, such was not really the case. Morphologic data available during the design of the 747, DC-10, and L-1011 indicated that the average width of the behind of US males had increased by 2-in (5.1 -cm) between the mid-fifties, when the 707 and DC-8 were designed, and the late sixties, when wide-body aircraft were conceived. Hence, wide-body aircraft became known by an unprintable epithet to engineering personnel involved in their design.

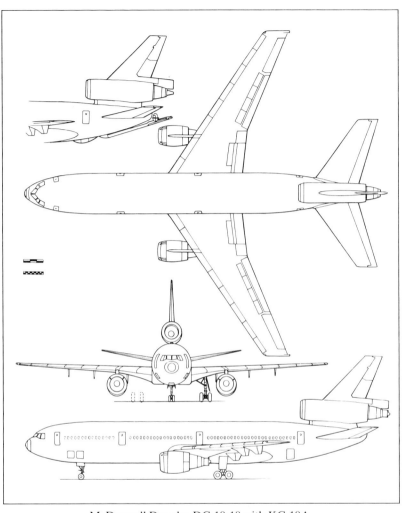

McDonnell Douglas DC-10-10 with KC-10A.

and staff to step up production of existing designs. None the less, Douglas could not afford to stay out of the wide-body aircraft market and financed design studies for two-, three-, and four-engined aircraft ranging from minimum-change developments of the stretched DC-8 with widened upper fuselage lobe and high bypass ratio turbofans to completely new designs. These efforts received a new impetus in the summer of 1966 when American Airlines circulated to manufacturers its specification for a twin-engined, wide-body aircraft conceived by its Chief Engineer, Franklin W Kolk. What American Airlines wanted was an aircraft with accommodation for 250 passengers in mixed-class configuration offering the wide-body passenger appeal of the Boeing 747. The aircraft was to be capable of carrying its full payload on routes of up to 1,750 naut miles (3,240 km)—such as West Coast points to Chicago—when operating from airports with long runways, or between New York and Chicago (640 naut miles, 1,185 km) when operating from the shorter runways of LaGuardia Airport. Furthermore, American Airlines specified that the aircraft's length had to be limited so that it could be taxied in and towed out in the confined space available between terminal fingers at LaGuardia Airport.

With Boeing fully occupied with the design of the 747, Douglas found itself in competition with its old rival from across town which, since the limited success of the propeller-turbine Lockheed Electra, had been out of the commercial aircraft business. Under the initial leadership of George Worley, the Douglas team first concentrated its efforts on twin-engined designs as requested by American Airlines. (A typical design, the Model D-966, is described and illustrated on pages 615 and 616 of Volume I.) Thereafter Douglas began to favour a three-engined configuration with US transcontinental range partially as a result of a survey of other potential customers which indicated that a twin-engined aircraft would not be required by most airlines until at least 1975, and partially due to concern over engine-out performance at the hot and high Denver Stapleton Airport—a major point on the network of United Air Lines, potentially the largest customer for the proposed aircraft. However, progress on the design was impaired by the increasing financial difficulty being experienced by Douglas. Finally, the advanced trijet transport project received the needed impetus when, following the April 1967, merger McDonnell provided additional working capital and assigned one of its executive, Robert Hage, as the new DC-10 Program Manager. Thus, the Douglas-conceived DC-10 was nurtured to life by McDonnell and became the first aircraft to deserve fully the McDonnell Douglas name.

By early autumn 1967, the design of the DC-10 had been finalized around a twin-aisle, wide-body fuselage providing accommodation for 250-340 passengers in up to nine-abreast seating[2], 35 deg wing sweep, and three engines (one beneath each wing and one in the tail). The choice of engine type was a difficult one as General Electric proposed the CF6 which had been developed from the TF39 powering the Lockheed C-5A, Pratt & Whitney offered its JT9D already adopted for the Boeing 747, and Rolls-Royce had an engine of considerable technical merit in its RB.211. In the event, as the straight-through duct adopted for the centre engine facilitated the installation of different power plants[3], McDonnell

[2] In service, this was eventually increased to a maximum of 380 passengers with ten-abreast seating.

[3] A feature not available with the rival Lockheed L-1011 due to the selection of a more conventional, and more elegant, split-S duct.

The number 2 and number 3 engines of a KC-10A of the 22nd Air Refueling Wing. *(René J. Francillon)*

Douglas left the selection of engine type[4] to the discretion of the customer airlines.

An early design decision, later fully justified by sales results, stemmed from the company's awareness of the need to design commercial aircraft with substantial growth potential both in terms of payload—through fuselage stretch—and in terms of range. Accordingly, the DC-10 was planned to have its undercarriage comprise a twin-wheel nose unit and four-wheel main units supplemented, if and when necessary, by a two-wheel centre unit to reduce pavement loads of future heavier versions. This played a significant role in prompting the KSSU (KLM, SAS, Swissair, and UTA) group, and later other airlines, to select the DC-10-30 in preference to proposed long-range derivatives of the L-1011 TriStar[5].

[4]   During the mid-seventies, in a determined bid to secure an order from British Airways, McDonnell Douglas offered to underwrite the additional certification costs for an RB.211-powered long-range DC-10-50 (or DC-10-30R) version. However, as it already had a fleet of medium-range Lockheed L-1011s, British Airways selected the TriStar 500 and ordered eight of these aircraft in spite of their higher seat-mile costs and shorter range.

[5]   Not having planned the use of a centre fuselage undercarriage unit, Lockheed could not easily retrofit such a unit as to do so would have necessitated the expensive relocation of equipment. Hence long-range versions of the TriStar were offered either without reduction in accommodation but with a redesigned wing to house six-wheel main undercarriage units—a costly redesign, or with standard undercarriage but reduced accommodation—a feature not liked by prospective airline customers.

277

The launch of the DC-10 programme did not come easily. McDonnell Douglas had taken the lead on 19 February, 1968, when American Airlines ordered fifty DC-10s (25 firm plus 25 options). Six weeks later, however, Lockheed leapt forward and announced staggering orders, including options, for 144 L-1011s from three traditional Douglas customers—Delta Air Lines, Eastern Air Lines, and Northeast Air-lines—and from TWA and the British Air Holdings group. Alarmed by Lockeed's apparent clean sweep of the market, the Board of Directors of McDonnell Douglas seriously considered cancelling the American Air-lines contract which had been accepted conditional upon further DC-10 orders being received within a six-month period. Fortunately, in late April 1968, United Air Lines ordered sixty DC-10s, including 30 on

Still bearing the temporary US registration N1341U on its fuselage, this DC-10-30 of UTA has its ultimate French registration (F-BTDA) partially painted out on the upper surface of its starboard wing. *(UTA)*

option, and with this order the future of the DC-10 was assured. Additional orders for the CF6-6 powered domestic version, now desig-nated DC-10-10, were received and orders for intercontinental range JT9D-powered DC-10-20s (later redesignated DC-10-40s) and CF6-50-powered DC-10-30s were received in October 1968 and in June 1969, respectively, from Northwest Orient Airlines and the KSSU group.

When ordering the DC-10, American Airlines had specified the use of 40,000 lb (18,144 kg) thrust General Electric CF6-6 turbofans and this powerplant selection was confirmed by other DC-10-10 customers. Thus, the prototype (N10DC, s/n 46500) was powered by three of these engines when on 29 August, 1970, it was flown for the first time from Long Beach to Edwards AFB by a crew captained by Clifford L Stout. This aircraft and the next four DC-10-10s underwent trials at Edwards AFB, and later at Yuma, Arizona, and the DC-10 received its FAA Type Approval on 29

This overhead view of a DC-10-10 of American Airlines shows well details of its power plant installation and leading edge slats. *(American Airlines)*

July, 1971. Only minor problems, including an over stiff undercarriage rendering smooth landings difficult to achieve, were encountered during the trials of the medium-range DC-10-10 and the long-range DC-10-20 (the first flight of which was made by s/n 46750, N141US, on 28 February, 1972) and DC-10-30 (s/n 46550, N1339U, first flown on 21 June, 1972). Confidence was then high that DC-10 sales would reach the 1,000-mark within 10 years, as predicted before the merger with McDonnell. Unfortunately, bad publicity following accidents in March 1974 and May 1979, the 1973 energy crisis and the ensuing downturn in airline activities, and changes in regulations which allowed twin-engined aircraft to provide EROPS (extended range operations) on long overwater routes combined to make it impossible for the DC-10 to reach the half-way mark in predicted sales. The 446th and last DC-10, a Series 30 (s/n 48318, N3024W), was delivered to Nigeria Airways on 27 July, 1989.

Production history

Remaining in production for over 20 years, the DC-10 was built in the following versions:

DC-10-10: Optimized for US domestic operations, the DC-10-10s were normally powered by three General Electric 39,300 lb (17,826 kg) thrust CF6-6D or CF-6K turbofans but could also be powered by 40,300 lb (18,280 kg) thrust CF6-6D1As. Series 10 aircraft were initially

Pending delivery of its Lockheed L-1011s, Delta Air Lines operated five leased DC-10-10s (including N610DA seen here at the Atlanta's Hartsfield International Airport) between October 1972 and May 1975. After acquiring nine DC-10-10s when it absorbed Western Airlines in April 1987, Delta again operated Douglas trijets. It disposed of the last of these aircraft in 1989. *(Delta Air Lines)*

certificated at the maximun take-off gross weight of 410,000 lb (185,973 kg), but a number of these aircraft were certificated at MGTOWs of 430,000 lb (195,045 kg), 440,000 lb (199,581 kg) and 455,000 lb (206,385 kg), the higher take-off weight resulting in increased FAR runway length requirements. The cockpit crew consisted of pilot (Captain), co-pilot (1st Officer), and flight engineer (2nd Officer) as was the case with all other DC-10 versions. Most DC-10-10s were delivered with galleys in the lower fuselage lobe with lifts[6] to bring the serving carts up to the main deck, but some carriers chose to have upper deck galleys in order to increase the volume and weight of cargo carried beneath the main deck. The prototype DC-10 (s/n 46500, which was registered N10DC during manufacturer's trials and was re-registered N101AA before being delivered to American Airlines on 8 December, 1972) first flew on 29 August, 1970, and this version went into service on 5 August, 1971. In all,

S/n 46938, N905WA, a DC-10-10 of Western Airlines taking off from the San Francisco International Airport in September 1975. *(René J. Francillon)*

122 DC-10-10s were delivered to six US carriers (American, Continental, Delta, National, United, and Western) and two foreign carriers (Laker and THY). The last DC-10-10 (s/n 48263, N1847U, the 353rd DC-10) was delivered to United Air Lines on 20 April, 1981.

A DC-10-10 leased from Continental Airlines was fitted with winglet surfaces projecting 10.5 ft (3.20 m) upward and 2.5 ft (0.76 m) downward from the wingtips. Six-month trials began on 31 August, 1981.

DC-10-10CF: Eight convertible passenger/cargo DC-10-10CFs were built for Continental Airlines and were fitted with reinforced floors and a 102 in by 140 in (2.59 m by 3.56 m) upward-hinged cargo floor on the forward port fuselage side for loading and unloading pallets or 8-ft by 8-ft

---

[6] Instead of being identified by the British word 'lift', the food cart conveying device was initially called by the corresponding US term of 'elevator.' However, when a rash of 'elevator problems' began to alarm the Federal Aviation Administration, 'elevators' quickly became 'lifts' to avoid confusing the cart conveying devices with the horizontal tail's movable control surfaces!

281

(2.44-m by 2.44-m) containers. They could be converted overnight to an all-cargo configuration by removal of seats, overhead baggage racks, upper deck galleys, coat compartments, and carpeting, and installation of freight loading tracks and rollers, cargo tiedown systems, and restraint nets. Passenger accommodation was similar to that provided in DC-10-10s but, with seats and other items removed, DC-10-10CFs could carry a maximum cargo load of 125,650 lb (56,995 kg). Usable main deck volume of 12,250 cu ft (346.9 m³) supplemented the 4,600 cu ft (130.3 m³) available below deck. Eight DC-10-10CFs (s/ns 47803 to 47810), powered by 40,000 lb (18,144kg) thrust CF6-6D turbofans and certificated at a MGTOW of 440,000 lb (199,581 kg), were delivered to Continental between February 1974 and March 1975. A ninth DC-10-10CF (c/n 48264, N1848U, which was the 379th DC-10 and the 2,000th Douglas jetliner) was specially built for assignment to the Civil Reserve Air Fleet (CRAF) and was delivered to United Air Lines on 20 September, 1982.

DC-10-15: Retaining the airframe of the Series 10 aircraft, Series 15 aircraft were powered by 45,500 lb (20,684 kg) thrust CF6-50C2-F turbofans, certificated at a MGTOW of 455,000 lb (206,385 kg), and specially intended for operations from hot and high airports such as Mexico City. Five were built for Mexicana and two for Aeroméxico with delivery taking place between June 1981 and January 1983.

DC-10-20: This designation was initially given to the JT9D-powered

Mexicana Airlines' McDonnell Douglas DC-10-15 widebody jets are equipped with three General Electric engines, each developing 46,500 pounds of thrust – an increase of 6,500 pounds over the standard Series 10 engine. The extra thrust allows operations from the 7,300-foot altitude of Mexico City with a full payload.

intercontinental version which was redesignated DC-10-40 before entering service with Northwest Orient Airlines. Still designated DC-10-20 and powered by 47,500 lb (21,546 kg) wet thrust Pratt & Whitney JT9D-20 turbofans, the prototype (s/n 46750, N141US) first flew on 28 February, 1972.

DC-10-30: The DC-10-30 was developed for intercontinental operations and was initially planned to be powered by three 48,400 lb (21,954 kg) thrust General Electric CF6-50A turbofans. However, the 166 DC-10-30s delivered between November 1972 and July 1989 were powered by either 50,400 lb (22,861 kg) thrust CF6-50C/-50CA/-50C2-R/ or -50Hs, 51,800 lb (23,496 kg) thrust CF6-50C1s or C2s, or 53,200 lb (24,131 kg) thrust CF6-50C2Bs. To meet customers' requirements, they

A US-owned and registered DC-10-30 of Aerovias de Mexico (Aeroméxico) landing at Paris-Orly. *(Christian Jacquet-Francillon)*

were certificated at MGTOW of 530,000 lb (240,404 kg), 555,000 lb (251,744 kg), 558,000 lb (253,105 kg), 565,000 lb (256,280 kg), 572,000 lb (259,455kg), 580,000 lb (263,084 kg), or 590,000 lb (267,620 kg). The necessary range extension was obtained by increasing the usable fuel capacity from the 21,762 US gallons (82,376 litres) of most DC-10-10s to 36,236 gallons (137,165 litres). Fuel capacity was further increased to 37,747 gallons (142,885 litres) for high gross weight DC-10-30ER (Extended Range) aircraft fitted with an auxiliary tank in the aft cargo compartment. Another DC-10-30ER option (as ordered by Finnair) increased capacity to 39,396 gallons (149,127 litres). Externally, the Series 30 aircraft were similar to DC-10-10s, but their wing span was increased by 10 ft (3.05 m) to 165 ft 4 in (50.39 m), and a third main undercarriage unit with twin wheels was added beneath the fuselage to offset partially the increase in MGTOW. In spite of their more powerful engines, Series 30 aircraft had increased FAR runway length require-

283

HS-TGA (s/n 46851), a DC-10-30 in the markings of Thai International, was leased from UTA between March 1975 and May 1977. *(Aviation Photo News)*

ments due to their greater take-off weight and longer take-off and landing runs. In most DC-10-30s, galleys were located on the main deck to increase cargo capacity in the lower compartments. Cargo capacity could be further increased, at the expense of seating capacity, by fitting baggage containers in the rear main deck, as originally specified by Lufthansa. The first DC-10-30 (s/n 46550, N1339U) began flight trials on 21 June, 1972.

DC-10-30CF: Passenger/cargo convertible DC-10-30CFs (simply designated DC-10-30Fs in the FAA type certificate) combined the airframe and powerplant installation of DC-10-30s with the reinforced flooring and main deck side-loading door of DC-10-10CFs. Passenger accommodation and cargo loads were similar to those of DC-10-10CFs. Thirty DC-10-30CFs were certificated with MGTOW of 555,000 lb (251,744 kg), 565,000 lb (256,280 kg), 572,000 lb (259,455kg), or 580,000 lb (263,084 kg) and delivered to Federal Express, Martinair, Overseas

The first DC-10-30CF (OO-SLA, s/n 47906) of Sabena-Belgian World Airlines. *(Aviation Photo News)*

284

National, Sabena, VARIG, Thai International, Trans International Airlines, and World Airways between April 1973 and September 1984.

In addition to aircraft built and delivered as DC-10-30CFs, at least one DC-10-30 passenger transport (s/n 46871 delivered as a DC-10-30 to SAS in January 1976, acquired by Federal Express in November 1984, and returned to service in December 1985 after being modified to a cargo configuration) has been converted as a convertible DC-10-30F. As more DC-10-30s are phased out from passenger service, more are likely to be converted to passenger/cargo convertible or all-cargo configurations.

DC-10-30F: Powered by 51,800 lb (23,496 kg) thrust CF6-50C2s and certificated at a MGTOW of 580,000 lb (263,084 kg), 10 all-cargo DC-10-30Fs were built for Federal Express and delivered between January 1986 and October 1988.

DC-10-40 (N144JC ex-Northwest N144US, s/n 46753) of Sun Country Airlines (aka Sunair) at Las Vegas' McCarran International Airport on 14 April, 1988. *(Jim Dunn)*

S/n 46752, N143US, a DC-10-40 of Northwest Orient Airlines. *(Northwest Airlines)*

DC-10-40:   Generally similar to Series 30 aircraft, the DC-10-40s were all-passenger, long-range intercontinental aircraft powered by Pratt &

285

Whitney turbofans. Twenty-two DC-10-40s each powered by three 47,500 lb (21,546 kg) thrust JT9D-20s and certificated at a MGTOW of 565,000 lb (256,280 kg) were delivered to Northwest Orient Airlines between March 1972 and December 1974. Ten DC-10-40Is (I for intercontinental) with 51,720 lb (23,4600 kg) thrust JT9D-59As and a MGTOW of 572,000 lb (259,455 kg) were delivered to Japan Air Lines between August 1976 and December 1981.

DC-10-40D: Produced for use on domestic and regional routes of Japan Air Lines, ten DC-10-40Ds were delivered between April 1976 and March 1983. They retained the JT9D-59A turbofans of the DC-10-40Is but were certificated at a lower gross weight (445,000 lb/201,849 kg) and were not fitted with the centre undercarriage unit.

KC-10: On 19 December, 1977, the USAF concluded the protracted ATCA (Advanced Tanker/Cargo Aircraft) competition between projected derivatives of the Boeing 747 and the McDonnell Douglas DC-10 by announcing its intention of ordering an initial batch of 20 tanker-cargo derivatives of the DC-10-30CF at a cost of approximately $680 million. At the same time, the Air Force awarded MDC a $28 million contract to begin engineering and related work necessary to convert the DC-10 into a military aircraft capable of carrying either fuel, cargo, or a combination of both. Designated KC-10A Extender, the resulting tanker/cargo aircraft was to be particularly well suited to supporting overseas deployments of tactical air units by simultaneously refuelling their aircraft and carrying their support equipment and maintenance personnel. The first KC-10A (s/n 48200, 79-0433) was first flown at Long Beach on 12 July, 1980.

For use in the tanker role, KC-10As were fitted with bladder fuel cells in the lower cargo compartments, thus boosting maximum usable fuel

During initial trials, the first KC-10A (s/n 48200) carried the N110KC civil registration instead of its Air Force serial, 79-0433. *(MDC)*

capacity to 54,455 gallons (206,130 litres), and with an air refuelling receptacle above and aft of the cockpit. In addition, a boom operator's station was provided beneath the rear fuselage, a McDonnell Douglas Advanced Aerial Refueling Boom (AARB) capable of transferring fuel at a maximum rate of 1,500 gallons (5,678 litres) per minute was attached on the centre line further aft beneath the fuselage, and a refuelling hose reel unit was installed on the lower starboard side of the rear fuselage. For use in the transport role, KC-10As were provided with reinforced main deck flooring with standard USAF 463L cargo handling and tie-down system and a 102-in by 140-in (2.59-m by 3.56-m) upward-hinged cargo

A KC-10A (79-1951) of the 22nd AREFW refuelling the prototype Northrop B-2 'stealth' bomber over the Mojave Desert in November 1989. (*USAF, courtesy of Northrop*)

loading door on the port side of the forward fuselage.

Powered by three 51,800 lb (23,496 kg) thrust General Electric CF6-50C2 turbofans and cleared for take-off at a maximum of 590,000 lb (267,620 kg), KC-10As were designed to transfer 200,000 lb of fuel (about 30,000 gallons/113,500 litres) to a receiver aircraft at a distance 2,200 miles (3,540 km) from base and then return home unrefuelled or to carry their maximum cargo load of 169,409 lb (76,843 kg) over a distance of 4,370 miles (7,030 km). Although designed to accommodate up to twenty-seven 463L pallets, KC-10As were intended to carry mixed upper deck loads which during typical overseas deployments were to include 75 people in airline-type seats and up to 17 cargo pallets.

The 60th and last KC-10A (s/n 48310, 87-0124; *see* Appendix C for the serials of the other KC-10As) was flown to the manufacturer's test facilities at Yuma, Arizona, on 29 November, 1988. There, this Extender was fitted with a British-built Mk 32B hose drum pod beneath each wing

287

S/n 48200, 79-0433, the first KC-10A, in the markings of the 32nd Refueling Squadron. *(René J Francillon)*

tip to convert it into a three-point tanker for probe-equipped aircraft. Earlier aircraft will be modified by mid-1993 to accept these pods and the USAF has ordered pods from Flight Refuelling Ltd to equip 40 of the KC-10As as three-point tankers.

Service history

Having taken delivery of their first DC-10-10s during a joint ceremony at Long Beach on 29 July, 1971, American Airlines and United Air Lines raced each other to complete crew training and pre-operational activities. The race was won by American which introduced the DC-10 on the Los Angeles-Chicago route in a luxurious 208-seat configuration (34 first class and 174 coach seats with lounges in both classes) on 5 August, 1971. United followed 11 days later by initiating DC-10 service between Los Angeles and Washington DC. Four other US trunk carriers—Delta Air Lines, Continental Airlines, National Airlines, and Western Airlines—began DC-10-10 service in 1971-72. Outside the United States, the only airlines to take delivery of new DC-10-10s were Laker Airways and Türk Hava Yollari (THY Turkish Airlines)[7]. The British company began DC-10 charter service on 21 November, 1972, and introduced *Skytrain* no-reservation transatlantic DC-10 operations on 26 September, 1977, but went out of business in February 1982. THY started DC-10 service in December 1972 and 17 years later still operated two Series 10 aircraft.

Although no other airlines ordered Series 10 aircraft, this version was later acquired on the second hand market by numerous carriers and aircraft leasing companies. Moreover, closely-related Series 15 aircraft were acquired by Aeromexico and Mexicana. By the end of June 1989, five DC-10-10s had been lost in accidents and 134 DC-10-10s,

---

[7] Their six DC-10-10s had been ordered by the Japanese trading company Mitsui and were intended to be delivered to All Nippon Airways. However, as a result of the later widely publicised bribery scandal, this Japanese carrier ordered Lockheed L-1011s and never flew DC-10s.

G-AZZC *Eastern Belle*, s/n 46905, was the 47th DC-10 built. It was delivered to Laker Airways on 26 October, 1972. Changing hands several times after Laker Airways went out of business in February 1982, this DC-10-10 was acquired by World Airways in May 1988. *(Laker)*

DC-10-CFs, and DC-10-15s remained in service with five airlines in the United States and six airlines abroad. The largest Series 10 US operators remained American and United, with 49 and 48 DC-10-10/10CF aircraft respectively. Abroad, the largest operator was Mexicana with six DC-10-15s.

A DC-10-40 of Northwest landing at the Spokane International Airport, Washington, on 1 July, 1974. *(Peter B Lewis)*

Before intercontinental versions of the DC-10 entered service, the type's long-range capabilities were demonstrated by a Series 40 aircraft which set three point-to-point world records during a one-week demonstration tour to Hong Kong, Tokyo, Honolulu, Buenos Aires, Rio de Janeiro, and back to Los Angeles in October 1982. The 7,677-mile (12,352-km) Los Angeles–Hong Kong sector was flown in 14 hr 44 min, the 7,800-mile (12,550-km) Honolulu–Buenos Aires sector in 14 hr 18 min, and the 6,300-mile (10,136-km) Rio de Janeiro–Los Angeles sector in 11 hr 52 min. On 13 December, 1972, two months after the type had beeen used for these record flights, the DC-10-40 entered service with Northwest on the Minneapolis/St Paul–Tampa route. The only other

JA-8539, a DC-10-40I, landing at Tokyo-Narita. *(Masanori Ogawa)*

carrier to order Series 40 aircraft was Japan Air Lines, which acquired DC-10-40Is for its intercontinental routes and DC-10-40Ds for its domestic and regional routes. An ex-Northwest DC-10-40 was destroyed on 10 August, 1986, while operated by American Trans Air, but at the end of June 1989 the remaining 41 Series 40s were still operated by

HB-1HA *St Gallen*, the first DC-10-30 for Swissair, was delivered on 30 November, 1972. It was acquired by Ecuatoriana (Empresa Ecuatoriana de Aviación) in September 1983 and registered EC-BKO. *(Swissair)*

Northwest and Sun Country Airlines in the United States and by Japan Air Lines and Japan Asia Airways abroad.

Although its prototype was flown four months after that of the JT9D-powered DC-10-20/40 version, the DC-10-30 became the first overwater version of the McDonnell Douglas wide-body trijet to be put into service when Swissair began DC-10 transatlantic service on 15 December, 1972. In spite of trailing behind the 747 by almost three years, the long-range version of the DC-10 initially achieved promising sales results as, with two-thirds of the capacity of the large Boeing, it was better suited than its larger rival to long-range routes with only moderate traffic (*eg*, Europe to Africa, Asia, and South America). Hence, many carriers operating 747s on North Atlantic routes added DC-10-30s to their fleet. Among these airlines, the most notable were several European and Asian flag carriers.

Beginning in 1975, however, the DC-10-30 faced stiffer competition from combi versions of the 747, which achieved seating capacity similar to that of the McDonnell Douglas trijet by trading seats for cargo on the main deck, and from the very long-range 747SP, which did so by having a shortened fuselage. Accordingly, MDC built the DC-10-30ER to match the long-range performance of the 747SP and proposed several stretched versions of the DC-10 to compete against the 747 combi. Several airlines (*eg*, Air New Zealand, Lufthansa, United, and Swissair) were about to order stretched DC-10-60s when an economic slowdown and adverse publicity following the loss of an American Airlines DC-10-10 at Chicago on 25 May, 1979, combined in forcing McDonnell Douglas to postpone development of that aircraft. The programme never recovered as major prospective customers could not wait for the availability of new DC-10 versions to increase capacity and switched to 747s. Finally, twin-engined EROPS by wide-body aircraft, which was initiated by Eastern Air Lines with A300Bs in December 1977 and had gained general acceptance by 1983-84, greatly reduced the potential DC-10-30 market.

One high-time DC-10-30 has already been retired (s/n 47846, N136AA, ex ZK-NZL of Air New Zealand) by American Airlines, another has been converted as a freighter, and six DC-10-30s and five DC-10-30CFs have been lost in accidents. Thus, at the end of June 1989 there were 196 Series 30 aircraft in service with six US carriers and 29 airlines. The largest operator of Series 30 aircraft was Federal Express which first obtained used DC-10-10CFs in March 1980, later acquired new and used DC-10-30CFs, and became the only operator of all-freight DC-10-30Fs in January 1986. In mid-1989, its DC-10 fleet included ten DC-10-30Fs, eight DC-10-10CFs, and six DC-10-30CFs. Abroad, the main Series 30 operators were Canadian Airlines International and VARIG (with 12 each), Lufthansa (with 11), and Scandinavian Airlines System and Swissair (with 10 each).

Following manufacturer's trials at Yuma and Air Force Operational Test and Evaluation at Yuma, Arizona, and Barksdale AFB, Louisiana, KC-10As entered service with the 32nd Air Refueling Squadron, 2nd

N306FE, an all-cargo DC-10-30F of Federal Express. *(Federal Express)*

S/n 46924, PP-VMA, a DC-10-30 of VARIG. *(DAC)*

Bombardment Wing, at Barksdale AFB in October 1981. Over the next four years, three additional Strategic Air Command squadrons received Extenders: the 9th AREFS, a component of the 22nd AREFW at March AFB, and the 344th and 911th AREFWs of the 68th AREFW at Seymour Johnson AFB, North Carolina. Since then, these four SAC squadrons have shared their aircraft with crews and maintenance personnel from the Air Force Reserve with AFRES flight crews at Barksdale AFB being assigned to the 77th AREFS (Associate), those at March AFB to the 78th AREFS (Associate), and those at Seymour Johnson AFB to the 79th AREFS (Associate). The 60th and final KC-10A was delivered to the 79th AREFS on 4 April, 1990.

In service, KC-10As have gained an excellent reputation with Air Force personnel due to their reliability, and the type has proved its usefulness in numerous deployments and routine exercises. Less usual activities have seen an Extender from the 22nd AREFW make a 17.8-

hour, nonstop, unrefuelled flight of 8,982 miles (14,452 km) from Riyadh, Saudi Arabia, to March AFB, California, in February 1985.

A KC-10A of the 22nd Air Refueling Wing touching down at Gowen Field in Boise, Idaho, on 17 July, 1988. *(René J Francillon)*

Aircraft from all KC-10A units provided air refuelling for F-111Fs and EF-111As during Operation *Eldorado Canyon*, the bombing of Libya by UK-based USAFE aircraft on 15 April, 1986.

Accident record
The non-specialized press, particularly in the United States, and special interest groups, such as the Airline Passengers Association, have repeatedly claimed that the DC-10 is unsafe or, at the very least, significantly less safe than other wide-body aircraft. There is no denying that an unusually large percentage of the DC-10 fleet has been lost in a variety of accidents. However, records show that only one of the 18 aircraft which have been destroyed since the type's entry into service was lost as the result of a design deficiency. This deficiency, the improper design of a cargo door latching mechanism, had already been identified and most aircraft had been modified when an unmodified Turkish DC-10 crashed in France in March 1974. The following is a chronological list of all DC-10/KC-10 accidents resulting in total airframe losses.

● 17 December, 1973: DC-10-30 (EC-CBN, s/n 46925) of Iberia crashed at Boston's Logan International Airport, Massachussetts. No fatalities. Primary cause: Undershot the runway during an instrument approach.
● 4 March, 1974: DC-10-10 (TC-JAV, s/n 46704) of THY-Turkish Airlines crashed near Ermenonville, France. All 346 occupants were

killed. Primary cause: Failure of controls following the loss of an unmodified rear baggage door which still had the original faulty latch mechanism and had been forcibly and improperly locked.

● 12 November, 1975: DC-10-30CF (N1032F, s/n 46826) of Overseas National aborted its take-off at New York's Kennedy International Airport and burned. No fatalities. Primary cause: Multiple bird strikes on engines.

● 2 January, 1976: DC-10-30CF (N1031F, s/n 46825) of Overseas National was destroyed in heavy landing at Istambul's Yesilköy Airport. No fatalities. Primary causes: Pilot error.

The ill-fated N1031F of Overseas National taking-off on a pre-acceptance flight from the Long Beach Municipal Airport. *(DAC)*

● 1 March, 1978: DC-10-10 (N68045, s/n 46904) of Continental Airlines aborted its take-off and burned at Los Angeles International Airport. Two passengers killed during evacuation. Primary cause: Multiple tyre bursts forced take-off to be aborted and aircraft burned when wheels and tyres overheated.

● 25 May, 1979: DC-10-10 (N110AA, s/n 46510) of American Airlines crashed on take-off at Chicago's O'Hare International Airport. All 279 occupants were killed. Primary cause: Improper maintenance procedure led to port engine separating from the wing and damaging controls. As a result of this accident, all US-registered DC-10s were grounded on order of the Federal Aviation Administration. The grounding order was rescinded by the FAA on 13 July, 1979, after it was determined that the design of the aircraft had not been a contributory factor to the accident.

● 31 October, 1979: DC-10-10 (N903WA, s/n 46929) of Western Airlines crashed at Mexico City's Aeropuerto Internacional Benito Juárez. All 74 on board, as well as two people on the ground, were killed. Primary cause: Pilot error. When he realized that his initial touchdown had been made on a closed runway encumbered with construction equipment, the pilot tried to go around and crashed into obstructions.

• 28 November, 1979: DC-10-30 (ZK-NZP, s/n 46910) of Air New Zealand crashed on Mount Erebus, Antarctica. All 257 occupants killed. Primary cause: An unauthorized descent below the minimum safe altitude when visibility was insufficient led to crash into the mountain. There were numerous other operational shortcomings.
• 2 February, 1981: DC-10-30 (AP-AXE, s/n 46935) of Pakistan International Airlines destroyed by fire at Karachi Airport. No fatalities. Primary cause: Hangar accident.

AP-AXD (s/n 46940), a DC-10-30 of Pakistan International Airlines at Heathrow Airport. *(Aviation Photo News)*

• 23 January, 1982: DC-10-30CF (N113WA, s/n 47821) of World Airways skidded off the runway at Boston's Logan International Airport. Two occupants were killed and 208 survived. Primary cause: Failure of airport authority to warn crew of icy runway condition.
• 13 September, 1982: DC-10-30CF (EC-DEG, s/n 46962) of Spantax aborted take-off at Málaga. Primary cause: Abort was initiated too late when the aircraft vibrated on take-off and the aircraft was destroyed by fire after overrunning on to a road.
• 23 December, 1983: DC-10-30CF (HL7339, s/n 46960) of Korean Air Lines collided on take-off with a Piper PA-31 Navajo light twin at the Anchorage International Airport. No fatalities. Primary cause: Crew used the wrong runway in fog.
• 10 August, 1986: DC-10-40 (N184AT, s/n 46751) of American Trans Air destroyed by fire at Chicago's O'Hare International Airport. Primary cause: Ground accident.
• 10 January, 1987: DC-10-30 (5N-ANR, s/n 46968) of Nigeria Airways destroyed by fire in touch-and-go accident at Ilorin, Nigeria. No fatalities. Primary cause: Pilot error during training flight.
• 17 September, 1987: KC-10A (82-0190, s/n 48212) of USAF burned during refuelling at Barksdale AFB, Florida. No fatalities. Primary cause: Servicing personnel error (improper procedures).

5N-ANN (s/n 46957), a DC-10-30 of Nigeria Airways. *(MAP)*

- 19 July, 1989: DC-10-10, (N1819U, s/n 46618) of United Air Lines crashed while attempting an emergency landing at Sioux City's Gateway Airport, South Dakota. 111 passengers and crew members were killed and 185 survived. Primary cause: Uncontained disintegration of fan section of No. 2 engine and subsequent failure of the triple redundant hydraulic system. As a result of this accident, McDonnell Douglas devised an hydraulic shutoff valve to prevent complete loss of control in the event of a catastrophic centre engine failure.
- 27 July, 1989: DC-10-30 (HL7328, s/n 47887) of Korean Air Lines crashed on final approach to Tripoli Airport, Libya. 78 passengers and crew members were killed and 121 survived. Primary cause: Pilot error.
- 19 September, 1989: DC-10-30 (N54629, s/n 46852) of UTA crashed in the Ténéré desert in southeastern Niger. All 171 occupants killed. Primary cause: Bomb.

S2-ACP (s/n 46995), a DC-10-30 of Biman Bangladesh Airlines, was purchased from Singapore Airlines in August 1983. It had been originally delivered to Singapore Airlines in April 1979. *(MAP)*

	DC-10-10	DC-10-30ER	DC-10-40	KC-10A
Span, ft in	155 4	165 4	165 4	165 4
(m)	(47.35)	(50.39)	(50.39)	(50.39)
Length, ft in	181 5	181 7	182 3	181 7
(m)	(55.30)	(55.35)	(55.55)	(55.35)
Height, ft in	58 1	58 1	58 1	58 1
(m)	(17.7)	(17.7)	(17.7)	(17.7)
Wing area, sq ft	3,550	3,610	3,647	3,958
(sq m)	(329.79)	(335.37)	(338.81)	(367.71)
Empty, lb	235,340		265,750	241,027
(kg)	(106,748)		(120,542)	(109,328)
MGTOW, lb	430,000	580,000	565,000	590,000
(kg)	(195,045)	(263,085)	(256,280)	(267,620)
Wing loading*, lb/sq ft	121.1	160.7	154.9	149.1
(kg/sq m)	(591.4)	(784)	(756)	(728)
Power loading*, lb/lb st	3.6	3.6	4.0	3.8
(kg/kgp)	(3.6)	(3.6)	(4.0)	(3.8)
Maximum speed, mph	589	594	594	610
(km/h)	(948)	(956)	(956)	(981)
Cruising speed, mph	574	574	574	564
(km/h)	(924)	(924)	(924)	(907)
Range with maximum payload,				
lb/miles	99,660/3,300		102,250/4,075	169,409/4,370
(kg/km)	(45,205/3,700)		(46,380/6,560)	(76,843/7,030)
Payload range with maximum				
fuel, lb/miles	51,000/4,375		40,200/6,100	
(kg/km)	(23,135/7,040)		(18,235/7,815)	
Ferry range,				
miles	5,000		6,735	11,500
(km)	(8,045)		(10,840)	(18,500)

* wing and power loadings are calculated at normal loaded weight and maximum take-off power.

A Mitsubishi-assembled F-15J (Japanese serial 22-8806) of the 204 Hikotai, Nihon Koku Jieitai (JASDF) at Hyakuri AB, Honshu, on 4 May, 1986. *(Masanori Ogawa)*

McDonnell Douglas F-15 Eagle

In the mid-1960s, the US aircraft industry was invited to study USAF requirements for an advanced tactical fighter capable of gaining and maintaining air superiority in the post 1975 period. This new aircraft was to achieve absolute superiority by defeating the advanced fighter threat in any and all types of aerial combat, at minimum weight and cost. Without compromising its primary air-to-air combat role, the aircraft was to be capable of performing air-to-ground missions. USAF interest in this twin-engined F-X (Fighter-Experimental) was confirmed with the issuance of Qualitative Operational Requirements (QOR) 65-14F on 6 October, 1965, and of a Request for Proposals (RFP) on 8 December, 1965.

Beginning in March 1966, USAF-sponsored studies of these requirements were made by Boeing, Lockheed, and North American while Grumman and McDonnell funded their own studies. A second set of government-funded studies was undertaken in December 1967 by General Dynamics and McDonnell Douglas with Fairchild-Republic, Grumman, Lockheed, and North American proceeding at their own expense. Bids for the Project Definition Phase (PDP) were requested from eight manufacturers on 30 September, 1968, and led to the award of PDP contracts to Fairchild-Hiller, McDonnell Douglas, and North American on 30 December. A year later, on 23 December, 1969, the McDonnell Douglas proposal was declared the winner and the company was authorized to proceed with a three 'item' programme. Item I covered the design and development phases, Item II the manufacture and testing of twenty FSD (Full Scale Development) aircraft, and Item III the production of 107 single-seat F-15s and two-seat TF-15s to equip a first wing and provide attrition aircraft.

Under the direction of Donald Malvern, General Manager, and Richard Noyes, Technical Program Manager, the F-15 Eagle was developed by MCAIR in St Louis. The basic requirements of high thrust-to-weight ratio (which, at normal loaded weight, came to 1.17:1 for the

298

F-15A versus 0.88:1 for the F-4E) and low wing loading (65.8 lb/sq ft, 321.2 kg/sq m, for the F-15A versus 76.5 lb/sq ft, 373.7 kg/sq m, for the F-4E) were combined successfully in an aerodynamic design emphasizing low drag at both low and high lift in order to achieve optimum manoeuvrability in all flight conditions. The MCAIR team rejected the use of a variable-geometry wing, which was judged to be too complex, too heavy, and too expensive, and adopted a large-area, fixed geometry wing

F-15A-18-MC of the 48th Fighter Interceptor Squadron firing an AIM-7F Sparrow missile. *(MCAIR)*

with 45 deg sweep on the leading edge. The use of advanced avionics and electronics, including a Hughes APG-63 X-band, pulsed Doppler, radar and HUD, made possible the single-seat configuration favoured by the Air Force. Other design features included twin vertical tail surfaces, and close-set Pratt & Whitney F100 afterburning turbofans fed by lateral intakes each of which were provided with three variable ramps, a variable diffuser ramp, and a variable bypass door. Air-to-air armament consisted of a forward-firing cannon[1] mounted in the starboard wing leading edge, four AIM-7 radar-guided Sparrow missiles on the lower corner of the fuselage, and four AIM-9 infrared-guided Sidewinder missiles[2] on wing stations. In addition, provision was incorporated for the carriage of three 610-US gallon (2,309-litre) external tanks or up to to 9,000 lb (4,082 kg) of air-to-ground stores on five stations.

[1] The projected replacement of the initially-fitted General Electric M61A-1 Vulcan six-barrel 20 mm cannon with a Philco-Ford GAU-7A 25 mm cannon had to be abandoned due to development problems.
[2] The USAF had planned to use AIM-82 short-range dogfight missiles which were then under competitive development by Aeronutronic (Ford), General Dynamics, and Hughes. Rising costs and the timely development of the AIM-9L version of the Sidewinder led to the cancellation of the AIM-82 development programme.

An order for twenty FSD aircraft—eighteen F-15As (71-0280/71-0289 and 72-0113/72-0120) and two TF-15As (71-0290/71-0291)—was initially placed and, following systems testing in St Louis, the first was shipped to Edwards AFB where its maiden flight took place on 27 July, 1972, with the manufacturer's chief test pilot, Irving L Burrows, at the controls. Flight trials proceeded smoothly with only three externally noticeable modifications being required. To eliminate a buffeting problem, four square feet (0.4 sq m) were removed from the trailing-edge of each wingtip, resulting in the Eagle's characteristic raked tips. Similarly, a flutter problem was corrected by cutting a snag on the inboard portion of

An F-15A-16-MC of the 555th Tactical Fighter Training Squadron showing off its large dorsal air brake as it lands at Luke AFB, Arizona. *(Peter J Mancus)*

the stabilator's leading-edge. Finally, the effectiveness of the dorsally-mounted speedbrake was markedly increased by enlarging its area 57.5 per cent. In addition, more than 30 engineering changes were made internally to improve systems reliability and to ease maintenance.

Development of the Eagle's Pratt & Whitney F100-PW-100 turbofans proved a laborious endeavour. Initial engine development milestones were passed on schedule. However, early during the aircraft's flight-test programme, the F100 ran into serious teething troubles (notably, a fan and turbine blade failed during a February 1973 test) and did not complete its 150-hour test until October 1973.

Once engine reliability increased, personnel of the Air Force Systems Command, the Air Force Logistics Command, the Tactical Air Command, and the manufacturer proceeded with an accelerated flight-test programme from three locations: the Air Force Flight Test Center at Edwards AFB, the Tactical Air Warfare Center at Eglin AFB, and the MCAIR facility in St Louis. Successful completion of these tests cleared the F-15 for delivery to Service units beginning in November 1974.

Production history

In addition to being built by MCAIR in St Louis, the Eagle has been produced under licence in Japan. Production at both locations will continue into the early 'nineties.

F-15A: A total of 384 single-seat F-15As, including 18 FSD aircraft, were built in Blocks 1 to 20 (*see* Appendix C for list of serials). Each was powered by two Pratt & Whitney F100-PW-100 turbofans, rated at 14,870 lb (6,744 kg) dry and 23,830 lb (10,809 kg) with afterburning. The fuel system consisted of (1) four fuselage tanks and two wing tanks, with a combined capacity increased from the initial 1,759 gallons to 1,790 gallons (6,659 to 6,776 litres); (2) up to three 610-gallon (2,309-litre) external tanks, those beneath the wings being seldom carried; and (3) a

F-15A-19-MC of the 7th TFS, 49th TFW, at Holloman AFB, New Mexico, on 4 May, 1989. *(René J. Francillon)*

boom-type air refuelling receptacle on the port wing, close to the air intake. Armament consisted of a 20-mm M61A-1 cannon mounted in the starboard wing, close to the air intake, and fed from a 940-round drum in the centre fuselage, four AIM-7 Sparrows on the lower fuselage corners, and four AIM-9 Sidewinders on wing pylons.

Beginning in 1983, aircraft 76-0086 was used for trials with the Vought ASM-135A air-launched anti-satellite (ASAT, also called the air-launched miniature vehicle or ALMV) missile mounted on the centreline station. Initial tests were promising and plans were made to modify twenty F-15As and to assign ASAT-carrying Eagles to two Fighter Interceptor Squadrons, the 48th at Langley AFB, Virginia, and the 318th at McChord AFB, Washington. However, Congress was unwilling to permit full-system testing and the ASAT programme was terminated in 1988.

Other F-15As used in experimental programmes have included 71-0281 and 71-0287, which were bailed to NASA as described below, and 77-0084, which became a test-bed for the Programmable Signal Processor modification subsequently incorporated in the APG-63 radar as part of the Multi-Stage Improvement Program. Funded in 1983, MSIP has provided for (1) increasing the memory capability of the APG-63 from 96K to 1,000k; (2) trebling its processing speed; (3) installing a Programmable Armament Control Set (PACS); (4) modifying the Electronic Warfare Warning Set (EWWS) into the more capable Tactical Electronic Warfare System (TEWS) with upgraded ALR-56C radar warning receiver and ALQ-135 countermeasure set; (5) adding an overload warning system to prevent pilots from accidentally exceeding 9g during combat manoeuvring; and (6) incorporating the necessary wiring for the eventual carriage of AIM-120A AMRAAM missiles.

NASA 835, the eighth FSD-F-15A (71-0287), during a test flight in 1986. *(NASA-Dryden Flight Research Center)*

Five refurbished FSD F-15As (72-0114, 72-0116/72-0118, and 76-0120) and 19 new aircraft (76-1505/76-1523) were delivered to the Heyl Ha'Avir. The Israeli Eagles initially differed from USAF F-15As by not having the EWWS, the IC-7 or ACES II ejection seat (IC-7 seat having been fitted to USAF aircraft to Block 17) replaced by the IG-7 seat, and minor other equipment changes. The most important difference, however, was the provision for carrying low-drag FAST Packs (Fuel And Sensor Tactical) on the sides of the fuselage. These 750-gallon (2,839-litre) conformal tanks, which were specially developed by McDonnell to meet a requirement of the Heyl Ha'Avir for greater range, actually decreased drag at subsonic speeds and only increased drag slightly at supersonic speeds. The FAST Packs, later renamed CFTs (Conformal Fuel Tanks), incorporated fittings for the Sparrow missiles normally mounted on the fuselage.

YF-15A: This designation was given to at least four FSD F-15As which were retained by the Air Force Systems Command in 1989 for development work at the Air Force Plant 84 (McDonnell) in St Louis and at the Air Force Flight Test Center, Edwards AFB.

F-15B (TF-15A):   First flown on 7 July, 1973, this two-seat operational training version retained the airframe of the F-15A without extensive structural alteration and without dimensional changes. Initially designated TF-15As, the two-seaters were differentiated from the single-seaters by their larger canopy and the removal of the Internal Counter-measure Set (ICS) to provide space for the rear cockpit and a full set of dual controls. In other respects single- and two-seat models were

TF-15A-8-MC (73-0111) from the 58th Tactical Fighter Training Wing at Luke AFB, Arizona, in June 1976. When entering service, the two-seat Eagles were still designated TF-15As. *(René J Francillon)*

identical. Two FSD aircraft (71-0290 and 71-0291) and 57 TF-15As/ F-15Bs (*see* Appendix C for list of serials) were built for the USAF. Two F-15Bs (76-1524 and 76-1525) were produced for the Heyl Ha'Avir.

Most USAF F-15Bs have been upgraded as part of MSIP. However, the two FSD TF-15As were not modified as they were used for a variety of experimental projects. Notably, 71-0291 successively served for flight testing FAST Pack conformal fuel tanks and for evaluating the *Pave Tack* laser designation pod and the LANTIRN (Low Altitude Navigation and Targeting Infrared System for Night) pod before becoming the development aircraft for the privately-funded Strike Eagle and Air Force-sponsored Dual Role Fighter programmes which culminated in the development of the F-15E. Also noteworthy was the use of a late production F-15B, 77-0166, as the test vehicle for the Integrated Flight Fire Control (IFFC)/Firefly III programme. As part of this programme, the aircraft was fitted with an Automatic Tracking Laser Illumination System (ATLIS) which was developed to enable air-to-ground weapons to be released while manoeuvring along a three-dimensional flight path.

NF-15B: Under a five-year contract awarded to McDonnell Douglas by the USAF's Flight Dynamics Laboratory on 1 October, 1984, MCAIR modified the first two-seat Eagle (71-0290) as part of the STOL and Maneuver Technology Demonstrator (S/MTD) programme. Intended to

The first TF-15A (F-15B) after it had been fitted with canard surfaces and thrust-vectoring, thrust-reversing engine nozzles as part of the S/MTD programme. *(MCAIR)*

develop technologies required for operations from damaged runways, the S/MTD Agile Eagle was intended to achieve balanced field operations from a 50-ft (15-m) wide, 1,000-ft (305-m) long runway under adverse weather conditions and without active ground-based navigational assistance. For the first phase of the demonstration programme, the F-15 S/MTD was fitted with movable canards mounted on the forward fuselage, a four-channel fly-by-wire integrated flight/propulsion control system, the latest cockpit controls and displays, and an improved undercarriage capable of sustaining landings on rough fields at high descent rate. After receiving these modifications, 70-0290 first flew at St Louis on 7 September, 1988. For the second phase of the programme, the standard convergent-divergent engine nozzles were replaced with rectangular, thrust-vectoring, thrust-reversing nozzles. First flight with the new exhaust nozzles was made at St Louis on 16 May, 1989, and the F-15 S/MTD was subsequently transferred to Edwards AFB for joint flight testing by the Air Force and McDonnell Douglas. The two-dimensional nozzles were first used in flight on 23 March, 1990.

YF-15B: This designation has been given by the Air Force to the FSD TF-15A modified as the Strike Eagle prototype.

F-15C: By the end of 1989, MCAIR had built 473 single-seat F-15Cs (409 for the USAF, 18 for the Heyl Ha'Avir, and 46 for the Royal Saudi Air Force with serials for all being given in Appendix C) in Blocks 21 to 42. No more F-15Cs were to be built for the USAF, but 17 were on order for delivery to Israel (five aircraft) and Saudi Arabia (12 aircraft) in 1991-92. Those for the USAF initially differed from F-15As only in having internal fuel capacity increased from 1,790 to 2,070 gallons (6,776 to 7,836 litres), provision for conformal fuel tanks, and undercarriage and brakes strengthened to cater for the increase in maximum gross take-off

F-15C-22-MC of the 4th TFS,18th TFW, at Kadena AB, Okinawa, on 23 August, 1985. *(Toyokazu Matsuzaki)*

F-15C-25-MC of the 22nd TFS, 36th TFW, USAFE, over Bitburg AB in June 1981. *(MCAIR)*

weight from 56,000 to 68,000 lb (25,401 to 30,844 kg). MSIP upgrades, as detailed in the F-15A description, were progressively incorporated during production and were retrofitted to early production F-15Cs. Most F-15Cs were delivered with F100-PW-100 turbofans but were intended to be re-engined with more reliable but slightly lower rated (maximum afterburning thrust being decreased from 23,830 to 23,450 lb—10,809 to 10,637 kg) F100-PW-220s. Provision was also added on some F-15Cs for carrying up to 18 cluster bombs or six Mk 82s, with the aircraft being cleared to release bombs at supersonic speeds. The first F-15C (78-0468) was flown on 26 February, 1979, and later was used for trials with tangential carriage of bombs on the conformal fuel tanks.

F-15Cs delivered to Israel and Saudi Arabia were not fitted with EWWS or TEWS. In addition, those for Israel were given additional air-to-ground capability (through installation of MER-10N bomb racks and of a data link pod for guiding GBU-15 standoff bombs) and were fitted with the IG-7 ejection seat instead of the ACES II of the USAF and RSAF aircraft.

F-15D: Corresponding to the F-15Cs, 61 two-seat F-15Ds were built for the USAF, eight for Israel, 12 for Japan (as F-15DJs), and 16 for Saudi Arabia (*see* Appendix C for list of serials). Aircraft for export customers were not fitted with EWWS or TEWS. The first F-15D (78-056) was flown on 19 June, 1979.

F-15D-3-MC (82-0044) of the 57th FWW landing at Nellis AFB on 25 April, 1989.
(René J. Francillon)

F-15DJ (12-8054) of the 204 Hikotai, a JASDF squadron based at Hyakuri AB.
(Dr Masahiro Yamasaki)

306

F-15DJ: This designation was given to identify 12 MCAIR-built and 17 Mitsubishi-built two-seat aircraft for the Nihon Koku Jieitai (Japanese Air Self-Defence Force). During production, the MCAIR-built F-15DJs were given USAF serials 79-0282/79-0287, 81-0068/81-0071, 83-0052 and 83-0053, but these were replaced by Japanese serials 12-8051/12-8054, 22-8055/22-8056, 32-8057/32-8060, and 52-8061/52-8062. The first four Mitsubishi-built F-15DJs were assigned Japanese serials 82-8063/82-8066.

F-15E: Following evaluation of the F-15B Strike Eagle prototype and the General Dynamics F-16XL, the Air Force selected the F-15E as its new Dual-Role Fighter in February 1984. Intended to supplement General Dynamics F-111s in the long-range, adverse weather interdiction role, two-seat F-15Es were designed to retain, virtually unchanged, the air-to-air capability of earlier Eagle versions. The first F-15E (86-0183) flew on 11 December, 1986, and production was expected to continue until 1993[3].

Although externally and dimensionally similar to F-15Ds, F-15Es were redesigned extensively to (1) strengthen their structure for longer service life and operations at maximum take-off weight of 81,000 lb/36,741 kg; (2) provide space for additional avionics (at the cost of a slight decrease in internal fuel capacity to 2,019 gallons/7,643 litres); (3) upgrade front and rear cockpits with multi-purpose cathode ray tube (CRT) displays being provided for improved navigation, weapons delivery, and systems operations; (4) increase air-to-ground weapon load to a maximum of 23,500 lb (10,659 kg) by adding six tangential racks on the corner of each conformal fuel tank; and (5) adapt engine bays for the eventual replacement of the 23,450 lb (10,637 kg) thrust F100-PW-220s by turbofans with up to 30,000 lb (13,608 kg) of thrust[4]. Principal mission avionics at the time of entry into service included the APG-70 radar, wide-field forward-looking infra-red (FLIR) and terrain-following radar pods beneath the starboard intake, and LANTIRN nav/attack pod beneath the port intake. Air-to-air armament was then normally limited to the internal gun and four Sidewinder missiles on wing stores pylons, but provision for Sparrow missiles was retained when not carrying bombs on tangential pylons.

F-15J: The selection of the F-15J to supplement and eventually replace the Lockheed F-104J interceptors of the Nihon Koku Jieitai was announced by Japan's National Defence Council in December 1977. The

[3] The Air Force had intended to procure 392 Dual-Role Fighters to equip four wings, and production had been expected to continue well into the second half of the 'nineties. In 1989, however, budgetary constraints forced the Air Force to limit F-15E procurement to just enough aircraft to equip one wing.

[4] In 1989, 87-0180 was fitted with F110-GE-129 engines to evaluate the compatibility of this General Electric advanced turbofan with the Strike Eagle. Six flight tests were made in St Louis and 20 others at Edwards AFB, but there then appeared little chance of the F110-GE-129 being adopted to re-engine the F-15E.

An F-15E dual-role fighter displaying its conformal tanks with tangential weapon pylons and pod-mounted LANTIRN nav-attack system. *(MCAIR)*

Japanese F-15Js were to differ from Air Force F-15Cs in omitting the ICS and EWWS sets, installing data link and MER-200P bomb racks, and providing for the installation of a Japanese-produced radar warning system. By the end of 1989, a total of 142 F-15Js had been ordered. The first two were built by MCAIR (USAF serials 79-0280/79-0281, Japanese serials 02-8801/02-8802) and the next eight were assembled by Mitsubishi from MCAIR knock-down kits (Japanese serials 12-8803, 22-8804/22-8810). All others were to be manufactured in Japan (*see* Appendix C for list of serials). The first Japanese-assembled F-15J (12-8803) flew at Komaki on 26 August, 1981.

Service history
The Eagle entered service in November 1974 when the 555th Tactical Fighter Training Squadron, 58th Tactical Fighter Training Wing, at Luke AFB, Arizona, received its first aircraft to begin operational evaluation and crew training. Three of the 58th TFTW squadrons, the 426th, 461st

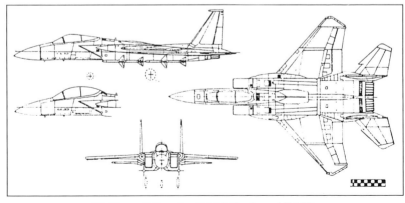

McDonnell Douglas F-15A Eagle and F-15B.

and 550th TFTS, later also converted to F-15A/Bs. The 555th TFTS added F-15C/Ds before all four F-15 training squadrons were transferred to the 405th Tactical Training Wing, also based at Luke AFB, in August 1979.

Before entering service with front-line units, the Eagle achieved fame when the last but one FSD F-15A (72-0119) broke eight world time-to-height records as part of Operation *Streak Eagle* conducted during the winter of 1974-75 at Grand Forks AFB, North Dakota. The records were:

Altitude	Time	Pilot	Date of record
3,000m/9,843 ft	27.57 sec	Maj R Smith	16 January, 1975
6,000 m/19,685 ft	39.33 sec	Maj W R Macfarlane	16 January, 1975
9,000 m/29,528 ft	48.86 sec	Maj W R Macfarlane	16 January, 1975
12,000 m/39,370 ft	59.38 sec	Maj W R Macfarlane	16 January,1975
15,000 m/49,212 ft	77.02 sec	Maj D W Peterson	16 January, 1975
20,000 m/65,617 ft	122.94 sec	Maj R Smith	29 January, 1975
25,000 m/82,021 ft	161.02 sec	Maj D W Peterson	26 January, 1975
30,000 m/98,425 ft	207.80 sec	Maj R Smith	1 February, 1975

Deliveries to the first combat ready wing, the 1st Tactical Fighter Wing at Langley AFB, Virginia, began in January 1976. Thereafter F-15A/Bs were initially assigned to re-equip two other wings (the 33rd TFW at Eglin AFB, Florida, and the 49th TFW at Holloman AFB, New Mexico) and one squadron of the 57th Fighter Weapons Wing (the 422nd Test and Evaluation Squadron at Nellis AFB, Nevada) in Tactical Air Command, one wing (the 36th TFW at Bitburg AB, Germany) and one independent squadron (the 32nd TFS at Soesteberg AB, The Netherlands) of the United States Air Forces in Europe, and one squadron (the 43rd TFS at Elmendorf AFB) in the Alaskan Air Command. With the exception of

An F-15C of the 53rd TFS, 36th TFW, USAFE, flying off the port wing of a fighter from the Armée de l'Air. *(Jean-François Lipka)*

309

the 49th TFW, all of these units were re-equipped with F-15C/Ds. Moreover, these more potent Eagles were also used to replace F-4s with the Pacific Air Forces' 18th TFW at Kadena AB, Okinawa, and TAC's 57th Fighter Interceptor Squadron at Keflavik, Iceland, and to equip a second squadron in the Alaskan Air Command (the 54th TFS at Elmendorf AFB).

The F-15A/Bs displaced by newer F-15C/Ds were used to replace F-106s in service with TAC's Fighter Interceptor Squadrons (the 5th at Minot AFB, North Dakota; the 48th FIS at Langley AFB; and the 318th at McChord AFB, Washington), to equip two Fighter Interceptor Training Squadrons (the 1st FITS and 2nd FITS at Tyndall AFB, Florida), and to upgrade three squadrons of the Air National Guard (the 122nd TFS at NAS New Orleans, Louisiana; the 128th TFS at Dobbins AFB, Georgia; and the 199th TFS at Hickam AFB, Hawaii). Finally, when TAC inactivated the 5th FIS and 318th FIS, their F-15A/Bs were respectively transferred to the 101st FIS, Massachusetts ANG, at Otis ANGB in 1987, and to the 123rd FIS, Oregon ANG, at the Portland International Airport in 1989. In addition, F-15A/Bs have been assigned in small numbers to the 4485th Test Squadron at the Tactical Air Warfare Center, Eglin AFB; the 6512th Test Squadron at the Air Force Flight Test Center, Edwards AFB; and the Warner Robins Air Logistics Center at Robins AFB, Georgia.

Following completion of OT&E (Operational Test and Evaluation) at Edwards AFB and *Seek Eagle* weapons carriage and separation testing at Eglin AFB, F-15Es were first delivered to the 425th TFTS, 405th TTW, at Luke AFB for crew training. The first operational F-15E squadron, the 336th TFS, 4th TFW, at Seymour Johnson AFB, North Carolina, began working up in early 1989. The two other squadrons of the 4th TFW are to complete their conversion from F-4Es to F-15Es in 1990 and 1991.

Two FSD F-15As, 71-0281 and 71-0287, were bailed to NASA in 1975. Assigned to the Dryden Flight Research Center at Edwards AFB, they have been used for several experimental programmes including the testing of the Space Shuttle's tiles on the inner starboard wing leading edge, and that of the Digital Electronic Engine Control and other advanced engine features for the Pratt & Whitney 1128 engine, a derivative of the F100-PW-100 which led to the development of the F100-PW-220. Aircraft 71-0281 was retired in 1983 and has since been put on display at Langley AFB, but 71-0287 (NASA 835) was still on the active list in 1990 when it was taking part in the NASA/USAF Highly Integrated Electronic Control (HIDEC) programme to test a flight control system capable of detecting in-flight failures and automatically reconfiguring the aircraft's ailerons, rudders and elevators so that the pilot can either continue his mission or land safely.

Eagles have been supplied to the air forces of Israel (under the *Peace Fox* programme), Japan (*Peace Eagle*, which also covered the licence

F-15As from the first batch of Eagles delivered to the Heyl Ha'Avir under *Peace Fox I. (MCAIR)*

production of F-15Js and F-15DJs), and Saudi Arabia (*Peace Sun*). Foreign service records to the end of 1989 are as follows:

Israel: Under the *Peace Fox I* and *II* programmes, the Tsvah Haganah le Israel – Heyl Ha'Avir (Israel Defence Force – Air Force, IDF-AF) received 46 Eagles (five refurbished FSD F-15As, 19 F-15As, two F-15Bs, 18 F-15Cs, and two F-15Ds) beginning in December 1976. Five additional F-15Cs will be delivered in 1991-92. Distributed among two squadrons (the first of which is believed to have been No.133), the F-15s of the Heyl Ha'Avir have been fitted to carry conformal fuel tanks with tangential bomb pylons, GBU-15 glide bombs, and indigenous Shafrir and Python air-to-air IR missiles.

The Israeli Eagles first went into battle on 27 June, 1979, when they claimed five Syrian MiG-21s in air combat over Lebanon. They again made the news by providing top cover for the Heyl Ha'Avir's F-16s which made a daring raid against the Osirak nuclear reactor near Baghdad on 7 June, 1981. A year later, they were at the forefront of combat activities during the Israeli invasion of Lebanon. Among the 40 'kills' obtained during operations over the Bekaa Valley, Israeli F-15 pilots claimed the destruction of at least two of the fast and high-flying MiG-25 reconnaissance aircraft of the Syrian Arab Air Force. In May 1983, an Israeli F-15 was successfully landed after losing most of its starboard wing in an inflight collision; it was repaired and put back into service.

Japan: By the autumn of 1989, the Nihon Koku Jieitai (Japanese Air Self-Defence Force, JASDF) had ordered 131 single-seat F-15Js and 29 two-seat F-15DJs. Eleven more were requested under the fiscal 1990 budget and additional orders are likely.

In 1981 training of a cadre of JASDF pilots and maintenance personnel was begun in the United States where the aircraft of the 555th TFTS at Luke AFB were supplemented by the first F-15DJs. Service evaluation by

The second Mitsubishi-built F-15J landing at Hyakuri AB on 1 July, 1984. The discrete marking on the outboard surface of the starboard fin identifies the aircraft as belonging to the 202 Hikotai. *(Toyokazu Matsuzaki)*

the Koku Jikkendan (Air Proving Wing) took place at Gifu AB, Honshu. Eagles were then declared ready for their Japanese service debut and the Rinji F-15 Hikotai (Temporary F-15 Squadron) was formed at Nyutabaru AB, Kyushu, in December 1981. A year later, this conversion unit was given permanent status as 202 Hikotai. In following years, F-15J/DJs replaced F-104J/DJs in 203 Hikotai and 207 Hikotai at Chitose AB, Hokkaido; 204 Hikotai and 305 Hikotai at Hyakuri AB, Honshu; and 301 Hikotai at Nyutabaru AB. A seventh F-15J squadron will be formed in 1993.

312

Kingdom of Saudi Arabia: Forty-six F-15Cs and 16 F-15Ds have been delivered to the Al Quwwat al Jawwiya as Saudiya (Royal Saudi Air Force or RSAF) beginning in January 1981. Bearing US markings, some of the early RSAF Eagles were used at Luke AFB to train a cadre of Saudi air and ground crews. In the Kingdom, F-15Cs and F-15Ds have been distributed among three squadrons, No 5 at King Fahad AFB in Taif, No 6 at King Khaled AFB in Khamis Mushayt, and No 13 at King Abdul Aziz AFB in Dhahran. On 5 June, 1984, Eagles from No 6 Squadron were vectored by a Boeing E-3 Sentry from the USAF's 552nd Airborne Warning and Control Wing toward McDonnell F-4Es of the Islamic

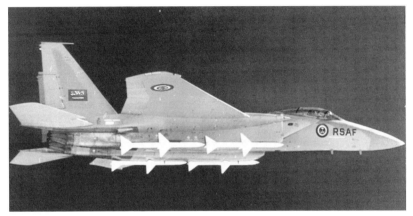

An F-15C of the Royal Saudi Air Force. *(Courtesy of William I Lightfoot)*

Republic Iranian Air Force which were threatening Saudi oil fields. Two of the Iranian aggressors were shot down by the RSAF.

Although the RSAF was pleased with its Eagles and wanted to acquire additional F-15C interceptors and to order F-15E long-range strike aircraft, US Congressional opposition to supplying more advanced aircraft to Saudi Arabia and the Kingdom's desire to diversify military aircraft procurement led instead to the ordering of Panavia Tornado IDS strike aircraft and ADV interceptors from Britain. However, in 1989 Saudi Arabia again sought to obtain additional F-15s for the RSAF and Congressional approval was obtained for the delivery of 12 additional F-15Cs in 1991-92.

Data for the F-15C:
   Span 42 ft 9.7³/₄ in (13.05 m); length 63 ft 9 in (19.43 m); height 18 ft 5¹/₂ in (5.63 m); wing area 608 sq ft (56.49 sq m).
   Empty weight 27,300 lb (12,383 kg); loaded (internal fuel and four Sparrows) 44,630 lb (20,244 kg); maximum 68,000 lb (30,844 kg); wing loading 73 lb/sq ft (546 kg/sq m); power loading 0.9 lb/lb st.
   Maximum speed 1,650 mph at 36,000 ft (2,655 km/h at 10,975 m) and 915 mph (1,472 km/h) at sea level; cruising speed 570 mph (917 km/h); climb rate over 50,000 ft/min (254 m/sec); service ceiling over 62,000 ft (18,900 m); ferry range with external tanks 2,880 miles (4,635 km); ferry range with conformal tanks 3,570 miles (5,745 km).

313

The first YC-15 in its original configuration with small wing and four Pratt & Whitney JT8D-17 turbofans. *(USAF)*

McDonnell Douglas YC-15

On 24 January, 1972, the USAF issued a Request for Proposal to the industry calling for an AMST (Advanced Medium STOL Transport) aircraft which could eventually be adopted as a larger successor to the Lockheed C-130 Hercules tactical transport. Bell, Boeing, Fairchild, Lockheed, and McDonnell Douglas submitted their proposals on 31 March, 1972, and the USAF awarded preliminary design contracts to Boeing and McDonnell Douglas on 10 November of that year. Two months later, both companies received an additional contract calling for the construction and testing of two prototypes, respectively designated YC-14s and YC-15s. To minimize cost and encourage competitors to seek innovative solutions, the USAF refrained from issuing detailed and rigid specifications and only required that the aircraft be capable of carrying 27,000 lb (12,247 kg) of cargo over a 400-naut mile (740-km) radius for STOL operations from 2,000-ft (610-m) runways. Later the payload/range requirement was modified to include the ability to lift in the conventional take-off mode a load of 38,000 lb (17,237 kg) for more than 2,600 naut miles (4,815 km).

Under the leadership of Marvin D Marks, AMST Program Manager, a McDonnell Douglas team at Long Beach chose a four-engined configuration with externally blown flaps for powered lift and a supercritical wing with only 5.9 deg of sweep at quarter-chord. The use of large double-slotted flaps, which extended over 75 per cent of the total span and over which the fan-shaped efflux of the engines was to be spread, was expected to result in exceptional STOL performance. This included an approach speed of only 98 mph (158 km/h) and a field length of 2,000 ft (610 m) at a landing weight of 150,000 lb (68,040 kg). To minimize costs, this team also decided to use as many existing components as possible including (1) the DC-10 cockpit adapted for two-man crew operations and fitted with a pair of lower windows on each side to improve forward and downward

314

visibility during short-field landings, (2) the main undercarriage of the Lockheed C-141 with increased stroke legs, and (3) a modified DC-8 nosewheel unit. The fuselage size and shape were dictated by the need to

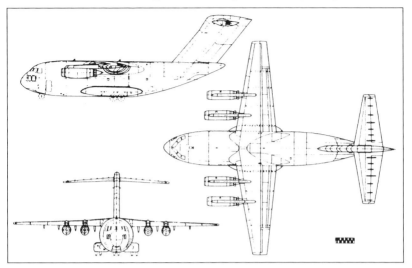

McDonnell Douglas YC-15.

accommodate 90 per cent of all Army divisional combat vehicles, including a 62,000 lb (28,123 kg) extended-barrel 8-in (203-mm) self-propelled howitzer. Vehicles were to be loaded by means of rear fuselage doors with built-in ramps. Finally, the decision was made to power the two prototypes with four readily available 16,000 lb (7,257 kg) thrust Pratt & Whitney JT8D-17 turbofans as used on some DC-9 models, but to design the pylons to accept alternative engines of advanced design then under development such as the 18,000 lb (8,165 kg) thrust JT8D-209, or 22,000 lb (9,979 kg) thrust General Electric/SNECMA CFM56 and Pratt & Whitney JT10D.

On the power of four JT8D-17s, the first YC-15 (70-1875) made its maiden flight from Long Beach to Edwards AFB on 26 August, 1975, and was joined by a second prototype (70-1876) in December of that year. By mid-1976, the two YC-15s had completed their USAF evaluation programme and, as the Boeing design was approximately one year behind in being tested by the Air Force, McDonnell Douglas decided to modify its two aircraft for additional testing. Consequently, the first YC-15 was returned to Long Beach where it was fitted with a larger wing (span was increased from 110 ft 4 in/33.64 m to 132 ft 7 in/40.41 m and area from 1,740 sq ft/161.65 sq m, to 2,107 sq ft/195.74 sq m) enabling the aircraft to achieve the 38,000 lb/2,600 naut mile (17,237 kg/4,815 km) requirement which had been added after the design of the original YC-15

315

wing had been frozen. In addition, this aircraft was experimentally fitted with a 22,000 lb (9,979 kg) General Electric/SNECMA CFM56 turbofan in the port outboard nacelle before resuming flight trials on 16 February, 1977. Meanwhile, the second aircraft, which retained the original wing, was fitted with an 18,000 lb (8,165 kg) Pratt & Whitney JT8D-209 turbofan in the port outboard nacelle and was returned to flight status on

The second YC-15 (70-1876) in tactical camouflage. *(DAC)*

4 March, 1977. On the basis of comparative engine evaluation, McDonnell Douglas stated in mid-1977 that it intended recommending the JT8D-209 as the engine for proposed production aircraft.

Soon after, however, the Air Force, which was satisfied that the C-130 was still the most cost effective tactical transport, concluded that an aircraft designed to meet the AMST requirement would not fill its most urgent airlift needs. Consequently, the AMST programme was terminated and in August 1979 the two YC-15s, as well as the Boeing YC-14s, were sent to the Military Aircraft Storage & Disposition Center (MASDC) at Davis-Monthan AFB, Arizona. For the taxpayers not all was lost as McDonnell Douglas incorporated features developed for the YC-15 in its winning CX proposal. The first YC-15 has been loaned to the Pima Air Museum since mid-1981.

Span 110 ft 4 in (33.64 m)*; length 124 ft 3 in (37.9 m); height 43 ft 4 in (13.2 m); wing area 1,740 sq ft (161.65 sq m)*.

Empty weight 105,000 lb (47,627 kg); loaded weight 216,680 lb (98,284 kg); maximum weight 219,180 lb (99,418 kg); wing loading 124.5 lb/sq ft (608 kg/sq m); power loading 3.4 lb/lb st (3.4 kg/kgp).

Maximum speed 500 mph (805 km/h); climb to 5,000 ft (1,525 m) in 3.2 minutes; service ceiling 26,000 ft (7,925 m); STOL payload/range 460 miles (740 km) with 27,000 lb (12,260 kg); conventional take-off payload/range 2,292 miles (4,815 km) with maximum payload of 38,000 lb (17,235 kg) maximum payload.

* On the first aircraft, span and area were later increased to 132 ft 7 in (40.41 m) and 2,107 sq ft (195.74 sq m).

AH-64A of the 1/130th Avn, North Carolina Army National Guard, at the Army Aviation Support Facility No. 1, Raleigh-Durham International Airport, on 14 June, 1989. *(René J. Francillon)*

Hughes/McDonnell Douglas AH-64 Apache

When the North Vietnamese Army began using Soviet tanks in support of its invasion of South Vietnam in the spring of 1972, the US Army had only two helicopters capable of firing anti-tank missiles[1], one in Germany and one in the United States. Both of these two TOW-armed Bell UH-1Bs were airlifted to the war zone in late April 1972 and achieved conspicuous success during six weeks of operations in the Vietnamese highlands. They were credited with the destruction of 26 tanks and numerous other armoured vehicles, and 73 of the 89 TOWs which were fired during that period achieved hits. Unfortunately, just as helicopters were proving their worth in anti-tank warfare, developmental problems and cost escalation forced the Army to terminate the development contract for the Lockheed AH-56 Cheyenne, its first purpose-built anti-tank helicopter, in August 1972.

Capitalizing on what had been learned during the protracted and unfruitful development of the Cheyenne[2], the Army's Advanced Attack Helicopter (AAH) Task Force invited the industry in November 1972 to

[1] Developed by Hughes to replace the Army's 106-mm recoilless rifle, the BGM-71 TOW (Tube-launched, Optically-tracked, Wire-guided) missile had been adapted as an airborne system and was to have been carried by Lockheed AH-56 Cheyenne attack helicopters. Two Bell UH-1Bs had been modified to serve in air-launching trials and had been fitted with a triple TOW launch tube on each side of their fuselages.

[2] Lessons from the AH-56 Programme included the need to adopt a twin-engined configuration for improved combat survivability (the Cheyenne having been powered by a single T56 turboshaft) and to dispense with the unduly demanding requirement for a ferry range of 2,100 naut miles to enable helicopters to be ferried between California and Hawaii and on to points in Southeast Asia.

submit proposals for an anti-tank helicopter capable of operating day or night, in adverse weather, and with great accuracy. For its primary mission, the helicopter was to be armed with eight anti-tank missiles and a 30-mm cannon, to climb at a minimum of 450 ft/min (2.3 m/sec), and to have a combat endurance of 1 hr 50 min when operating at an altitude of 4,000 ft (1,220 m) on a 95°F (35°C) day. The AAH Task Force also stressed the importance of designing the helicopter for easy maintenance and for maximum survivability to combat damage and specified that power was to be provided by a pair of General Electric T700-GE-100 turboshafts which had already been selected to power the Utility Tactical Transport Aircraft System (UTTAS), the assault transport helicopter

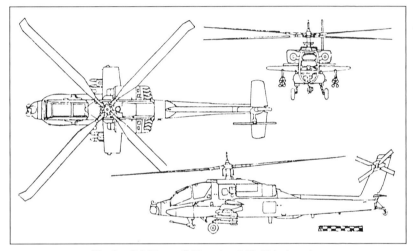

Hughes/McDonnell Douglas AH-64A Apache.

then being designed by Boeing Vertol (YUH-61A) and Sikorsky (YUH-60A). After reviewing proposals submitted by Bell, Boeing Vertol, Lockheed, Hughes, and Sikorsky, the Source Selection and Evaluation Board announced on 22 June, 1973, that competitive engineering development contracts would be awarded to Bell and Hughes. Both firms were to build a ground test vehicle (GTV), a static test airframe, and two flying prototypes.

Under the direction of John N Kerr, the Hughes team designing the Model 77 strove to minimize size, weight, and cost while achieving higher margins of survivability and agility than previously incorporated into armed helicopters. This concern led to the selection of a narrow fuselage with vertically-staggered cockpits (that for the co-pilot/gunner being forward and below that of the pilot), a large blister on each side of the nose to house most of the avionics (thus placing equipment within easy reach for maintenance and replacement), and engines on each side of the upper centre fuselage section (to facilitate maintenance and reduce the

318

likelihood of both engines being disabled simultaneously). Power from the two 1,694-shp engines was to be transmitted to a four-blade main rotor of conventional design and to a 'scissor' (*ie* with unequal spacing between blade pairs) four-blade, low noise tail rotor. Fuel was to be carried in two crash resistant fuselage cells with a combined capacity of 376 US gallons (1,423 litres). Most structural components were designed to survive hits by a 12.7-mm machine-gun and the main rotor later was demonstrated to be capable of surviving hits by 23-mm cannon gunfire and continue operating for more than 5 hours before failing. Other early design decisions led to planning for the installation of an advanced

An AH-64A carrying eight Hellfire missiles and two Aerial Rocket Delivery System pods. *(MDHC)*

targeting and night vision system (the Target Acquisition Designation Sight and Pilot's Night Vision Sensor or TADS/PNVS then under competitive development by Martin Marietta and Northrop) in a nose turret and for the carriage of the primary armament (up to eight guided missiles as specified by the Army) on wing stubs. Secondary armament, a 30-mm cannon, was to be mounted externally beneath the fuselage.

Although Hughes first ran its GTV (serial 74-22247) on 22 June, 1975, nine weeks after Bell had initially tested its YAH-63A ground test vehicle, Hughes did manage to fly the first YAH-64A (74-22248) one day ahead of the YAH-63A. The maiden flight of the Hughes prototype was made by Robert Ferry and Raleigh Fletcher at the Palomar Airport in San Diego County, California, on 30 September, 1975. The second YAH-64A flew on 22 November, 1975, and both Hughes prototypes were flown extensively in preparation for six months of competitive testing against the Bell YAH-63A which began at Edwards AFB in June 1976. Much as had been the case $10^1/_2$ years earlier when the Hughes YOH-6A easily defeated the Bell YOH-4A, the YAH-64A clearly won the AAH flyoff. Lighter, possessing sprightlier performance, and less noisy (the two-blade main rotor of the Bell made it more quickly detected audibly) than the YAH-63A, the YAH-64A was announced the winner on 10 December, 1976. Shortly afterwards, Hughes received an order for three additional prototypes and was authorized to proceed with production engineering. After test and development activities lasting more than five years, full production was authorized in March 1982 and during the following month the Martin Marietta TADS/PNVS was selected over the competing Northrop system to equip production AH-64A Apaches.

Winning the AAH competition more than made up to Hughes for the loss of the related missile competition as, in February 1976, the Army had selected the Rockwell AGM-111 Hellfire (an acronym for Helicopter-launched Fire-and-Forget missile) laser-guided missile over the Hughes BGM-71 TOW wire-guided missile as primary armament for its new anti-tank helicopter. Moreover, Hughes also had the satisfaction of seeing its specially developed XM230 30-mm single-barrel Chain Gun adopted in 1976 in preference to the General Electric XM188 three-barrel 30-mm cannon as the secondary armament for its AH-64.

Production history

Whereas the YAH-64As were built by Hughes in Culver City, the fuselage of production Apaches have been and continue to be built by Teledyne Ryan Aeronautical in San Diego, with final assembly undertaken by McDonnell Douglas in a new plant at Mesa, Arizona. The first production Hughes AH-64A was rolled out at Mesa on 30 September, 1983. Twenty-eight months later, by which time 70 AH-64As had been delivered to the Army, the manufacturer's name was changed officially to McDonnell Douglas.

In the spring of 1990, as only one export customer had been found and

The Apache can carry two Sidearm *(far right)* anti-radiation missiles; two Sidewinder *(far left)* or four Mistral *(foreground)* air-to-air missiles; 1,200 rounds of 30-mm ammunition; seventy-six 2.75-in/70-mm rockets; sixteen Hellfire anti-tank missiles; or four Stinger (two in each wingtip) air-to-air missiles. *(MDHC)*

as the number of AH-64As to be procured by the US Army was likely to be reduced from 975 to 807 as part of overall budget cuts, production was expected to end in 1993.

YAH-64A: This designation was given to the non-flyable GTV (74-22247), which was used primarily to test the propulsion system, as well as to two prototypes (74-22248/74-22249) ordered for competitive trials against Bell YAH-63As and three development vehicles (77-23257/77-23259) ordered after Hughes had been declared the winner of the AAH competition. The YAH-64As provided accommodation for a crew of two in vertically-staggered tandem cockpits and were fitted with a non-retractable conventional undercarriage with single main and tail wheels. Power was provided by two General Electric T700-GE-701 turboshafts with normal maximum rating of 1,694 shp increased to 1,723 shp in the event one engine became inoperative.

The first YAH-64A flying prototype (77-22248) was flown by Robert Ferry and Raleigh Fletcher at the Palomar Airport on 30 September, 1975, and the first development aircraft (77-23257) flew on 31 October, 1979. During the summer and autumn of 1978, the rotor system of the two prototypes was modifed: the mast was lengthened by 6 in (15.24 cm), the diameter of the tail rotor was increased by 3 in (7.62 cm), and the tips of

AV-02 (74-22248), the first flying prototype of the Apache. *(MDHC)*

The second development Apache (77-23258) modified as a test vehicle for the Advanced Digital Flight Control System. *(MDHC)*

the main rotor blades were swept back. The three development vehicles incorporated the rotor system modifications from the outset and were fitted with revised tail surfaces, the T-tail of the prototypes being replaced by conventional surfaces with a low-mounted all-moving stabilator[3], to eliminate a tendency for the helicopter to pitch-up while flying at low speeds. Other modifications, which were also retrofitted to the two prototypes, included (1) the relocation of the tail rotor 2 ft 6 in (0.76 m) higher up the port side of the vertical fin; (2) a 10-in (25.4-cm) increase in tail rotor diameter; and (3) the substitution of 'Black Hole' infrared

---

[3] Initially, the first prototype was to have been fitted with a low-mounted tailplane but this had been replaced by T-mounted horizontal surfaces with endplates before the first flight. The second prototype was flown without endplates for its T-mounted surfaces of reduced span.

suppression system for the fan-cooled exhaust system initially mounted at the aft end of the engine nacelles. The YAH-64As were flown with both the Martin Marietta and Northrop TADS/PNVS systems.

The second development aircraft (77-23258) was modified in 1985 as a test vehicle for the Advanced Digital Flight Control System designed by MDHC for the LHX programme. The forward cockpit was reconfigured to simulate single-pilot operation with a fly-by-wire digital control system as contemplated for the LHX while the aft cockpit remained mostly unchanged for use by a back-up pilot. The modified aircraft first flew on 12 October, 1975.

AH-64A: Incorporating the modifications developed during trials with the prototypes and service test vehicles, production AH-64As retained the powerplant and rotor system of the YAH-64As. The first production Apache was flown in January 1984, a few days after Hughes Helicopters had been taken over by McDonnell Douglas.

Four pylons were provided beneath the stub wings which had a span of 17 ft 2 in, 5.23 m). Each pylon was wired for carrying either four

AH-64A of the 1/130th Avn, NC ArNG. *(René J. Francillon)*

AGM-114 Hellfire laser-guided missiles[4], an Aerial Rocket Delivery System pod with 19 2.75-in (70-mm) rockets, or a 230-gallon (871-litre) ferry tank. An M230 30-mm Chain Gun was mounted in an unfaired, hydraulically-driven turret beneath the forward fuselage and provided with a rotating magazine for up to 1,200 rounds. The Target Acquisition and Designation Sight of the Martin Marietta TADS/PNVS system was mounted in a turret beneath the nose of the Apache and consisted of direct-view optics, a television camera, a laser spot tracker, and a laser range finder/designator. The Pilot's Night Vision Sensor portion of the system was mounted atop the nose and consisted of a stabilized FLIR

[4]   Laser target designation was to be provided by the AH-64A co-pilot/gunner by means of the TADS, by other aircraft (such as OH-58 scout helicopters), or by troops on the ground. Hellfires were designed to be launched in single, rapid, or ripple modes either before or after obtaining a laser lock-on.

An Apache firing an AIM-9M Sidewinder air-to-air missile at the Army's White Sands Range in New Mexico, November 1987. *(MDHC)*

Photographed in December 1989 near Mammoth, Arizona, during the filming of a motion picture, this AH-64 is fitted with twin AIM-92 Stinger air-to-air missiles at the tip of the wing stubs. *(Charles T Robbins)*

(forward-looking infrared) receiver. In addition, the pilot and co-pilot/ gunner were provided with a helmet-mounted IHADSS (Integrated Helmet And Display Sighting System) which was not only to serve as a head-up display, but was also to be used to cue the sensors and ready the missiles by merely looking at the target.

To endow the AH-64A with additional air combat capability (for which the Chain Gun already provided limited capability[5]), MDHC and the Army have been working on various air-to-air missile installations. Notably, AIM-9M Sidewinders mounted at the tips of the stub wings were first fired over the White Sands Missile Range, New Mexico, in November 1987, and AIM-92A Stingers mounted at the wingtips in paired launchers were first fired at the Yuma Army Proving Ground, Arizona, in October 1987. Work has also proceeded for integrating up to four Matra Mistral IR-homing missiles and captive tests with these French-built missiles were completed in March 1988. In addition, the use of the TADS in air-to-air range determination and in maintaining a laser spot on a target aircraft, thus enabling Hellfires to be used for air-to-air combat, has been evaluated during tests against other helicopters and fixed-wing aircraft. Similarly, AGM-12 Sidearm anti-radar missiles were first fired in April 1988, during tests aimed at providing the AH-64A with a limited defence suppression capability.

Prototype installation of a millimetre-wave Longbow fire control radar. *(Martin Marietta)*

[5] Studies continued to be made in 1989 to improve the effectiveness of the Chain Gun as an air-to-air weapon by digitizing turret control and pre-programming firing patterns, using a longer barrel for greater muzzle velocity, and developing improved 30-mm ammunition to reduce time-of-flight to the target.

Under a Multi-Stage Improvement Program (MSIP) for which initial funding was provided in August 1988, AH-64As will eventually be fitted with updated avionics, radar and laser warning systems, and more capable targeting and weapons systems. MSIP Stage I was under development in 1989 to sustain Apache effectiveness until the turn of the century. If funding can be provided, Stage I would also give an air combat capability to the Apache, with MDHC supplying and installing AIM-92 Stinger kits beginning in 1992.

MSIP Stage II, which was scheduled to begin in the mid-to-late 'nineties, would include more advanced mission equipment packages. In particular, up to 227 Apaches may be fitted with a mast-mounted Longbow radar. This millimetre wave fire control radar, which in 1989 was being jointly developed by Martin Marietta and Westinghouse, would be used with new radar-guided Hellfire missiles to give the AH-64A a fire-and-forget capability under reduced visibility conditions.

MDHC has made numerous proposals for co-production of the AH-64 with European partners, for direct sales of AH-64s to export customers and for Apache versions tailored to the needs of the Marine Corps and the Navy. For the latter, the Sea Apache has been offered for use in the anti-ship and escort roles for which the TADS/PNVS, gun, and Hellfire missiles of the Army version were to be replaced with an APG-65 multi-mode radar, AGM-84 Harpoon anti-ship missiles, and Sidewinder air-to-air missiles. However, most of these proposals had not reached fruition by the end of 1989, and the only export customer was Israel, which is to receive 19 AH-64As, beginning in September 1990.

Service history
Training of a small cadre of Army personnel was begun at Yuma during the spring of 1981 in preparation for operational tests conducted with

An AH-64A during field operations with USAREUR (US Army Europe). *(MDHC)*

three YAH-64As by the Army Combat Development Experimentation Command at Fort Hunter-Liggett, California, between 1 June and 31 August, 1981. Successful conclusion of these tests was a vital factor leading to the production go-ahead which was given in March 1982.

Training began in earnest following the delivery of production AH-64As to the Army Aviation Training Center at Fort Rucker, Alabama, and the Army Aviation Logistics School at Fort Eustis, Virginia, in January 1985. However, another 18 months went by before the first combat unit, the 3rd Squadron of the 6th Cavalry Brigade (abbreviated as 3/6th Cav), was fully trained, equipped, and fielded at Fort Hood, Texas. Other regular AH-64 Advanced Attack Helicopter Battalions[6] fielded in the United States by the end of 1989 were the 1/3rd Avn, 2nd Armored Division, the 1/6th Cav and 4/6th Cav, 6th Cavalry Brigade, and the 1/227th Avn, 1st Cavalry Division, all at Fort Hood; the 1/82nd Avn, 82nd Airborne Division at Fort Bragg, North Carolina; the 1/101st Avn and 2/101st Avn, 101st Airborne Division, at Fort Campbell, Kentucky; and the 2/229th Avn, XVIII Corps, at Fort Rucker. Those based in Germany with USAREUR (US Army Europe) were the 3/1st Avn, 1st Armored Division, at Ansbach; the 2/6th Cav, VII Corps, at Illesheim (which in January 1988 became the first Apache unit to be activated overseas); the 5/6th Cav, V Corps, at Wiesbaden; the 3/227th Avn, 3rd Armored Division, at Hanau; and the 4/229th Avn, VII Corps, at Illesheim. In addition, at the end of 1989, four units of the Army National Guard were flying Apaches, these being, in chronological order of activation, the 1/130th Avn in North Carolina, the 1/151st Avn in South Carolina, the 1/111th Avn in Florida, and the 1/211th Avn in Utah.

In service, whether operating independently or designating targets for 'fast movers' (notably Fairchild Republic A-10s and General Dynamics F-16s armed with AGM-65E Laser Maverick missiles), the Apache has proved to be a potent anti-tank weapon with outstanding night operation capability. Its advanced and complex systems, however, have been found difficult to maintain in the field and in 1989 the mission-ready rate remained below expectation. Highlights of the first three years of operations with front-line units included the first air-to-air combat exercise at NATC Patuxent River in April 1987; the first participation of AH-64As in a REFORGER (Return of Forces to Germany) exercise in September 1987; the first live firing of a Hellfire missile by an operational unit (the 1/6th Cav) at the Yuma range in February 1988; and the first night operation from the deck of an amphibious assault ship (by the 1/82nd Avn aboard the USS *Nassau*, LHA-4, sailing 50 naut miles/93 km off the Virginia coast) in July 1988. The 1/82nd Avn also became the first unit to use the Apache in combat when in December 1989 its AH-64As were used in Panama during Operation *Just Cause*.

[6] Typically, a battalion has 18 AH-64A attack helicopters, 13 Bell OH-58C/D Kiowa scout helicopters, and three Sikorsky UH-60A Blackhawk utility helicopters.

In April 1988, the 1/130th Avn, North Carolina, became the first Guard unit to be fielded with Apaches. *(René J. Francillon)*

Rotor diameter 48 ft (14.63 m); maximum length with both rotors turnings 58 ft 3¹/₈ in (17.76 m); fuselage length with tail rotor turning 48 ft 2 in (14.68 m); height 15 ft 3 in (4.65 m); rotor disk area 1,809.56 sq ft (168.1 sq m).

Empty weight 10,760 lb (4,881 kg); loaded weight 14,445 lb (6,552 kg); maximum weight 21,000 lb (9,525 kg); rotor loading 8 lb/sq ft (39 kg/sq m); power loading 4.2 lb/shp (1.9 kg/hp).

Maximum speed 184 mph (296 km/h); cruising speed 170 mph (274 km/h); maximum vertical rate of climb 2,500 ft/min (13 m/sec); service ceiling 21,000 ft (6,400 m); hover ceiling in ground effect 15,000 ft (4,570 m) on a standard day and 10,200 ft (3,110 m) on a 95°F/35°C day; hover ceiling out of ground effect 11,500 ft (3,505 m) on a standard day and 7,000 ft (2,135 m) on a 95°F/35°C day; range with internal fuel 260 miles (420 km); ferry range 1,057 miles (1,700 km).

An AV-8B of VMA-331 flying low over the desert in northern Nevada during a training sortie from NAS Fallon in October 1985. *(MCAIR)*

McDonnell Douglas/British Aerospace AV-8 Harrier II

Interest in the British P.1127/Kestrel/Harrier V/STOL ground attack aircraft was first shown by the Douglas Aircraft Company during the pre-merger period, and discussions between Douglas and Hawker Siddeley towards the possible manufacture of the British aircraft by the Long Beach firm had reached an advanced stage by the time Douglas was acquired by McDonnell. These discussions later led to McDonnell Douglas obtaining the licence rights for the Harrier with the intention that the aircraft would be built in St Louis in the event that Congress should mandate that the production of the aircraft ordered for the Marine Corps be undertaken in the United States. However, in the end all 102 single-seat AV-8As and eight two-seat TAV-8As for the USMC—which had first been ordered in 1969 and entered service in 1971—as well as eleven AV-8As and two TAV-8As for the Arma Aérea de la Armada Española (Spanish Naval Air Arm) were built in the United Kingdom with McDonnell Douglas providing support through its St Louis facilities. Subsequently, McDonnell Douglas developed the modernization pro-gramme through which 47 AV-8As were upgraded to the AV-8C configuration. More significantly, the American firm and Hawker Siddeley (later British Aerospace[1]) co-operated in the development of

[1] Readers unfamiliar with the British aircraft industry are reminded that Hawker Siddeley, the firm with which the Harrier originated, became part of British Aerospace (BAe) in April 1977 as the result of the Aircraft and Shipbuilding Industries Act 1977. Hawker Siddeley continued trading under its old name until the end of that year, but thereafter its identity disappeared. Hence, reference in the following text to Hawker Siddeley and British Aerospace as the Harrier manufacturer in the United Kingdom depends on the period.

advanced versions of the Harrier, including the projected AV-8+ and AV-16, respectively a minimum development of the AV-8A and a more extensive redesign.

As the anticipated cost of the AV-16 programme was found excessive, the Department of Defense chose instead to sponsor the development of a less complex version for the USMC while work proceeded in Britain on a 'Super Harrier' tailored to RAF needs. Initial studies for the AV-8B, the new version proposed to meet the Marine Corps requirement for an advanced vectored thrust STO/VL[2] light attack aircraft, were begun in May 1975, and approval of the AV-8B development was announced on 27 July, 1976. Using the AV-8A's Rolls-Royce Pegasus 11 vectored-thrust turbofan, but with improvements to increase maximum thrust to 21,500

The AV-8B mock-up at the McDonnell plant in August 1975. *(MCAIR)*

lb (9,760 kg), and, initially, the basic AV-8A fuselage, the AV-8B was to incorporate major changes designed to increase range and load carrying ability and to improve reliability and maintainability.

In a first step, changes were to include (1) the use of a McDonnell-designed supercritical wing of larger area (230 versus 201 sq ft for the AV-8A, 21.37 versus 18.67 sq m) made primarily of carbon-epoxy materials (thus saving some 330 lb/150 kg) and incorporating a new high-

---

[2]   Whereas in Great Britain the Harrier is classified as a V/STOL (Vertical/Short Take-Off and Landing) aircraft, it is regarded as a STO/VL (Short Take-Off/Vertical Landing) aircraft in the United States. In squadron service, the aircraft seldom makes vertical take-offs, as in this mode its useful load is considerably less than when taking-off after a short run; thus, the STO/VL appellation is more accurate.

lift system with large slotted flaps and drooped ailerons; (2) new elliptical air intakes with improved internal flow; (3) zero-scarf front exhaust nozzles; and (4) Lift Improvement Devices (LIDS) consisting of two longitudinal strakes and a retractable forward fence (thus improving VTOL performance by capturing the reflected jet exhaust to increase lift). Additional changes incorporated at a later stage included (1) a revised forward fuselage with raised cockpit and bubble canopy; (2) a lengthened rear fuselage; and (3) Leading Edge Root Extensions (LERX) developed by British Aerospace to improve air combat performance as required by the Royal Air Force (a Memorandum of Understanding covering the acquisition of Harrier IIs, as Harrier G.R. Mk 5s, for the RAF had been signed in August 1981, after the cost of developing the all-British 'Super Harrier' exceeded budget).

Before approval of the AV-8B was announced, MCAIR had already begun modifying a no-longer flyable AV-8A (BuNo 158385) for use in wind tunnel tests at NASA's Ames Research Center, the aircraft being fitted with a metal replica of the new wing, LIDS, and air intakes of various shapes. Next MCAIR was authorized to modify two AV-8As (BuNos 158394/158395) as YAV-8B prototypes with the composite wing, LIDS, and revised air intakes but without major changes to the fuselage. BAe test pilot Charles Plummer first flew the YAV-8B in St Louis on 9

The first YAV-8B at the time of its completion in September 1978. *(MCAIR)*

November, 1978. The second YAV-8B was first flown on 19 February, 1979, but was lost nine months later, on 15 November, as the result of an engine flame-out. Fortunately, the programme was not significantly delayed as four FSD (full-scale development) AV-8Bs and two structural test airframes had been ordered in 1978.

Flight trials with the FSD aircraft began in St Louis on 5 November, 1981, (again with BAe test pilot Charles Plummer at the controls) and proceeded smoothly with the first phase of NPE (Navy Preliminary Evaluation) beginning at the NATC Patuxent River in June 1982. The first pilot production AV-8B flew on 29 August, 1983, and OPEVAL (Operational Evaluation), which was undertaken in 1984, confirmed that the AV-8B possessed performance markedly superior to that of the AV-8A. In particular, as its maximum STO take-off weight was 26 per cent greater than that of the AV-8A (24,600 versus 31,000 lb, 11,158 versus 14,061 kg), it proved able to lift twice the warload or to carry the same load twice as far. Moreover, it did so significantly more accurately.

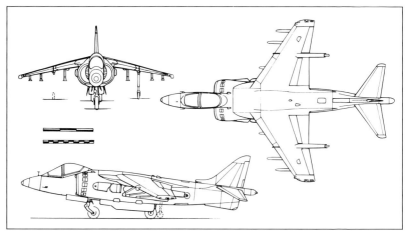

McDonnell Douglas/British Aerospace AV-8B Harrier II.

Deliveries to the USMC began in January 1984. The first BAe-assembled Harrier G.R. Mk 5 (ZD318) was first flown at Dunsfold on 30 April, 1985, and deliveries to the Royal Air Force began in May 1987.

Production history
Whereas the first AV-8 versions for the US Marine Corps and the Spanish Navy were built by Hawker Siddeley, later versions were, and continue to be co-produced as provided by the 1981 Memorandum of Understanding. Those for the USMC and Spain are built by McDonnell from components built by MCAIR, DAC, and BAe (fin and aft and centre fuselage sections), the split being 60-40 in favour of McDonnell Douglas. Those

332

for the RAF are built by BAe (with components manufactured at Kingston-upon-Thames and Brough and final assembly at Dunsfold) and incorporate wings and forward fuselage sections produced by MCAIR and DAC, the British-US split being 50-50. For the engine, regardless of customer, the split is 75-25 in favour of Rolls-Royce with Pratt & Whitney as junior partner.

The following AV-8 versions, whether Hawker-built/McDonnell-supported, McDonnell-built, or BAe-assembled, have been produced:

AV-8A (Harrier Mk 50): After taking part in the Tri-Service evaluation of Hawker XV-6A Kestrel V/STOL demonstrators in the United States in 1966 and evaluating the Hawker Siddeley Harrier at RAE Farnborough in 1968, the US Marine Corps placed contracts for a total of 102 Hawker Siddeley Harrier Mk 50s. Designated AV-8As in America, these British-built aircraft[3] were given BuNos 158384/158395, 158694/158711, 158948/158977, 159230/159259, and 159366/159377. Except for the 11th and 12th AV-8As which became YAV-8Bs, all were either retrofitted or delivered with 21,500lb (9,752 kg) thrust Rolls-Royce Pegasus 11 Mk 103 vectored-thrust turbofans (US designation F402-RR-401).

TAV-8A (Harrier Mk.54): To complement its single-seat AV-8As, the Marine Corps acquired eight British-built Harrier Mk.54 two-seat trainers. Designated TAV-8As in the United States, they were BuNos 159378/159385. Like the single-seaters, the TAV-8As were powered by the F402-RR-401. The first TAV-8A flew on 16 July, 1975.

YAV-8B: To serve as prototypes for the Harrier II with MCAIR-designed composite wings, LIDS, and other improvements, two AV-8As (BuNos 158394 and 158395) were modified by McDonnell. When first flown on 9 November, 1978, BuNo 158394 was not yet fitted with LERX.

After completing Navy trials, the first YAV-8B was transferred to the Ames Research Center at Moffett Field, California, as NASA 704. It was photographed on 1 August, 1986, at Travis AFB, California. *(Jean-Michel Guhl)*

[3] The first AV-8A flew in England on 20 November, 1970, and was delivered to the USA on 26 January, 1971.

333

BuNo 158395 crashed on 15 November, 1979, and, after completing Navy trials, BuNo 158394 was transferred to the Ames Research Center at Moffett Field, California, as NASA 704 (N704NA).

AV-8B: Including four FSD aircraft and production aircraft ordered through FY91 under a multi-year buy approved in 1988, 252 AV-8Bs have been built or are on order for the USMC (*see* Appendix C for BuNos). In addition to aerodynamic and structural changes as incorporated in the YAV-8Bs, production Harrier IIs were fitted with a revised

BuNo 161573, the first Block 2 Harrier II, flying over the Mississippi River. *(MCAIR)*

nose and cockpit arrangement. They differed from AV-8As in having more sophisticated nav/attack systems and in carrying heavier weapons loads. For precise navigation and accurate weapons delivery, the AV-8Bs were delivered with an integrated, computer-controlled system comprising a Hughes Angle Rate Bombing Set (ARBS) to pinpoint targets with laser- or TV-contrast tracking, an Inertial Navigation System (INS), a Head Up Display (HUD), a Multi-purpose Display, and a Stores Management Set. They were fitted with one centreline pylon and six wing pylons to carry a maximum external load[4] of 9,200 lb (4,173 kg) and were armed with a General Electric GAU-12/U five-barrel, 25-mm rotary cannon mounted in two pods beneath the fusclage (the left pod containing the gun and the right pod containing 300 rounds of linkless ammunition).

During the course of production, engine models have been changed several times. The FSD aircraft were powered by the 21,500 lb (9,752 kg) F402-RR-404 or -404A (use of the latter leading to the replacement of the

[4] Typical external loads: 16 Mk.82 general purpose bombs, four Mk.83 laser guided bombs, four AGM-65 Maverick (IIR-, TV-, or laser-guided) missiles, eight CBU-59B or 12 Rockeye cluster bomb units, 10 LAU-68 rocket launchers, four 300-gallon (1,136-litre) external fuel tanks, or four AIM-9L Sidewinder air-to-air missiles.

Carrying four Mk 82 Snakeye retarded bombs and two AGM-65E laser-guided Maverick air-to-ground missiles and bearing the markings of Air Development Squadron Five (VX-5), this Night Attack AV-8B was photographed over Twentynine Palms Marine Base, California, in May 1988. *(MCAIR)*

double row of auxiliary doors on the intakes by a single row), early production aircraft had the 21,450 lb (9,730 kg) thrust F402-RR-406, and aircraft delivered since March 1987 had the similarly-rated F402-RR-406A incorporating a digital fuel control system. Finally, following Pegasus 11-61 engine trials in Britain (with a modified Harrier G.R.5) and at Edwards AFB (with a modified AV-8B), the 23,800 lb (10,795 kg) thrust F402-RR-408 engine was to replace the F402-RR-406A beginning with aircraft delivered in August 1990. Earlier engines will then be progressively brought up to F402-RR-408 standards. The internal fuel tanks of the AV-8Bs have a capacity of 1,103 gallons (4,175 litres), a 45 per cent increase over the capacity of AV-8A tanks which have a capacity of 759 gallons (2,873 litres).

Following the testing of a prototype (BuNo 162966, first flown on 26 June, 1987), aircraft delivered since September 1989 have been given night attack capability. In addition to the nav/attack system of earlier AV-8Bs, night attack Harrier IIs have been fitted with a forward-looking infrared sensor (FLIR) mounted atop the nose, modified cockpit lighting compatible with the use of night vision goggles (NVG), a wide field of view HUD, and a colour digital moving map display. Controls for the digital map display and FLIR have been located on the HOTAS (Hands-On-Throttle-And-Stick). In 1989, the Marine Corps hoped to have earlier AV-8Bs, beginning with the 167th airframe, retrofitted to the night attack configuration.

TAV-8B: BuNo 162747, the prototype for the two-seat conversion trainer of the Harrier II, was included in the FY84 buy. Fitted with a revised forward fuselage which provided accommodation for the instructor in a cockpit above and behind the student and increased overall length

The first production TAV-8B hovering during a test flight at MCAIR in St Louis in July 1987. *(MCAIR)*

to 50 ft 3 in (15.32 m), and a 1 ft 5 in (43 cm) taller fin, the TAV-8B made its maiden flight on 21 October, 1986. It became on that occasion the first US Harrier II to fly with the F402-RR-406A incorporating a digital fuel control system. By the end of 1989, twenty-four TAV-8Bs (*see* Appendix C for list of BuNos) either had been delivered to the Marine Corps or were on order.

AV-8C: To extend the life and usefulness of AV-8As until sufficient AV-8Bs were available to re-equip three Marine squadrons, McDonnell engineered a Harrier modernization package. This CILOP (Conversion In Lieu Of Procurement) programme called for various comm/nav improvements and the installation of LIDS (as developed for the AV-8B), radar warning receivers, on-board oxygen generating system, and chaff/flare dispensers. BuNo 158384 was modified by McDonnell as the AV-8C prototype in 1979. By 1983, 46 other AV-8As had been brought up to AV-8C standard by the Naval Air Rework Facility at MCAS Cherry Point, North Carolina.

Harrier G.R. Mk 5:   Assembled in Great Britain and making use of a greater percentage of airframe and equipment manufactured in the United Kingdom, the British Aerospace/McDonnell Douglas Harrier G.R.5s for the Royal Air Force are quite similar to the McDonnell Douglas/British Aerospace AV-8Bs for the Marine Corps. Contracts were placed for two Development Batch (DB) aircraft (ZD318 and ZD319) and 94 production aircraft (*see* Appendix C for list of serials). However, only the two DB aircraft (first flown at Dunsfold on 30 April, 1985) and the first 39 production aircraft were completed to G.R.5 standards. These aircraft will eventually be brought up to G.R.7 standards.

Principal differences distinguishing Harrier G.R.5s from AV-8Bs were (1) the use of a slightly higher rated Pegasus Mk.105 engine (21,750 lb/9,866 kg thrust); (2) the addition, forward of the outrigger pylons, of a

336

A Harrier GR 5 from No 233 OCU at the French air base in Colmar (BA 132 Colmar-Meyenheim) on 20 May, 1989. *(Michel Fournier)*

missile launch rail for AIM-9L Sidewinder air-to-air missiles (thus freeing other pylons for carriage of offensive stores); (3) the installation of British defensive avionics (*eg* Marconi Zeus RWR/ECM suite with nose, wingtip, and ventral antennae, and Plessey missile approach warning (MAW) system in the tail cone); (4) the fitting of a moving map display in the cockpit; (5) the elimination of the chaff/flare dispenser beneath the aft fuselage; and (6) the substitution of a pair of Royal Ordnance Factory 25-mm cannon in place of the GAU-12/U gun. Plans to add a MIRLS (Miniature Infra-Red Linescan System) had to be cancelled for financial reasons, but the G.R.5s retained the fairing beneath the nose which had been originally provided for that system.

One of the G.R.5s, ZD402, was modified as a test bed for the 23,800 lb (10,795 kg) thrust Pegasus 11-61 (F402-RR-408) engine. Flight trials began at Rolls-Royce facilities in Bristol on 9 June, 1989; shortly thereafter, ZD402 was used to set four time-to-height records in the FAI Class H.

Harrier G.R. Mk.5A: The 42nd to 62nd aircraft for the Royal Air Force have been completed to a revised standard to facilitate their future conversion as night attack G.R.7s. In particular, the FLIR blister has been installed and instrument lighting has been made compatible with the use of night vision goggles.

Harrier T. Mk.6:   Pending availability of the Harrier T. Mk.10, a small number of Harrier T. Mk.4s (two-seat version corresponding to the earlier Harrier G.R. Mk.3 single-seaters) were fitted with night attack avionics for use in the G.R.7 pilot training programme.

337

An EAV-8B for the Arma Aérea de la Armada Española photographed from a KC-10A during its delivery flight from St Louis to Rota, Spain, in October 1987. *(MCAIR)*

Harrier G.R. Mk.7:   The G.R.7 designation has been given to aircraft with night attack capability similar to that of late production AV-8Bs. Night attack equipment will be fitted during production beginning with the 63rd aircraft, and G.R.5s and G.R.5As will be brought up to that standard.

Harrier T. Mk.10:   This designation has been given to two-seat combat trainers fitted with FLIR and night-attack equipment. An initial batch of 14 was ordered for the RAF in 1990.

VA.1 Matador (AV-8S or Harrier Mk.55): To circumvent diplomatic disagreement over the status of Gibraltar, Harriers for Spain's Arma Aérea de la Armada Española were ordered through US Navy channels and delivered by McDonnell. Given the designation VA.1 in Spain, AV-8S in the United States, and Harrier Mk.55 in Great Britain, these aircraft were virtually identical to AV-8As of the Marine Corps. They were assigned BuNos 159557/159562 and 161174/161178 before delivery and were renumbered VA.1-1 to VA.1-10 in Spanish service (the exception being BuNo 159558 which was written off before delivery).

VAE.1 Matador (TAV-8S or Harrier Mk.58):   To complement its single-seat Matadors, the Arma Aérea de la Armada Española obtained two two-seat Harrier Mk.59 trainers via McDonnell Douglas (BuNos 159563 and 159564 which became VAE.1-1 and VAE.1-2 in Spanish service).

VA.2 Matador II (EAV-8B):   Twelve McDonnell-built Harrier IIs (designated EAV-8Bs in the United States and VA.2 Matador IIs in Spain) were given BuNos 163010/163021 for contractual purposes and

The first Matador II (BuNo 163010, Spanish Serial VA.2-1) in service with Escuadrilla 009, Arma Aérea de la Armada Española, in Rota, Spain. *(Christian Boisselon)*

numbered VA.2-1 to VA.2-12 in Spanish service. With the exception of minor equipment changes, the VA.2s were delivered in the same configuration as Block 9 AV-8Bs.

Service history

As British Harriers (before the Mk.5s) and Sea Harriers, US AV-8As and TAV-8As, and Spanish VA.1s and VAE.1s were not McDonnell products, their service careers are not included in this history of aircraft built by MDC, its subsidiaries, and forebears. Suffice it to say that Harrier G.R.Mk.1s entered service in 1969 with No.1 Squadron, Royal Air Force, at RAF Wittering, that AV-8As were first assigned in 1971 to VMA-513, USMC, at MCAS Yuma, Arizona, and that Matadors became operational in 1976 with Escuadrilla 008, Arma Aérea de la Armada Española, at Rota.

The operational life of the much more capable Harrier II began in January 1984 when AV-8Bs were delivered to VMAT-203 at MCAS Cherry Point to begin crew training in preparation for assignment of AV-8Bs to operational squadrons. Beginning with VMA-513 at MCAS Yuma which was commissioned on 30 January, 1985, and achieved IOC

A Block 8 AV-8B of VMA-513 at MCAS Yuma, Arizona on 10 May, 1989. *(René J Francillon)*

(Initial Operational Capability) in August 1985, three combat squadrons (VMA-231, VMA-513, and VMA-542) exchanged their AV-8A/Cs for AV-8Bs. Harrier IIs were next used to replace Douglas A-4M Skyhawks with VMA-211, VMA-214, VMA-223, and VMA-311. The last to do so, VMA-214 at MCAS Yuma, was the first to receive AV-8Bs with night attack capability when it converted from A-4Ms in the autumn of 1989. AV-8Bs have also been assigned to the Naval Air Test Center at NAS Patuxent River and VX-5 at NAS China Lake, California.

Normally CONUS-based at MCAS Cherry Point with the 2nd MAW (Marine Aircraft Wing) and at MCAS Yuma with the 3rd MAW, the Marine AV-8B squadrons have made deployments to Europe and have been assigned on a six-month rotational basis to the 1st MAW at MCAS Iwakuni, Japan. In addition, they have deployed and continue to deploy

BuNo 162971 a TAV-8B of VMAT-203 at MCAS Chery Point, North Carolina, in January 1988. *(MCAIR)*

regularly aboard ships of the US Navy, primarily alongside Marine transport and attack helicopters aboard LHA-, LHD-, and LPH-class Amphibious Assault Ships. The first major sea deployment was made by VMA-331 aboard the USS *Belleau Wood* (LHA-3) from January to June 1987. On that occasion, the *Bumblebees* from VMA-331 were able to maintain an impressive 91 per cent fully mission capable rate and a 98 per cent mission capable rate while operating in temperatures ranging from 26°F to 102°F (-3°C to 39°C). In other respects, AV-8Bs have also proved themselves in service. Notably, they completed all their sorties during a Red Flag exercise in 1986 without suffering a single simulated 'kill' even though they were exposed to surface-to-air defences and air-to-air interceptors. Moreover, AV-8Bs have repeatedly demonstrated their ability to take care of themselves in air-to-air combat within visual range[5].

Spain, which had ordered twelve EAV-8Bs from McDonnell Douglas in late 1982, received its first three aircraft in October 1987. As training of an initial group of Spanish crews had been begun earlier by VMAT-203 at MCAS Cherry Point, Escuadrilla 009, Arma Aérea de la Armada Española, became operationally ready in 1988. In addition to operating from their shore base at Rota, the Matador IIs will deploy regularly

[5] In simulated air-to-air combat within visual range, the AV-8B has won four times as many battles as it has lost (the 'kill-to-loss' ratio decreasing to 2-to-1 in simulated combat against high-performance fighters). Obviously, lacking radar and not being armed with medium-range missiles, the AV-8B is a much easier prey at longer ranges.

aboard the *Principe de Asturias*, a new carrier built in Spain and fitted with a 12-deg ski jump to enhance the operating capability of the STO/VL aircraft.

The United Kingdom was the third nation to place the advanced version of the Harrier in service. Training of HCT (Harrier Conversion Team) instructors on Harrier G.R.5s was begun by No.233 OCU at RAF Wittering in March 1988. Beginning in July 1988, Harrier G.R.5s were next assigned to the Strike/Attack Operational Evaluation Unit (SAOEU) at Boscombe Down. Also based at RAF Wittering, No.1 Squadron received its first G.R.5s in November 1988 as replacements for less capable G.R.3s and became operationally ready in October 1989. Next to re-equip with G.R.5s was No. 3 Squadron, RAF Germany, at Gütersloh, which became combat-ready in April 1990, with No.1417 Flight in Belize to follow. The first squadron of night capable G.R.7s, No.4 at Gütersloh, began its conversion in mid-1990. All G.R.5 squadrons, as well as No.1417 Flight, will eventually be re-equipped with G.R.7s.

Data for AV-8B:

Span 30 ft 4 in (9.25 m); length 46 ft 4 in (14.12 m); height 11 ft 7³/₄ in (3.55 m); wing area 238.7 sq ft (22.18 sq m).

Empty weight 13,086 lb (5,936 kg); maximum VTO take-off weight 18,930 lb (8,587 kg); typical loaded weight 22,950 lb (10,410 kg); maximum STO take-off weight from 1,500-ft (460-m) runway 31,000 lb (14,061 kg); maximum VTO weight 18,950 lb (8,596 kg); wing loading 96.1 lb/sq ft (469.3 kg/sq m); power loading 1.1 lb/lb (1.1 kg/kg).

Maximum speed 647 mph (1,041 km/h) at sea level; combat radius with seven 500-lb (227-kg) bombs, short take-off, 542 miles (872 km); ferry range 2,380 miles (3,830 km).

An F/A-18A of VFA-125, the Hornet training squadron in the Pacific Fleet, during carrier qualifications aboard the USS *Kitty Hawk* (CV-63) in March 1985. *(René J. Francillon)*

McDonnell Douglas F/A-18 Hornet

With space aboard a carrier always at a premium, combining fighter and attack capabilities into a single aircraft always was a concept of greater interest to the Navy than to the Air Force. Evaluated before the Second World War, this concept gained much prominence during the last months of that war when the threat of Japanese suicide operations required that as many fighters as possible be embarked aboard the carriers of TF (Task Force)38 and TF58 while at the same time the need to provide air support to ground forces slugging it out on Okinawa and Iwo Jima forced the retention of large numbers of bomb-carrying aircraft. Capable of carrying as heavy a load of bombs and rockets as the Curtiss SB2C Helldiver dive-bombers and being at the same time the world's best carrier-borne fighters, the Vought F4U-1D Corsairs and Grumman F6F-5 Hellcats of fighter bomber squadrons (VBFs) flew the types of missions in 1945 which are now assigned to McDonnell Douglas F/A-18 Hornets of strike fighter squadrons (VFAs).

Nevertheless, the advent of the first carrier jet fighters, with their limited weight carrying ability and range, once again brought about the separation of the fighter and attack roles. However, combining these two missions into a single airframe remained a most desirable objective for Navy planners and was revived when the strike mission became almost synonymous with carrying a single nuclear store. Thus, during the mid-fifties, several VA squadrons were equipped with fighter aircraft such as McDonnell F2H-2B Banshees, Grumman F9F-8B Cougars and North American FJ-4B Furies. Moreover, development of the McDonnell F4H

343

An AF/A-18A of No. 3 Squadron, RAAF. *(RAAF)*

Phantom II, the primary naval fighter for most of the sixties and seventies, began with the award of a contract for two prototypes of the AH-1 attack fighter. Later optimized for all-weather fighter operations as the F-4B and F-4J, carrier versions of the Phantom II carried a hefty load of conventional air-to-ground ordnance.

By then, however, clearly separated fighter and attack communities were in existence and during the Southeast Asia War the Navy deliberately fostered this state of affairs further when it dropped its VFAX requirements for a multi-purpose fighter/light attack aircraft and instead ordered the Grumman F-14 Tomcat as a fleet defence fighter. Plans were rapidly dropped to provide the F-14 with a load carrying capability and visual delivery accuracy equal to that of the Vought A-7E Corsair II and later to develop an 'F-14C' with an upgraded avionic

F/A-18A of the *Blue Angels* at NAS Fallon, Nevada, in October 1988. *(René J Francillon)*

system for all-weather attack and reconnaissance. Consequently, the F-14 entered service in 1974 as a pure fleet air defence fighter, with only a limited air-to-ground ordnance carrying potential, while attack needs continued to be satisfied by a mix of LTV A-7Es and Grumman A-6 Intruders.

While favoured by many within the Navy, this mix of fighter and attack aircraft soon came under attack. A thorough analysis of Vietnam operations revealed that separating attack and fighter missions into clearly distinct roles only had merit when, as had been the case over North Vietnam, air-to-air opposition was limited. However, according to the proponents of the dual-capable strike fighter concept, this mix placed bomb-carrying attack aircraft in great jeopardy wherever and whenever air superiority was not clearly established, such as could be the case in the event of war in Europe. At about the same time, the OSD (Office of the Secretary of Defense) directed the Navy to seek a lower cost alternative to continued procurement of the F-14.

As a result of these activities, requirements for a new VFAX were drawn up during the second half of 1973, and an RFP was issued to the industry in June 1974. Congress, however, short-circuited this scheme and on 28 August, 1974, instructed the Navy to select one of the Air Force-sponsored lightweight fighter projects, the General Dynamics YF-16 or the Northrop YF-17, as the NACF (Navy Air Combat Fighter). On 2 May, 1975, an enlarged and much redesigned version of the YF-17, which had been jointly developed by McDonnell Douglas and Northrop, was announced as the winner of the NACF competition. The aircraft was then intended to be procured in three closely related models: the single-seat F-18, to replace the F-4 in the fighter role, the single-seat A-18, to succeed the A-7 in the attack role, and the two-seat TF-18A combat

F/A-18A of VFA-106 at NAS Cecil Field, Florida, in February 1985. *(Peter B Mersky)*

345

trainer. Differences between the F-18 and A-18 versions were to be limited to store attachments and avionic details while the TF-18A was to retain the mission flexibility and armament of the single-seater but to have slightly reduced internal fuel capacity. However, careful redesign eventually enabled the two single-seat variants to be merged into a single F/A-18A version and the combat-capable two-seat trainer was successively redesignated TF/A-18A and F/A-18B.

As development work progressed, before and after the selection of the McDonnell Douglas Model 267 as the F-18 naval fighter, the revised design retained the characteristic appearance of the Northrop P-630 (the YF-17 lightweight fighter prototype for the USAF) with its twin canted tail surfaces and wingroot leading-edge extensions (LEX). Structural changes, however, were numerous. The airframe and undercarriage had to be strengthened for carrier operations, wing folding and arrester hook had to be incorporated, fuel capacity had to be increased to meet the Navy specified mission radius in the fighter escort and strike roles, and power had to be increased by replacing the 15,000-lb (6,804-kg) thrust General Electric YJ101 turbofans with their F404-GE-400 derivatives rated at 16,000 lb (7,257 kg) with afterburner. Moreover, the small radar of the YF-17 was to be replaced by a more powerful set and at the end of 1977 the Hughes AN/APG-65 digital multi-mode set was selected in preference to the Westinghouse design. Although retaining wingtip-mounted Sidewinder air-to-air IR missiles and the internally-mounted 20-mm M61 cannon of the YF-17, the F-18 was to be provided with a corner station beneath both sides of the fuselage to carry Sparrow air-to-

The first Hornet (BuNo 160775) during initial trials in November 1978. *(MCAIR)*

air missiles and four wing stations and a centreline station for external stores.

Significant technical innovations incorporated into the F-18 design included (1) a quadruplex fly-by-wire flight control system; (2) HOTAS (hands on throttle and stick); (3) HUD (head-up display); (4) two multi-function CRT (cathode ray tube) displays; (5) BIT (built-in test) system; and (6) an APU (auxiliary power unit) for engine starting and ground pneumatic, electric, and hydraulic power. Moreover, the F-18 was to make extensive use of advanced materials, with lightweight aluminium accounting for 55.4 per cent of its total weight, steel for 14.1 per cent, carbon fibre/epoxy for 10.3 per cent (40 per cent of the outer skin), titanium for 8.4 per cent, and fibreglass and other materials for the remaining 11.8 per cent.

The F-18 programme went ahead with the award of letter contracts in November 1975 to General Electric for the development of the F404 turbofans and in January 1976 to McDonnell for nine single-seat and two two-seat FSD (full scale development) aircraft. At that time, first flight was expected to take place in July 1978. However, as the redesign of the YF-17 into the F-18 entailed more work than initially estimated, delays were incurred and the first F-18 (BuNo 160775) was rolled-out at St Louis on 13 September, 1978. First flight took place at Lambert Field, St Louis, on 18 November with Jack E Krings at the controls. Beginning in January 1979, most flight development work—including NPE (Navy Preliminary Evaluation) and BIS (Board of Inspection and Survey) trials—were undertaken at the Naval Air Test Center, Patuxent River. Carrier qualifications were begun with the third FSD aircraft (BuNo 160777)

The third Hornet (BuNo 160777) trapping aboard the USS *Carl Vinson* (CVN-70) in April 1982. *(MCAIR)*

aboard the USS *America* (CV-66) off the Virginia Cape on 30 October, 1979.

Trials revealed a number of problems and deficiencies which, for the most part, could easily be corrected. This was notably the case of (1) excessive nosewheel lift-off speed and take-off roll which were solved by filling the snag on the inboard leading edge of the stabilator and automatically toeing in the rudders on take-off; (2) insufficient acceleration speed above Mach 1 which was corrected through engine improvements; (3) inadequate main undercarriage strength which led to the use of a twin-chamber oleo leg; (4) unsatisfactory external tanks which brought a switch from elliptical to circular cross-section tanks and a slight increase in capacity from 315 to 330 US gallons (1,192 to 1,249 litres); and (5) roll rate below specification which required that outboard wing panels be strengthened and the length and area of ailerons be increased.

More serious was the range shortfall which, in spite of several airframe modifications (including the filling of the boundary layer slots in the LEX and the elimination of the dog-tooth from the wing leading-edge to reduce drag) and engine improvements to reduce specific fuel consumption, was never fully corrected. Although the F/A-18 range remained less than specified after all changes had been incorporated, it was still greater in the fighter escort role than that of the McDonnell F-4J it replaced. In the strike role the F/A-18 range was found to be 10 to 12 per cent shorter than that of the LTV A-7E. Nevertheless, as in all other respects the Hornet met or exceeded specifications with air combat capability and weapon delivery accuracy being particularly outstanding, the range deficiency did not prevent the Navy from ordering the aircraft into full scale production without the need to approve a proposed increase in internal fuel capacity through the installation of tanks in a dorsal fairing aft of the cockpit.

Hornet BuNo 162878 of VFA-192 at NAF Atsugi, Japan. *(Dr Masahiro Yamasaki)*

Production history

By the end of 1989, a total of 878 Hornets had been delivered to the US Navy, US Marine Corps, Canadian Armed Forces, Royal Australian Air Force, and Ejército del Aire Español, and orders had been placed by Kuwait, Switzerland, and Korea.

F/A-18A: Single-seat aircraft were initially to have been completed in two slightly different configurations, the F-18As being optimized for use in the fighter escort and air superiority roles and the A-18As being tailored for the strike role. However, careful redesign of two store pylons (stations 4 and 6) on the lower corner of the air intakes eventually enabled the two variants to be merged into a single F/A-18A single-seat version, the AIM-7 Sparrows carried when operating in the fighter role being replaced by the AN/AAS-38 forward-looking infrared (FLIR) on the left side and the AN/ASQ-173 laser spot tracker (LST) on the right side when operating in the strike role. Centreline and inboard wing racks (stations 3, 5, and 7) were provided for 330-gallon (1,249-litre) external tanks or air-to-ground ordnance. Armament common to both roles was to include a centrally-mounted 20-mm M61 cannon, with 570 rounds, and wingtip-mounted AIM-9 Sidewinders. As a fighter, the F/A-18A would also carry an AIM-7 or two AIM-9s on the outboard wing racks (stations 2 and 8). As a strike aircraft, it would carry up to 17,000 lb (7,711 kg) of mix ordnance including special weapons, AGM-65 Maverick or AGM-88 HARM missiles, laser guided or general purpose bombs, cluster or fuel air explosive bombs, and rocket pods.

Power was provided by two 16,000 lb (7,257 kg) General Electric F404-GE-400 afterburning turbofans, and the 1,700-gallon (6,435-litre) internal fuel capacity was supplemented by up to three 330-gallon (1,249-litre) external tanks and inflight refuelling (for which a retractable probe was provided in the upper starboard fuselage side).

The F/A-18A (then still designated F-18A) first flew on 18 November, 1978. Production for the US Navy and the US Marine Corps ended with the delivery of the 380th F/A-18A. The total included nine FSD aircraft in Blocks 1 to 3 and 371 production aircraft in Blocks 4 to 22. BuNos for these aircraft are given in Appendix C.

AF/A-18A: Ordered in October 1981 to replace Dassault Mirage IIIO in RAAF service, 57 single-seat AF/A-18As (Blocks 14 to 28 aircraft bearing Australian serials A21-1 to A21-57), the AF/A-18As were essentially similar to the F/A-18As of the USN and USMC but were fitted to carry a reconnaissance pod. The AF/A-18As were assembled by the Government Aircraft Factory (now renamed ASTA, Aerospace Technologies of Australia) at Avalon, Victoria, from US, Spanish, and Australian components. Their F404 turbofans and their avionics were respectively assembled in Australia by Commonwealth Aircraft Corporation and British Aerospace Australia Ltd. The first Australian-assembled Hornet was flown on 3 June, 1985, and the last is to be delivered in 1991.

349

Australian AF/A-18As flying along the coast of New South Wales. These Hornets belong to No. 77 Squadron *(bottom)*, No 3 Squadron *(middle)*, and No. 2 OCU *(top)*. *(RAAF)*

BuNo 161712, an A/F-18A of VMFA-314.

CF-18A: Differing from the US F/A-18As in having ILS (Instrument Landing System) equipment in place of the ACLS (Automatic Carrier Landing System) of the naval aircraft and in being fitted with a spotlight

350

A Canadian Armed Forces CF-18A (188723) making an emergency landing at Hill AFB, Utah, on 20 July, 1988. *(René J Francillon)*

on the port side of the forward fuselage to enable night identification of other aircraft, 98 Canadian single-seat Hornets were ordered in April 1980. Intended to replace Canadair CF-104s and McDonnell CF-101Bs of the Canadian Armed Forces, CF-18As were given Canadian military Serials 188701 to 188798. All were built by McDonnell in Blocks 9 to 23, the first flying on 29 July, 1982, and the last being delivered in September 1988.

EF-18A (C.15):   Ordered in May 1973, 60 single-seat EF-18A Hornets were built by McDonnell for the Ejército del Aire Español to which they are known as C.15s. Bearing Spanish serials C.15-13 to C.15-72, they were included in McDonnell's Blocks 18 to 31 and were similar to US F/A-18As.

EF-18A (C.15-17) of Ala de Caza 15. *(Michel Fournier)*

F/A-18B (TF/A-18A): Two full-scale development two-seaters (BuNos 160781 and 160784) were followed by 39 F/A-18Bs in Blocks 4 to 21 (BuNos are listed in Appendix C). Initially designated TF/A-18As, these aircraft were essentially intended as trainers but retained full combat capability. To make room for the instructor's cockpit, internal fuel capacity was reduced by under 6 per cent.

AF/A-18B: Ordered at the same time as the AF/A-18As and corresponding to the F/A-18Bs in US service, the 18 two-seat AF/A-18Bs (Australian serials A21-101 to A21-118) were delivered to the RAAF. Two were built by McDonnell and were ferried to Australia in May 1985 whereas the 16 others were assembled in Australia by GAF/ASTA.

CF-18B: Also built by McDonnell, the 40 two-seat CF-18Bs came from Blocks 8 to 25 and were given Canadian military serials 188901 to 188940.

CF-18B (188932) at Hill AFB, Utah, on 20 July, 1988. *(René J. Francillon)*

EF-18B (CE.15): The US EF-18B designation and Spanish CE.15 designation identified 12 two-seat combat trainers which were similar to the F/A-18Bs in US service. Included in Blocks 17 to 21, these aircraft were delivered to the Ejército del Aire Español and bore serials CE.15-1 to CE.15-12.

F/A-18C: Beginning with Block 23 aircraft, single-seat Hornets for the Navy and the Marine Corps were built to a new standard and featured (1) a Martin-Baker NACES (Navy Aircrew Common Ejection Seat) in place of the Martin-Baker VS 10S ejection seat; (2) an improved mission computer; (3) an airborne self-protection jammer; (4) a flight incident recording and monitoring system; and (5) provision for carriage of AIM-120 AMRAAM air-to-air and AGM-65F IIR Maverick and AGM-84 Harpoon air-to-ground missiles. Moreover, beginning with aircraft delivered in October 1989, F/A-18Cs were optimized for night attack missions and fitted with a Hughes AN/AAR-50 TINS (thermal imaging navigation set), FLIR, raster HUD, and instrumentation and cockpit arrangement modified for use with night vision goggles.

Two F/A-18Cs of VF-81, CVW-1, assigned to the USS *America* (CV-66). BuNo 163467, the aircraft bearing the side number 300, is shown in the fighter escort configuration with a 330-US gallon external tank, six Sidewinder short-range missiles, and two Sparrow medium-range missiles. BuNo 163465, the aircraft with side number 314, is in the attack configuration with an external tank, eight Mk 83 bombs, two Sidewinders, and two Sparrows. *(MCAIR)*

The first F/A-18C (BuNo 163427) was flown on 3 September, 1987. This version, which replaced the F/A-18A on the assembly line at St Louis, has also been ordered by Kuwait, Switzerland, and Korea. Production F/A-18Cs were initially powered by 16,000-lb (7,257-kg) thrust F404-GE-400 turbofans built by General Electric or Pratt & Whitney, but 17,700-lb (8,029-kg) thrust General Electric F404-GE-402 turbofans are to be fitted to Kuwaiti F/A-18s beginning in August 1991, to USN/USMC Hornets from April 1992, to Swiss aircraft starting in May 1993, and to Korean aircraft beginning in the autumn of 1993.

At the option of export customers, French-built short-range Magic II and medium-range Mica air-to-air missiles can be substituted for Sidewinders and Sparrows.

F/A-18D: Intended to be used primarily in the all-weather night attack role, the two-seat F/A-18Ds currently in production are equivalent to the single-seat F/A-18Cs configured for night attack with FLIR, TINS, raster HUD, and instrumentation and cockpit arrangement modified for use with night vision goggles. Unlike F/A-18Bs which are fitted with dual controls, F/A-18Ds have flying controls only in the front cockpit; if

The prototype of the night attack F/A-18D (BuNo 163434). *(MCAIR)*

required for training missions, however, a stick and throttle can be installed in the rear cockpit. Normally, flight officers in the aft cockpit of F/A-18Ds are provided with two stationary hand controls, one on each side of the seat, to operate the weapons systems. The prototype for the night attack version of the Hornet, an F/A-18D (BuNo 163434), was first flown at St Louis on 6 May, 1988.

F-18L: In 1974, when they undertook to develop the Northrop P-630 design into the McDonnell Douglas Model 267, the two manufacturers agreed that McDonnell would be prime contractor for the naval strike fighter—with Northrop becoming an associate contractor with responsibility for 30 per cent of airframe development and 40 per cent of airframe production, but that these roles and work shares would be reversed in respect of future land-based versions of the basic F-18.

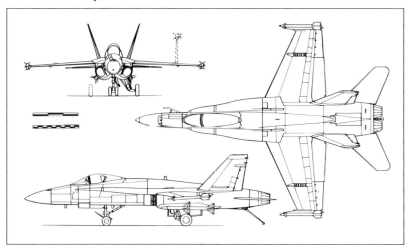

McDonnell Douglas F/A-18A Hornet.

Accordingly, during the late 'seventies and early 'eighties, Northrop actively marketed F-18L land-based versions of the Hornet, often in direct competition with McDonnell which was endeavouring to sell basic F/A-18s to various air forces. Not intended for carrier operations, proposed F-18L versions were expected to be significantly lighter and better performing than the F/A-18. However, Northrop was unsuccessful in its endeavours and development work on the F-18L and, after settling a dispute with McDonnell Douglas in April 1985 and agreeing that henceforth the St Louis firm would be prime contractor for all existing and future versions of the Hornet, Northrop terminated its F-18L programme.

F/A-18(R): To evaluate the feasibility of producing a single-seat reconnaissance version of the Hornet, McDonnell was funded to modify a Block 4 F/A-18A (BuNo 161214) and to install a twin-sensor package in place of the 20-mm cannon. Conversion back to the gun-armed standard fighter/strike configuration could be accomplished overnight. The modified aircraft first flew on 15 August, 1984, and sensors evaluated during trials in St Louis and at NATC Patuxent River included low-altitude cameras, low- to medium-altitude panoramic cameras, and infrared linescan. Substitute plans to procure Advanced Tactical Air Reconnaissance System (ATARS)[1] sensor packages to enable F/A-18Ds to supplement F-14A (TARPS) in Navy service and replace RF-4Bs with the Marines have not yet been finalized.

F/A-18B of VFA-125 on a starboard side elevator aboard the uss *Kitty Hawk* (CV-63) in March 1985. *(René J. Francillon)*

[1] ATARS will record digitised imagery for data link to ground stations and onboard editing and review.

F/A-18C (BuNo 163455) in the defence suppression configuration with AGM-88 HARM anti-radiation missiles beneath the wings. *(MCAIR)*

356

The Hornet in US service

Following trials at NATC Patuxent River and follow-on test and operational evaluation by VX-4 and VX-5 at PMTC Point Mugu and NWC China Lake, California, the F/A-18 was declared ready for assignment to training and operational squadrons beginning with VFA-125. This first Hornet Fleet Replacement Squadron (FRS) which was commissioned at NAS Lemoore, California, on 13 November, 1980, received its first Hornets three months later. As F/A-18As were primarily intended to replace Marine F-4s and Navy A-7Es and, to a lesser extent, Navy F-4s, VFA-125 initially provided conversion training for experienced attack and fighter pilots transitioning from Marine VMFA squadrons and Navy VA and VF squadrons. As time went on, VFA-125 focused increasingly on training new pilots having just received their wings but having no experience with a Fleet squadron. In this role, VFA-125 was later joined by an Atlantic Fleet FRS, VFA-106 at NAS Cecil Field, Florida, and by a Marine Training Squadron, VMFAT-101 at MCAS El Toro, California.

Marine Fighter Attack Squadrons 314 and 323 (VMFA-314 and VMFA-323) at MCAS El Toro became the first operational units to convert to the Hornet, their first F/A-18s being received in January and March 1983 respectively. With the Navy, VA-113 and VA-25 at NAS Lemoore were redesignated VFA-113 and VFA-25 before beginning their conversion from A-7Es to F/A-18As in the autumn of 1983. Other active duty squadrons which have been re-equipped with Hornets since then include all Marine operational squadrons previously flying F-4s (VMFA-115, -122, -212, -232, -235, -251, -312, -333, -451, and -531), two Navy F-4 squadrons (VFA-151 and VFA-161), and 12 Navy squadrons previously equipped with A-7s (VFA-15, -81, -82, -83, -86, -87, -131,

F/A-18A of VMFA-333 at Komatsu AB, Honshu, Japan, on 18 April, 1989.
(Toyokazu Matsuzaki)

357

-132, -136, -137, -146, and -147). VFA-82 and -86 were the first to deploy with F/A-18Cs when they went aboard the USS *America* in August 1989. It is expected that all remaining A-7 active squadrons will have been re-equipped with F/A-18s by 1992. In addition, Hornets were delivered to the Naval Air Reserve beginning in October 1985 and by mid-1989 equipped VFA-203, -303 and -305 with one more A-7 reserve squadron to convert. The first unit to be equipped with night-capable Hornets, VMFA(AW)-121 at MCAS El Toro, Arizona, put the aircraft into service in May 1990 when it converted from Grumman A-6Es to F/A-18Ds. Two reserve Marine Fighter Attack Squadrons, VMFA-112 and VMFA-321, will exchange their F-4Ss for Hornets beginning in 1990.

With increased service experience, a problem not uncovered during the trials programme came to light as higher than expected usage of the F/A-18 in the high angle of attack region, where loads on the tail are particularly severe, resulted in fatigue-related cracks in the tail area. McDonnell quickly developed a modification kit, which consisted of adding four-inch (10.2-cm) long steel doublers to two of the mountings and replacing a non-structural fairing with a stronger fairing, and absorbed the costs of the modification. Later, an ungainly plate was bolted atop the LEXs to divert the airflow away from the fins, thus enabling F/A-18 pilots to continue flying their aircraft at angles of attack higher than possible with other aircraft.

During the first operational cruise by Hornet squadrons, VFA-25 and VFA-113 deployed to the Western Pacific and the Indian Ocean aboard the USS *Constellation* (CV-64) as part of Air Wing Fourteen (CVW-14). Lasting from 21 February until 24 August, 1985, this cruise established the Hornet as an exceptionally reliable aircraft requiring about half the maintenance hours of the F-14 A and A-6E/KA-6D. Flying 4,160 hours, the F/A-18As of the two squadrons maintained high mission-capacity

BuNo 161950, a Block 12 F/A-18A of VFA-125, at NAS Fallon, Nevada, on 19 June, 1989. The ungainly steel plate bolted atop the starboard LERX to divert the airflow away from the fins can be seen clearly. *(René J Francillon)*

rates (89 per cent mission-capable rate and 87 per cent fully mission-capable rate) during an otherwise uneventful seven months at sea.

The next Hornet cruise saw Air Wing Thirteen take four F-18A squadrons (two from the Navy, VFA-131 and VFA-132, and two from the Marine Corps, VMFA-314 and VMFA-323) as part of CVW-13 (Air Wing Thirteen) aboard the USS *Coral Sea* (CV-43) for what was expected to be another routine deployment to the Atlantic and the Mediterranean. However, after the Sixth Fleet was ordered by President Reagan to begin Freedom of Navigation operations in the Gulf of Sidra to demonstrate the United States' resolve to operate freely in international waters, *Coral Sea's* F/A-18As repeatedly intercepted Libyan MiG-23s, MiG-25s, Su-22s, and Mirage F.1s while flying on FORCAP (Task Force combat air patrol). Then, in the course of 'retaliatory' actions on 24/25 March and 15 April, 1986, Hornets were called on for the first time to fly combat missions, firing HARM missiles during defence suppression sorties and flying TARCAP (target combat air patrol) sorties during joint USAF/Navy strikes against targets in and around Tripoli and Benghazi.

In February 1986, the Navy announced that F/A-18As would replace the Douglas A-4Fs of the *Blue Angels* flight demonstration squadron. For

F/A-18B of the *Blue Angels* at NAS Fallon in October 1988. *(René J Francillon)*

that purpose, one aircraft was fitted by McDonnell with a smoke generation system and a new seat harness to help its pilot handle the weightlessness caused by some manoeuvres. Ten more early production Hornets were modified at the Naval Air Rework Facility at NAS North Island, Califonia. The *Blue Angels* began training with F/A-18s during the winter of 1986.

In 1985, the Navy transferred five FSD F/A-18As (BuNos 160777, 160778, 160780, 160782, and 160785), the first FSD two-seater (BuNo 160781), and two early production F/A-18As (BuNos 161251 and 161251) to NASA to be used at the Ames-Dryden Flight Research Facility for chase and proficiency flying. In addition, NASA has used its Hornets for a

F/A-18A BuNo 160780 returning to the NASA Ames-Dryden Flight Research Facility at Edwards AFB after a High Alpha research flight. *(NASA)*

variety of research projects, the first being the High Alpha programme which began in March 1987 to investigate airflow surrounding the aircraft in high angle-of-attack attitudes and post-stall manoeuvrability assisted by thrust vectoring.

The Hornet in foreign service

By the end of 1989, Hornets had been ordered by five air forces. Brief summaries of overseas deliveries and foreign service history are given by country in chronological order of date of entry in service.

Canada: A total of 138 Hornets, including 98 single-seat CF-18As and 40 two-seat CF-18Bs, was delivered to the Canadian Armed Forces between October 1982 and September 1988. The first CAF unit to convert to the new fighter was No.410 Squadron, the operational conversion unit at CFB Cold Lake, Alberta. Operational units which have re-equipped with CF-18s are Nos.416 and 441 Squadrons at CFB Cold Lake, Nos.425 and 433 Squadrons at CFB Bagotville, Quebec, and Nos.409, 421, and 439 Squadrons with No.1 Canadian Air Group at CFB Baden Söllingen, West Germany.

Australia: In May 1984, McDonnell shipped components for the first two AF/A-18As to the Government Aircraft Factory at Avalon. The first Australian-assembled Hornet was flown on 3 June, 1985, and the 73rd and last (including 16 two-seat AF/A-18Bs) is to be delivered in 1991. In addition, two two-seat Hornets for the RAAF were built by McDonnell, with the first being flown at St Louis on 29 October, 1984. No.2 OCU at RAAF Williamstown, New South Wales, began training Hornet pilots in the summer of 1985. Deliveries of GAF-assembled AF/A-18s to operational squadrons, which began in August 1986, have enabled the RAAF to convert three Mirage squadrons, No.3 Squadron and No.77 Squadron

A Royal Australian Air Force AF/A-18B from No. 2 OCU *(bottom)* and an AF/A-18B from No. 3 Squadron *(top)* over RAAF Williamstown, NSW, in May 1989. *(RAAF)*

at RAAF Williamstown and No 75 Squadron at RAAF Tindal, Northern Territory.

Spain: The first four CE.15s for the Ejército del Aire Español were ferried from St Louis to Zaragoza-Valenzuela in July 1986 to enable Ala de Caza 15 to begin training pilots and maintenance personnel both for its two squadrons (Escuadrón 151 and Escuadrón 152) and for two

An EF-18A (Spanish serial C.15-17) of Ala de Caza 15, Ejército del Aire Español. *(Christian Boisselon)*

squadrons (Escuadrón 121 and Escuadrón 122) of Ala de Caza 12 at Torrejón de Ardoz. The 72nd and last Hornet from the first batch of aircraft (60 single-seat C.15s and 12 two-seat CE.15s) ordered by Spain will be delivered in 1990.

Kuwait: An agreement covering the delivery of 40 Hornets to the Al Quwwat al Jawwiya al Kuwaitiya (Kuwait Air Force) was signed in August 1988. These F/A-18Cs and F/A-18Ds, which are to be powered by more powerful F404-GE-402 turbofans, will be delivered between 1992 and 1994.

Switzerland: In October 1988, the Swiss Government announced its selection of the Hornet as the next fighter for the Schweizerische Flugwaffe/Troupe d'Aviation Suisse (Swiss Air Force). Thirty-four F/A-18Cs and F/A-18Ds with F404-GE-402 turbofans are to be delivered to equip three squadrons of the Überwachungsgeschwader/Escadre de Surveillance (Surveillance Wing) beginning in 1993.

Republic of Korea: After a protracted competition pitting it against the F-16, a type already in service with the Republic of Korea Air Force,

362

the F/A-18C was declared the winner of the Korean Fighter Program (KFP) in December 1989. Twelve Hornets, including F/A-18Cs and F/A-18Ds, will be manufactured by MCAIR in St Louis and will be delivered to the ROKAF beginning in the autumn of 1993. Thirty-six F/A-18Cs and F/A-18Ds will then be assembled by Samsung Aerospace Industries at Sachon, Korea, from kits supplied by MCAIR. Finally, 72 Hornets will be manufactured under licence by Samsung. Similarly, 27 F404-GE-102 turbofans will be supplied by General Electric while Samsung will assemble 10 engines from General Electric subassemblies, 71 from subassemblies built in Korea and parts supplied by General Electric, and 144 wholy manufactured in Korea. Some of the more sensitive equipment, such as the APG-65 radar, will be supplied by United States companies.

Data for the F/A-18A:
Span 40 ft 4³/₄ in (12.31 m); span (wings folded) 27 ft 6 in (8.38 m); length 56 ft (17.07 m); height 15 ft 3¹/₂ in (4.66 m); wing area 400 sq ft (37.16 sq m).
Empty weight 23,050 lb (10,455 kg); typical take-off weight (fighter mission) 36,710 lb (16,651 kg); typical take-off weight (attack mission) 49,225 lb (22,328 kg); maximum take-off weight 56,000 lb (25,401 kg); wing loading 92 to 123 lb/sq ft (448 to 601 kg/sq m); power loading 1.15 to 1.54 lb/lb st (1.15 to 1.54 kg/kg st).
Maximum speed more than Mach 1.8 at 40,000 ft (12,190 m); initial climb rate 60,000 ft/min (305 m/sec); service ceiling 50,000 ft (15,240 m); typical combat radius (fighter mission) 460 miles (740 km); typical combat radius (attack mission) 660 miles (1,060 km); ferry range 2,400 miles (3,860 km).

A DC-9-83 (MD-83) of Air Liberté landing at Paris-Orly. *(Christian Jacquet-Francillon)*

McDonnell Douglas MD-80 and MD-90

To all intents and purposes the MD-80 was not a new aircraft and, indeed, continued to be operated under an amendment to the original DC-9 Type Certificate[1]. Nevertheless, for marketing (leading the uninitiated public to believe it was a new design) and internal reasons (associating the aircraft more closely with the new corporate structure[2]) MDC decided in 1983 to refer to the Douglas DC-9 Series 80 (or Super 80) as the McDonnell Douglas MD-80. Notwithstanding this new designation, the MD-80 was, and still is, merely a further stretched version of the successful DC-9 (*see* Volume I for details on the early DC-9 models) with refanned engines and modernized avionics.

With its tradition of stretching the fuselage of its airliners going back to 1934 when the 12-seat DC-1 was stretched into the 14-seat DC-2, the MDC subsidiary in Long Beach (the Douglas Aircraft Company) had become by the mid-seventies the almost undisputed champion of capacity increase through fuselage lengthening. The DC-1 to DC-2 stretch had been followed by that of the DC-4 into the DC-6 in 1946, DC-6A in 1949, DC-7 in 1953, and DC-7C in 1955, and by that of the DC-8 into the Series 60 in 1966. The DC-9 had itself been stretched from the 104 ft 5 in (31.82 m) Series 10 to the 119 ft 5 in (36.39 m) Series 30 in 1966, the 125 ft 7 in (38.27 m) Series 40 in 1967, and the 133 ft 7 in (40.71 m) Series 50 in 1974.

Notwithstanding that the DC-9-50 was already representing a greater stretch than had been previously achieved with other airliners (overall

---

[1] The amendment covering the first variant, the DC-9-81, was approved on 26 August, 1980. All models have since been approved under additional amendments to the DC-9 Type Certificate. According to these amendments, 'The official designation for the McDonnell Douglas DC-9-81, -82, -83, or -87 is the DC-9-81, -82, -83, or -87. The MD designator may be used in parentheses, but must be accompanied by the official designator, *i.e.*, DC-9-81 (MD-81).' The amendment covering the MD-88, however, does use MD-88—not DC-9-88—as the official designation for this model.

[2] MDC has gone as far as keeping segregated records for DC-9s and MD-80s. Those of us who were at Long Beach when the DC-9 first flew on 25 February, 1965, have more difficulty in getting used to the new nomenclature. A rose is a rose…

length and maximum certificated seating capacity had been increased 26.4 and 54.4 per cent over corresponding figures for the DC-9-10), the Long Beach team knew that the DC-9 could be stretched further to achieve still better seat-mile costs. However, as increasing concern over all forms of pollution was leading regulatory agencies to plan stricter noise regulations, engineers also knew that another stretch of the DC-9

N779JA, s/n 48079, a DC-9-82 (MD-82) of Jet America at the Long Beach Municipal Airport. Jet America, one of the many carriers which emerged as the result of the deregulation of the US airline industry, went out of business in October 1987. *(John Wegg)*

fuselage would either entail a significant reduction in range (to keep take-off weight within limits that could be accommodated with existing engines without boosting power and thus noise emission) or require quieter engines. Fortunately for the future of the DC-9 and, as it later turned out, for the continuance of the long line of Douglas airliners, Pratt & Whitney's timely development of refanned versions[3] of the JT8D turbofan opened a new line of development.

Before the keenest prospective customer, Swissair, was able to obtain a production commitment from MDC, the further stretched and re-engined twinjet went through several proposed configurations (*eg* DC-9RSS—Refanned-Stretch-Strech, DC-9-55, DC-9-SC with a new

[3]   The development of a refanned JT8D was initially sponsored by NASA. By combining the HP (high pressure) compressor, HP turbine spool, and combustion section of the proven JT8D-9 with a new six-stage LP (low pressure) compressor and LP turbine, and adding a new by-pass duct, Pratt & Whitney was able to develop the JT8D-200 series. Compared with earlier JT8D versions, the new series offered increased thrust as well as substantial reductions in noise and specific fuel consumption. Engine length and diameter were increased respectively from 120 to 150 in (3.05 to 3.81 m) and from 42.5 to 56.34 in (1.08 to 1.43 m), but this still enabled refanned JT8Ds to be installed in nacelles not significantly larger than those of earlier JT8D versions (by comparison, the CFM56 later adopted for the rival Boeing 737-300 had a length of 95.7 in/2.43 m and a diameter of 72 in/1.83 m).

Under a NASA contract, a DC-9-32 (N54638, s/n 47649) was experimentally fitted with a pair of JT8D-109s, prototypes of the refanned engines. It first flew on 9 January, 1975. Re-engined with JT8D-11s, it was delivered to Adria Airways as YU-AJR in March 1976, but crashed six months later. The refanned engine was next flight tested in 1977 when a JT8D-209 replaced the port outboard JT8D-17 of the first YC-15.

supercritical wing, etc) while Douglas was also considering the joint development with Dassault-Breguet of the ASMR (Advanced Short-to-Medium Range) derivative of the French-designed Mercure. In the end, a new model of the DC-9 proved less costly to develop and manufacture than the ASMR and, as it would reduce training, spares, and facility requirements, was clearly more attractive to existing DC-9 operators. The MDC Board of Directors, however, was unwilling to authorize programme go-ahead until at least 25 orders from three or more

OE-LMB, s/n 49279, a DC-9-81 (MD-81) of Austrian Airlines. *(MAP)*

customers could be obtained. Finally, on the strength of orders from Austrian Airlines (8 firm orders and 4 options), Southern Airways (4 plus 4), and Swissair (15 plus 5), the DC-9 Series 80[4] was announced on 19 October, 1977.

In addition to the most obvious changes (the insertion of a 152-in/3.86-m plug forward of the wing and of a 19-in/0.48-m plug aft as well as the use of JT8D-209s), the initial production model of the Series 80 was to differ from Series 50 aircraft principally in having (1) a modified wing in which were inserted a $62\frac{1}{2}$ in/1.59-m plug at the root on each side of the fuselage and a 24-in/0.61-m constant-chord plug between the aileron and the wing tip, thus increasing area from 1,000.7 to 1,279 sq ft (92.97 to 118.82 sq m) and span from 93 ft 5 in to 107 ft 10 in (28.47 to 32.87 m); (2) an improved high-lift system with additional inboard flap and slat sections and a 'dial-a-flap' control system to enable pilots to select any flap position between fully up and fully down; (3) an increase in fin area; (4) a strake added on the lower outboard side of each engine nacelle to improve airflow over

[4] The DC-9 Series 60 was an earlier proposal for a version which was to have been powered by '20-tonne' CFM56 or JT10D engines. Hence, the version announced in October 1977 should have been designated DC-9 Series 70 (DC-9-70) but, as it was scheduled to enter service in 1980, the opportunity presented itself for marketing it as the Series 80 (or Super 80) for the 'eighties.

the tail when flying at high angles of attack; (5) standard fuel tank capacity increased by 1,520 US gallons (5,754 litres) to 5,779 gallons (21,875 litres); (6) strengthened undercarriage to cater for higher take-off weights (the DC-9-81 being initially certificated at a maximum weight of 140,000 lb/63,503 kg versus 121,000 lb/54,885 kg for the DC-9-51); and (7) improved avionics including a digital flight guidance system (DFGS), a Category IIIA autoland system, and a Head Up Display (HUD).

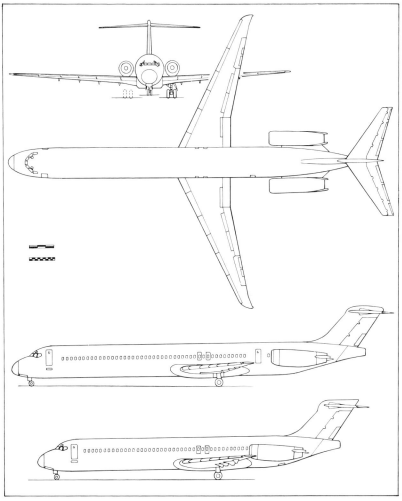

McDonnell Douglas DC-9-81 (MD-81) with side view of the DC-9-87 (MD-87)

The restyled cabin with enclosed overhead compartments and 'wide look' panelling was to provide accommodation for a maximum of 172 passengers (versus 139 in the DC-9-50 and 115 in the DC-9-30) in single-class configuration or 137 passengers in mixed-class configuration (versus 114 in the DC-9-50 and 93 for the DC-9-30). In addition, underfloor cargo volume was to be increased from 895 cu ft/25.4 m³ for the DC-9-30 and 1,140 cu ft/32.3 m³ for the DC-9-50 to 1,294 cu ft/36.6 m³.

Flight tests began on 18 October, 1979, when the first Series 80 (N980DC, s/n 48000, the 909th DC-9 off the assembly line) was flown by H H Knickerbocker and John P Lane, with Virginia A Clare as flight-test engineer, from Long Beach to Yuma, Arizona, where Douglas had its flight test facilities. Trials proceeded smoothly until 17 December when the aircraft ran into problems during a departure stall manoeuvre. Recovery was effected by deploying the anti-spin chute which had been fitted in the tail for initial trials and a permanent solution was provided by modifying the stick-shaker and automatic stall recovery system. Four and a half months later, N980DC was damaged in a heavy landing at Edwards AFB while taking part in new FAA test requirement to ascertain the

S/n 48089, N311RC. a DC-9-82 (MD-82) of Republic Airlines landing at Los Angeles International Airport. *(John Wegg)*

minimum distance required from a height of 50 ft (15 m) to touchdown. The crew was safe and the aircraft was repaired[5].

The second Series 80 aircraft (s/n 48001, the 917th aircraft from the DC-9 line) was less fortunate. First flown on 6 December, 1979, it was damaged in a landing accident at Yuma on 19 June, 1980, during simulated hydraulic failure trials. It could have been repaired but the boom of a crane being used to move the aircraft off the runway broke off and fell across the fuselage causing additional damages and rendering repair uneconomic. Fortunately, no other mishaps occured and on 25 August, 1980, the initial production model, the DC-9-81, was certificated under an amendment to the FAA Type Certificate for the DC-9. Significantly, tests had confirmed that Series 80 aircraft would meet the latest noise regulations, including ICAO (CAN 5) and FAA Part 36, and hence would be good neighbours when operating from airports surrounded by densely populated areas.

Production history

As stockholders were informed in successive annual reports, DC-9-80 sales gained tempo at a painfully slow rate. The 1978 Annual Report gave a total of 50 orders. That number grew to 72 in 1979 and only to 92 in 1980, the year during which the new jetliner was put into revenue service. Moreover, the number of orders placed in 1981 and 1982 remained disappointingly low and put the programme in jeopardy. Convinced that the DC-9-80 was a good aircraft and had solid potential, DAC management obtained approval from the MDC Board of Directors to offer an exceptionally attractive lease package to key potential customers in order to generate enough orders to keep the production line open until the demand for airliners would again be sufficient for resumption of normal sales procedures. In early 1983, American Airlines and TWA availed themselves of this opportunity to add quiet, fuel-efficient aircraft to their

I-DAWB, a DC-9-82 (MD-82) of Alitalia taxi-ing with its thrust reversers deployed. *(Bob Neumeier)*

[5] Swissair refused to accept the repaired aircraft and N980DC was retained by Douglas. Later, it was re-engined with JT8D-217s for use in the development of the DC-9-82 and modified again as the trial aircraft for the proposed propfan powered MD-90.

fleets without major capital outlay, thus assuring the future of the newly redesignated MD-80. More conventionally-financed orders were secured later in 1983, notably from Alitalia. By the end of 1985, when 266 MD-80s had been delivered, 180 were on firm order and 214 were reported as conditional orders or options. The twinjet was well on its way to becoming the most successful jetliner ever built at Long Beach. This became the case early in 1989 when MD-80 deliveries and firm orders exceeded the DC-9 production total and went over the 1,000 mark.

Even though sales were disappointing and production was thus kept below the planned rate, initial deliveries were made behind schedule due to the combined effects of a three-month strike at Long Beach in 1978, later strikes at sub-contractors, material and parts shortages, and the delayed completion of the flight-test programme. Deliveries were back on schedule by the end of 1981 but again fell behind less than seven years later and remained a major problem to the end of 1989. This time, the primary reason for late deliveries was a typical case of not enough success turning into (almost) too much success as the booming demand for MD-80s brought back the production nightmare which had beset Douglas just before its merger with McDonnell in 1967. Once more, MDC was forced to initiate sweeping management changes[6] to increase production efficiency and improve quality control. It was hoped that these changes would enable the MD-80 annual production rate, which fell slightly from 121 in 1988 to 119 in 1989 instead of rising to the predicted level of 137, to go up to 138 in 1990 and 151 in 1991. Should this be achieved, deliveries would once again be on schedule in 1990.

Initially, Series 80 were produced on a common line with earlier DC-9 models. However, after 108 DC-9-81s and DC-9-82s and 976 earlier DC-9s had been built, DAC no longer built DC-9s. Thus, starting with

An Irish-registered DC-9-83 (MD-83) in the markings of Unifly Express. *(MAP)*

[6] The bombastically named Total Quality Management System (TQMS) was irreverently nicknamed 'Time to Quit and Move To Seattle' by Douglas old timers who apparently were suggesting that perhaps the time had come for them to send their curriculum vitae to Boeing.

the 1,085th, a DC-9-82 delivered to VIASA in December 1982, all aircraft from that line have been Series 80s/MD-80s. During the course of production, a number of improvements have been offered for incorporation, at the customer's option, in any of the MD-80 models. These improvements included (1) a cruise improvement package with low-drag flap-hinge fairings, fuselage/engine pylon fairings, a fairing over the APU (auxiliary power unit), and improved sealing on the horizontal tail surfaces; (2) a revised, squared off tail cone to reduce drag and fuel consumption; (3) more modern avionics and flight management systems such as an EFIS (electronic flight instrument system) with four colour CRTs (cathode ray tubes)—two to display primary flight information and two to display navigational data—for which FAA certification was received in May 1987; and (4) a wind shear alert and guidance system which was approved by the FAA in June 1989.

By the end of 1989, the DC-9 Series 80/MD-80 with refanned JT8D turbofans had been built in four models with fuselage length as announced in 1977 and one model with a shorter fuselage. Production of these models was expected to continue until the late 'nineties. Moreover, in early 1990 receipt of enough orders enabled MDC to proceed with the development of yet another DC-9 derivative, the MD-90.

DC-9-81 (MD-81):   The first model in the Series 80 was certificated in August 1980 at a maximum gross weight of 140,000 lb (63,503 kg). It later was also certificated at 142,000 lb (64,410 kg). Most DC-9-81s (MD-81s) have been delivered with two Pratt & Whitney JT8D-209 turbofans rated at 18,500 lb (8,391 kg) thrust for take-off, with an emergency thrust reserve of 750 lb (340 kg). The Type Certificate, however, has been amended to allow the use of 21,000/21,700 lb (9,525/9,843 kg) thrust JT8D-219s and 20,000/20,850 lb (9,072/9,456 kg) thrust JT8D-217s, -217As, or -217Cs. The first flight was made on 18 October, 1979, and

JA8461, s/n 48032, a DC-9-81 (MD-81) of Toa Domestic Airlines (now Japan Air System). *(Dr Masahiro Yamasaki)*

S/n 48026, N10028, a DC-9-81 (MD-81) of Muse Air. *(John Wegg)*

deliveries began in September 1980. This model remained in production in 1990.

DC-9-82 (MD-82): For improved airfield performance, particularly when operating from hot and high airports, most DC-9-82s (MD-82s) have been delivered with JT8D-217s or -217As[7] rated at 20,000 lb (9,072 kg) thrust for take-off, with an emergency thrust reserve of 850 lb (386 kg), and have been certificated for operations at maximum gross weights of 147,000 lb (66,678 kg) or 149,500 lb (67,812 kg). In other respects, MD-82s were similar to MD-81s. So far ordered in greater numbers than other models, the MD-82 was first flown on 8 January, 1981.

S/n 48096, N941PS, a DC-9-82 (MD-82) of PSA at San Diego on 3 March, 1983.
(René J Francillon)

[7] With option to use JT8D-209s, -217Cs, or -219s.

In accordance with an agreement signed in April 1985, between Shanghai Aviation Industrial Corporation (SAIC), China Aviation Supply Corporation (CASC), and McDonnell Douglas Corporation, 25 MD-82s were to be assembled by SAIC in a factory located on the outskirts of Shanghai. Parts, major subassemblies, avionics, and engines were to be shipped by Douglas and its sub-contractors. The first SAIC-assembled MD-82 (s/n 49415, Chinese registration B2106) was first flown in Shanghai on 2 July, 1987. It received a certificate of airworthiness issued by the FAA four days later and was put into regular service from Shenyang by The General Administration of Civil Aviation of China (CAAC) on 4 August. A second SAIC-assembled MD-82 was delivered in 1987, and four came off the Shanghai assembly line in 1988. The production rate was increasing during the first half of 1989, when political turmoil in China and late deliveries of components from Long Beach slowed down the programme. Shanghai-assembled MD-82s joined five DAC-built aircraft in service with CAAC. In May 1988, when CAAC was

The first DC-9-82 (MD-82), s/n 49140, for CAAC still carrying its temporary US registration (N1004S). In China it was re-registered B2101. *(DAC, courtesy of John Wegg)*

S/n 49328, N417AA, a DC-9-82 (MD-82) of American Airlines landing at the Sacramento Metro Airport on 4 March, 1988. *(René J Francillon)*

split into regional airlines, US- and Chinese-built MD-82s were distributed to China Eastern and China Northern Airlines.

As Chinese orders for twinjet transports were hotly contested, with CAAC eventually ordering MD-82s as well as Boeing 737-200s and -300s, MDC had agreed in 1979 to have SAIC build undercarriage doors for all MD-80s. Following the signing of the agreement providing for the assembly of MD-82s in China, work by SAIC was increased to include the manufacture of cargo doors, access and service doors, door frames, and wing components. In July 1988, MDC awarded additional contracts covering the manufacture of complete MD-80 nose sections by the Chengdu Aircraft Corporation and of MD-80 horizontal stabilizers by SAIC, with Chinese-built components to be shipped to Long Beach.

DC-9-83 (MD-83):   Long-range MD-83s differed from MD-81s and MD-82s only in having fuel capacity increased from 5,779 to 6,939 gallons

S/n 49396, SE-DHB, a DC-9-83 (MD-83) of Transwede. *(MAP)*

S/n 49602, D-ALLF, a DC-9-83 (MD-83) landing at Sacramento Metro Airport during an acceptance flight on 17 December, 1987, four days before being delivered to Aero Lloyd. *(Jim Dunn)*

(21,875 to 26,266 litres) through the installation of two 580-gallon (2,195-litre) tanks in the cargo compartment. Maximum certificated gross weight was increased to 160,000 lb (72,575 kg) and power provided by two 21,000/21,700 lb (9,525/9,843 kg) thrust JT8D-219s (with options to use lower rated JT8D-209s, -217s, -217As, or -217Cs). The first MD-83 flight (with JT8D-217s, pending availability of the higher rated JT8D-219s) was made on 17 December, 1984.

DC-9-87 (MD-87): Primarily intended as a DC-9-30 replacement for use on routes with lower traffic density, the MD-87 combined the wing and powerplant installation of MD-80s with a shorter fuselage—its 119 ft 1 in/36.30-m length being only 4 in (10 cm) shorter than that of the DC-9-30—providing accommodation for 139 passengers in high density configuration or 108 passengers in typical mixed-class configuration. The MD-87 differed also from other MD-80 models in having no aft passenger

The DC-9-87 (MD-87) was first put into revenue service by Finnair, in November 1987. *(DAC)*

loading doors on either side of the rear fuselage, a longer strake located further forward on the outboard side of the engine nacelles, and a taller fin. First flown on 4 December, 1986, the MD-87 has been certificated at gross weights of 125,000lb (56,699 kg), 135,000 lb (61,235 kg), 140,000 lb (63,503 kg), 147,000 lb (66,678 kg), and 149,500 lb (67,812 kg). Customers were given options to specify either 20,000/20,850 lb (9,072/9,457 kg) thrust JT8D-217Cs or 21,000/21,700 lb (9,525/9,843 kg) JT8D-219s, and either standard tanks (5,779 gallons/21,875 litres) or long-range tanks (6,939 gallons/26,266 litres).

MD-88: When an order from Delta Air Lines for 30 (plus an option on a further 50) was announced in January 1986, the MD-88 appeared to

S/ns 49403 (OH-LMA) and 49411 (OE-LMK), the first DC-9-87s for Finnair and Austrian Airlines. *(DAC)*

be quite different from the MD-82. It was notably to feature more advanced cockpit systems and avionics (FMS, EFIS, and wind shear detection which have since been made available for installation on other MD-80 models), a wider aisle (at the expense of seat width) to facilitate movement in the cabin with food and beverage carts in use, and ground air conditioning and potable water connections relocated to the nose to ease servicing. The most important new feature, however, related to the powerplant installation with the MD-88s to be delivered with JT8D-219s and with provision for substituting propfan engines at a later date. As

An MD-88 (N930DL, s/n 49717 of Delta Air Lines at Raleigh-Durham Airport, North Carolina, in June 1989. *(René J Francillon)*

McDonnell Douglas later had to terminate work on propfan-powered MD-90s, Delta Air Lines' MD-88s differed little from late production MD-82s with digital cockpit systems.

As digital cockpit systems had not yet been approved by the FAA, the first eight MD-88s were delivered to Delta in 1988 without these systems but were later retrofitted. Powered by JT8D-219s derated to 20,000 lb (9,072 kg) thrust to increase engine life, MD-88s were certificated at a weight of 149,500 lb (67,812 kg). The first flight of an MD-88 was made on 15 August, 1987.

UHB Demonstrator: As propfan engines could easily be substituted for the rear-mounted turbofans of its MD-80, whereas neither Airbus Industrie nor Boeing could do so with their A320 or 737 due to the use of wing-mounted engines, Douglas made intensive efforts between 1985 and 1989 to convince the world's airlines that the novel engine should power the next generation of short-to-medium-range transports. In particular, Douglas claimed that a propfan-powered airliner would burn 25 to 35 per cent less fuel than the most advanced turbofan-powered aircraft then under development and as much as 50 per cent less than the MD-80.

To demonstrate the potential of its proposed re-engined MD-88 and propfan-powered MD-90 series, Douglas modified the MD-80 prototype as a test-bed for ultra-high-bypass (UHB) engines developed by General Electric and Allison. The first phase of this demonstration programme

The UHB Demonstrator with its original 8 by 8 counter-rotating fan driven by a General Electric GE36 Unducted Fan engine. *(DAC)*

The PW-Allison 578-X installation in the port nacelle of N980DC. *(United Technologies)*

saw the port JT8D-217 replaced by a 16,000 lb (7,257 kg) thrust General Electric GE36 Unducted Fan engine. Flight trials began on 17 June, 1987, at Mojave, California, and after a few flights the 8 by 8 counter-rotating fan (*ie* with two rows of eight blades) was replaced by a quieter 10 by 8 unit (10 blades in the front row and eight blades in the aft row). Results were encouraging and the UHB demonstrator was next modified to flight-test the 20,000 lb (9,072 kg) thrust 578-DX propfan engine which had been jointly developed by Allison and Pratt & Whitney and drove two sets of six-bladed counter-rotating propfans. The first flight with the PW-Allison 578-DX mounted in the port nacelle was made at Edwards AFB on 13 April, 1989. By then, however, Douglas was about to concede that the development of propfan-powered airliners was not yet justified[8].

The UHB Demonstrator landing at the Mojave Airport during trials with the PW-Allison 578-X ultra-high bypass engine. *(United Technologies)*

The proposal for the propfan-powered MD-90 had elicited much curiosity but steady fuel prices and concerns over both potentially difficult engine maintenance and lack of public acceptance of a 'propeller-powered' aircraft finally convinced airlines that the UHB era was not about to start. Accordingly, further work on UHB-powered MD-80 derivatives was ended in mid-1989 and in their place McDonnell Douglas announced that it would offer a new turbofan-powered MD-90 series.

MD-90: The MD-90 designation was first used publicly in 1983 to identify a proposed development of the MD-80, with a shorter fuselage and JT8D-217/-218 or CFM56-3 turbofans, which was intended as a replacement for the DC-9-30. This proposal did not at first attract airline interest (but eventually led to the development of the MD-87) and the MD-90 designation was next used for proposed UHB-powered versions

[8]   No better luck attended the proposed development of a military version. Douglas had entered a propfan-powered MD-87 derivative in the US Navy's Long Range-ASW Capable Aircraft (LRAACA) competition, but, in October 1988, the Navy selected the Lockheed P-7, a development of the P-3 Orion.

of the MD-80. When this proposal failed to find favour with the airlines, McDonnell Douglas announced a new MD-90 series[9] which will be powered by IAE V2500 turbofans[10]. The first order (50 firm and 110 options) was placed by Delta Air Lines in November 1989. MD-90s will be built alongside MD-80s on a common assembly line.

MD90-10: Proposed version with fuselage shorter than that of the MD-88 to provide accommodation for 114 passengers in mixed-class configuration. Preliminary data include a maximum take-off weight of 139,000 lb (63,049 kg) with V2500-D2 turbofans rated at 22,000 lb (9,979 kg) for take-off. None ordered up to April 1990.

MD90-20: Designation not used up to April 1990.

MD90-30: Basic version which before April 1990 had been ordered by Delta Air Lines, Alaska Airlines, Japan Air System, and International Lease Finance Corporation (ILFC). The MD90-30 has a fuselage 4.2 ft (1.28 m) longer than that of the MD-88 and will provide accommodation for 153 passengers in typical mixed-class configuration. Preliminary data include a maximum take-off weight of 156,000 lb (70,760 kg) with V2500-D1 turbofans rated at 25,000 lb (11,340 kg) for take-off. Flight trials will begin in 1992 with the original MD-80 prototype being partially brought up to the MD90-30 configuration.

MD90-40: Proposed version with fuselage length increased further to provide accommodation for 180 passengers in mixed-class configuration. Preliminary data include a maximum take-off weight of 165,000 lb (74,843 kg) with V2500-D5 turbofans rated at 28,000 lb (12,701 kg) for take-off. None ordered up to April 1990.

Service history

Swissair began DC-9-81 service on 5 October, 1980, on its Zürich–London route and Pacific Southwest Airlines (PSA) became the first US carrier to fly Series 80 aircraft when it inaugurated service in California

---

[9] In a sudden and unexplained aberration, McDonnell Douglas is using the MD-90 designation with a hyphen to identify the new series of aircraft powered by V2500 turbofans but without a hyphen when referring to a specific model. Thus, in a news release dated 30 January, 1990, DAC advised editors as follows: 'When you refer to the MD-90 as a family of aircraft, insert a hyphen between 'MD' and '90,' If you are referring to a specific model of MD-90, do not insert a hyphen between 'MD' and '90,' using a single hyphen before the model number only. Example: MD90-10, MD90-30 and MD90-40.' Clearly, implementation of the Total Quality Management System is making significant contributions to DAC's product lines...

[10] The use of forebears of the V2500 engine to power Series 80 derivatives had been first considered by Douglas in 1980 when the Anglo-Japanese RJ-500 was suggested for the proposed Super 80S and Super 80LR. IAE V2500s were first offered for the stillborn 170-seat MD-89 in 1985.

HB-IND, s/n 48003, a DC-9-81 (MD-81) of Swissair at the Aéroport de Genève-Cointrin. *(P Miche, courtesy of John Wegg)*

from its San Diego base on 17 December, 1980. The MD-82 entered service with Republic Airlines in August 1981, the MD-83 with Finnair in July 1985[11], the MD-87 with Austrian Airlines and Finnair in November 1987, and the MD-88 with Delta Air Lines in January 1988.

Like earlier DC-9 models, the DC-9 Series 80 was certificated for two-pilot operation. However, the Airline Pilots' Association (ALPA) strenuously opposed the two-pilot crewing arrangement and attempted to impose a three-pilot crew on US carriers. As a result of the ALPA stance, Southern Airways had to cancel its DC-9-80 order and other long-term DC-9 customers, notably Delta Air Lines and Eastern Air Lines, were initially unable to order Series 80 aircraft as they could ill-afford to comply with the demand from ALPA. Hence, the first airline to operate DC-9-80s in the United States was PSA as its non-union crews were prepared to fly the aircraft with two pilots as certificated. Had ALPA's stance regarding two-crew operation remained unchallenged, the future of the MD-80 would indeed have been grim. Fortunately, a Presidential task force ruled in 1981 that a third crew member was not required for safety purposes, thus opening the way for large scale orders. For example, after availing itself in October 1982 of McDonnell Douglas's unique marketing offer to lease its first 20 MD-82s for an initial two-year period, American Airlines first purchased 67 MD-82s and optioned 100 more in February 1984. Including aircraft ordered under later contracts, American Airlines had 165 MD-80s in service in August 1989—the largest fleet of any single type of aircraft outside the USSR—and had 135 additional MD-80s either on order or option.

In the autumn of 1989, the largest non-US customers were Scandinavian Airlines System (which had 61 MD-81/-82/-83/-87s in service or on

[11] Four aircraft delivered to Alaska Airlines earlier in 1985 were not true MD-83s as they were still powered by JT8D-217s. They were subsequently brought up to MD-83 standard when they were re-engined with JT8D-219s late in 1985.

N432AA, a DC-9-82 (MD-82 of American Airlines, with extended tail cone and other drag reducing improvements, landing at the Sacramento-Metropolitan Airport on 17 December, 1987. *(Jim Dunn)*

order and held 37 options), Alitalia (which, with its domestic subsidiary ATI, had 40 in service and 80 on order or option), and Japan Air System (the former Toa Domestic Airlines, which had 19 MD-81s and MD-87s in service and 19 on order, and held options on more MD-80s). Outside the United States MD-80s not only were being flown on scheduled domestic

A DC-9-81 (MD-81) of US Air landing at the McCarran International Airport, Las Vegas, Nevada, on 24 April, 1989. *(René J Francillon)*

and regional routes[12] but also had found a ready market among charter airlines as their payload/range performance was particularly well-suited to operations from Northern Europe to places in the sun in North Africa, Spain and its islands, and Eastern Mediterranean countries. Many of their aircraft were then owned by major leasing companies (including GPA Group Ltd, International Lease Finance Corp, etc.) which have acquired large numbers of MD-80s for that purpose.

[12] The longest scheduled sector—2,301 miles/3,703 km from Vienna to Riyadh was flown by MD-87s of Austrian Airlines.

So far, no MD-80s have been ordered for military or governmental use. However, large numbers of these jetliners have been committed by US carriers to the Civil Reserve Air Fleet (CRAF) for use in the aeromedical evacuation role during times of national emergency. For this contingency, E-Systems Inc of Greenville, Texas, has developed a kit requiring no prior modifications to enable MD-80s to carry litters and other equipment.

Since entering service in 1980, DC-9 Series 80/MD-80s have seen widespread service around the world. The 618 delivered by mid-1989 had been flown for a total of nearly 6 million hours (with the high-time aircraft approaching the 29,000-hour mark). Four aircraft (two MD-81s and two

G-PATB, s/n 49400, a DC-9-83 (MD-83) of Paramount Airways. *(MAP)*

DC-9-87 (MD-87) S/n 49586 (HB-IUB) of CTA over the Swiss Alps. *(CTA)*

MD-82s had been lost in accidents, one MD-81 (the erstwhile UHB demonstrator) was in storage, and 613 aircraft were in service (95 MD-81s, 366 MD-82s, 87 MD-83s, 25 MD-87s, and 40 MD-88s) were in service with 24 airlines in Europe, nine in the United States, five in Asia, four in Latin America, two in the Caribbean, and one in Africa. By the beginning of 1990, deliveries had reached 686 aircraft while MDC held orders and other commitments for 911 DC-9-80s and 240 MD-90s.

	DC-9-81	DC-9-83	DC-9-87
Span, ft in	107 10	107 10	107 10
(m)	(32.87)	(32.87)	(32.87)
Length, ft in	147 10	147 10	119 1
(m)	(45.06)	(45.06)	(36.30)
Height, ft in	29 8	29 8	30 6
(m)	(9.04)	(9.04)	(9.30)
Wing area, sq ft	1,270	1,270	1,270
(sq m)	(118)	(118)	(118)
Operating weight empty, lb	78,421	80,563	73,157
(kg)	(35,571)	(36,543)	(33,183)
Maximum take-off weight, lb	140,000	160,000	140,000
(kg)	(63,503)	(72,575)	(63,503)
Wing loading*, lb/sq ft	110	126	110
(kg/sq m)	(538)	(615)	(538)
Power loading*, lb/lb st	3.8	3.8	3.5
(kg/kg st)	(3.8)	(3.8)	(3.5)
Maximum speed, mph/ft	575/30,000	575/30,000	575/30,000
(km/h at m)	(925/9,145)	(925/9,145)	(925/9,145)
Normal cruising speed, Mach	0.76	0.76	0.76
FAA take-off field length**, ft	7,250	8,375	6,100
(m)	(2,210)	(2,555)	(1,860)
Maximum operating altitude, ft	37,000	37,000	37,000
(m)	(11,280)	(11,280)	(11,280)
Payload range, (passengers/miles)	155/1,800	155/2,880	130/2,730
(passengers/km)	(155/2,895)	(155/4,635)	(130/4,395)

* wing and power loadings are calculated at maximum take-off weight and normal take-off thrust.

** field length at sea level/standard day computed at maximum take-off weight and normal take-off thrust.

BuNo 162787, the first T-45A Goshawk, during manufacturer's trials. *(DAC)*

McDonnell Douglas T-45 Goshawk

During the late 'seventies, while planning the replacement of ageing North American T-2Cs and Douglas TA-4Js equipping intermediate and advanced training squadrons of the Naval Air Training Command (NATRACOM), the Naval Air Systems Command (NAVAIR) considered several alternatives (*ie* extending the service life of the T-2Cs and TA-4Js, acquiring foreign-designed trainers, or sponsoring the development of a new trainer) before inviting the industry to submit proposals for the VTXTS jet training system. Intended to improve the quality of training while lowering costs substantially by replacing two types of trainers with a single, more fuel efficient type and by making extensive use of simulation, the complete VTXTS package was to be comprised of jet trainers, flight simulators, computer-aided training devices, a computer-based integration system, and contractor operated logistics support.

In answer to an RFP issued by the Navy in March 1980, teams of aircraft manufacturers and system designers submitted proposals[1] and, in August of that year, NAVAIR awarded study contracts to six of the teams, including the McDonnell Douglas team composed of Douglas Aircraft, British Aerospace, and Sperry. Over the next six months, the MDC team refined proposals for a new Douglas design and a modified version of the BAe Hawk with both alternatives being complemented by simulators and computer-based training systems for which Sperry was to be the prime sub-contractor. Following NAVAIR evaluation, the

[1] Proposals for new aircraft were submitted by a General Dynamics/American Airlines team, a McDonnell Douglas/British Aerospace team, a Northrop/Vought team, and Rockwell. In addition, Lockheed and Dassault-Breguet teamed up to offer a version of the Alpha Jet, McDonnell Douglas and BAe proposed a modified Hawk, Rockwell submitted an alternate proposal for the T-2X modernised version of its T-2C, and Aermacchi entered its MB.339.

training package based on the Hawk derivative was announced the winner of the VTXTS competition on 18 November, 1981. The aircraft was designated T-45A (and named Goshawk in June 1985) and the complete package became the T-45 Training System (T45TS).

Following its selection, the MDC/BAe/Hughes[2] team worked on the T45TS programme at a relatively slow pace under small pre-development and sustained engineering contracts until the award of a $438 million full

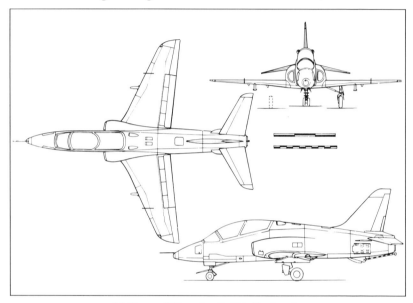

McDonnell Douglas T-45A Goshawk.

scale development contract in October 1984. Thereafter, in adapting the land-based Hawk and its Rolls-Royce Turboméca Adour turbofan to carrier operations, changes were kept to a minimum to minimize costs. Principal differences between the BAe Hawk and the McDonnell Douglas T-45A Goshawk include (1) new twin-wheel nose unit with steering system and catapult tow bar; (2) main undercarriage with longer stroke, larger wheels, and high pressure tyres, moved outboard to increase track from 10 ft 11½ in to 12 ft 9½ in (3.34 m to 3.90 m); (3) installation of a tailhook and under fuselage fairing in place of the dual ventral strakes; (4) addition of small horizontal surfaces (side mounted unit root fins or Smurfs) on the rear fuselage sides; (5) substitution of two fuselage-side air-brakes for the ventral air-brake; (6) local strengthening

---

[2] The Sperry Corporation's subsidiary which was responsible for the design and manufacture of instrument flight trainers (IFTs) and operational flight trainers (OFTs) was acquired in 1988 by Hughes Aircraft Company. Hence, Hughes replaced Sperry in the T-45 team.

of the airframe to compensate for higher stress during carrier operations; (7) anti-corrosion treatment; and (8) addition of a back-up fuel control. In addition, a new version of the Adour turbofan, the 5,450 lb (2,474 kg) thrust Rolls-Royce Turboméca F405-RR-400L, was initially selected to power the Goshawk. The capacity of the fuselage and integral wing tanks remained unchanged at 450 US gallon (1,703 litres) but the capacity of the external tanks was increased from 120 to 156 gallons (454 to 591 litres). Finally, whereas Hawks in RAF service have provision for a ventral cannon and for carrying missiles or bombs on four underwing points, Goshawks were to be limited to a single store beneath the fuselage and practice bombs on multiple racks when replacing the external tanks.

As agreed among the T45TS partners, the wings, flying controls, centre and rear fuselage, canopy, and tail surfaces of the T-45A were to be

The second Goshawk, BuNo 162788. *(DAC, courtesy of NATC)*

manufactured by British Aerospace in Great Britain and the forward fuselage by Douglas in Long Beach. British Aerospace, as principal T-45A sub-contractor, was also to produce two airframes, one for drop tests and one for fatigue testing. Douglas Aircraft, as the prime contractor, was to be responsible for final assembly, with that of the development aircraft taking place in the Long Beach plant and that of production aircraft at US Air Force Plant 42 in Palmdale, California[3]. The F405-RR-400L turbofan was to be produced by Rolls-Royce in Britain and the flight simulators were to be manufactured by Hughes at Reston, Virginia.

In accordance with this arrangement, construction of two development aircraft (BuNos 162787 and 162788) was begun in February 1986 and the

[3] In December 1989, MDC announced that the management of the T-45 programme and the production of that aircraft would be transferred from DAC to MCAIR. This move was undertaken to balance the workload of the two divisions and stabilize their employment in spite of a decrease in the backlog of military business in St Louis and an increase in backlog of commercial business in Long Beach.

In being adapted for carrier operations, the McDonnell Douglas Goshawk has lost some of the gracefulness and pleasant handling characteristics of its forebear, the land-based British Aerospace Hawk. *(DAC)*

first T-45A was unveiled on 16 March, 1988. Exactly a month later, Fred Hamilton first flew BuNo 162787 at the Long Beach Municipal Airport. The second Goshawk joined the test programme three months later with most of the contractor trials taking place in Yuma, Arizona, while Navy testing was undertaken at the Naval Air Test Center at Patuxent River. Tests revealed the prototypes to be underpowered, to possess poor stall characteristics and inadequate directional stability, and to have unsatisfactory air brakes. Corrective modifications evaluated during the summer of 1989 included a 6-in (15.2-cm) fin extension and reinstallation of ventral fins to boost lateral stability, modified leading edge and other aerodynamic devices to improve stall characteristics, and an increase in take-off thrust to 5,845 lb (2,651 kg) to achieve more satisfactory hot-and-high airfield performance

The US Navy is planning to acquire a total of 302 T-45As (of which 38 had been ordered by the summer of 1989 including the two development aircraft, the 12-aircraft production Lot I, and the 24-aircraft Lot II) with the last of these aircraft to be delivered in 1997. Goshawks are to enter NATRACOM service at NAS Kingsville, Texas, in 1991. Later, T-45As will also replace T-2Cs and TA-4Js at NAS Chase Field, Texas, and NAS Meridian, Mississippi.

Span 30 ft 9³/₄ in (9.39 m); length 35 ft 9 in (10.89 m); height 13 ft 5 in (4.09 m); wing area 179.6 sq ft (16.69 sq m).
Empty weight 9,394 lb (4,261 kg); maximum weight 12,758 lb (5,787 kg); wing loading 71 lb/sq ft (346.7 kg/sq m); power loading 2.3 lb/lb st (2.3 kg/kgp).
Maximum speed 620 mph at 8,000 ft (997 km/h at 2,440 m); initial climb rate 6,980 ft/min (35 m/sec); service ceiling 42,250 ft (12,875 m); ferry range 1,150 miles (1,850 km).

The first MD-11 on the occasion of its maiden flight on 19 January, 1990. *(MDC)*

McDonnell Douglas MD-11

As befits its long tradition of offering stretched versions of its airliners, Douglas had from the very beginning of the DC-10 project planned to offer versions of its trijet with extended fuselages. Indeed, conceptual designs of stretched DC-10 models were included in brochures and audiovisual presentations shown to prospective customers in 1967-68. Unfortunately, the anticipated early launch of stretched DC-10 versions was repeatedly frustrated as the result of downturns in airline traffic, unfortunate effects of the DC-10 crash at Chicago in May 1979, and internal MDC problems.

In November 1983, when the airline industry was going through a particularly difficult period and Douglas had no more DC-10s on order, the MDC Board of Directors decided that all work should be stopped on the MD-100, a proposed derivative of the DC-10. It thus appeared to most industry observers that McDonnell Douglas was bowing out of the commercial aircraft market and that no stretched DC-10s (or MD-100s) would ever be built. However, less than two years later, signs of a vigorous upturn in airline business prompted the MDC Board of Directors on 29 July, 1985, to authorize Douglas again to seek orders for a wide-cabin trijet transport derived from the DC-10, the MD-11. Nevertheless, 17 months went by before enough orders and other commitments were obtained from 12 airlines to enable the MD-11 programme to be officially launched on 30 December, 1986. In the meantime Airbus Industrie had decided to proceed with the development of the similarly-sized A340. Announced on 27 January, 1986, the A340 was to be a four-engined design combining the fuselage cross-section of the A300/A310 twin-engined series with an all-new wing, whereas the MD-11 was to be a more modest project directly derived from the DC-10 trijet. Consequently, the MD-11 was expected to have slightly higher operating costs but to be less expensive to acquire and to be available two years earlier than the A340.

Before going ahead with the MD-11, Douglas contemplated the adoption of several major new design features, such as all-new wings, to improve substantially the new aircraft's operating economics. However, it was felt that quite a significant reduction in direct operating costs could be achieved without having to undertake such a drastic and costly

The first MD-11 on rotation at the Long Beach Municipal Airport. *(MDC)*

redesign of the DC-10. Accordingly, it was decided to retain most of the DC-10 airframe virtually unchanged but to (1) use more advanced engines and introduce aerodynamic modifications to reduce fuel burn and drag; (2) lengthen the fuselage to reduce seat-mile costs by providing accommodation for more passengers; and (3) redesign the cockpit for two-pilot operations to eliminate the need for a third crew member. Moreover, composite materials were to be used extensively to reduce airframe weight.

The most obvious external change came from the addition of winglets, while further drag reductions resulted from the adoption of modified wing aerofoils with increased camber near the trailing edge, smaller horizontal tail surfaces with 2,000-US gallon (7,571-litre) integral tanks, and a lengthened tail cone. Combined with the use of more efficient engines (airlines being given a choice between 60,000 lb/27,216 kg thrust Pratt & Whitney 4460 turbofans, 61,500 lb/27,896 kg thrust General Electric CF6-80C2 turbofans, and 65,000 lb/29,484 kg thrust Rolls-Royce RB.211-524L Trent turbofans), these aerodynamic improvements were predicted to result in a 20 per cent reduction in fuel burn per trip. More operating cost savings were to be derived from the adoption of an all-digital flight deck with six CRT displays, wind shear detection and guidance devices, and a dual flight management system as the new cockpit arrangement would enable a reduction in the flight crew from three to two.

As design work progressed, the MD-11 was offered in three standard models, in an extended range version with a shorter fuselage, and in a stretched derivative. However, only the three standard MD-11 models had been ordered by the end of 1989. The standard passenger model offered accommodation for up to 405 passengers in high-density config-uation, 323 passengers in a typical two-class configuration, or 293 passengers in a three-class arrangement, as well as more below-deck cargo capacity (6,850 cu ft/194 m³ in which to carry fourteen LD-3 containers and six pallets) than any other passenger jetliner. New

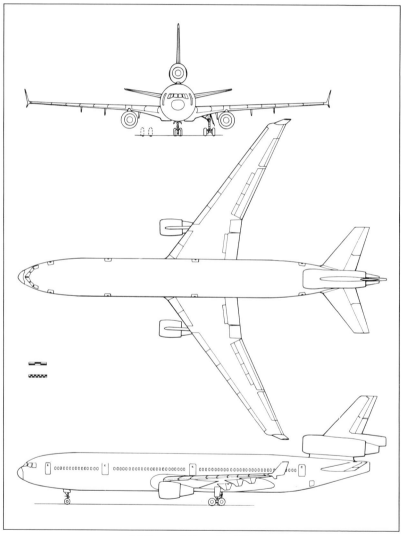

McDonnell Douglas MD-11.

features to improve passenger and crew comfort and to provide greater operating flexibility included (1) carry-on baggage compartments with 50 per cent greater capacity; (2) improved lighting and air conditioning systems; (3) lavatories and galleys mounted on seat tracks for quick cabin reconfiguration; and (4) optional 'Skybunk' crew rest area. In addition, Douglas proposed the installation of an optional 'Panorama Deck' beneath the main deck with accommodation for either 44 business class or 66 economy class passengers.

The all-freighter model, first ordered by Federal Express, was designed to carry a maximum payload of 205,700 lb (93, 304 kg), with 14,600 cu ft (413.4 m³) available on the upper deck and 6,850 cu ft (194 m³) below deck. The 'combi' model, which was first ordered by Alitalia, carries up to 173 passengers in a three-class configuration and six 88 in by 125 in (2.24 m by 3.18 m) pallets on the main deck, plus fourteen LD-3 containers and six additional pallets below deck.

Being a direct derivative of the DC-10, the MD-11 had been expected to be developed rapidly and first flight had been predicted to take place in March 1989, with FAA certification to be obtained in April 1990. To that end, fabrication of the first parts had begun in March 1987, assembly of the first MD-11 had started in March 1988, and the first wing-to-fuselage

Airborne for the first time, MD-11 N111MD shows off its winglets and revised tail cone, the two principal features distinguishing it externally from the DC-10.
(MDC)

393

join was accomplished in October 1988 as scheduled when the programme was launched in December 1986. In January 1989, McDonnell Douglas was still expecting 'the MD-11 first flight to be in early 1989 and MD-11 certification for passenger use for early 1990.' Unfortunately, this was not to be as shortly thereafter the company recognized that it had managerial problems of major proportion which took precedence. Finally, powered by CF6-50C2 turbofans, the first MD-11 (N111MD,s/n 48401) was flown from Long Beach to Edwards AFB on 10 January, 1990, with John I Miller in command. Also powered by CF6-50C2s, the second MD-11 (N211MD) was first flown on 1 March, 1990.

After use in engine performance and aerodynamic flight testing and for avionics testing respectively, the first two MD-11s will be refurbished before delivery to Federal Express. The third MD-11, which first flew on 26 April 1990, is to be used for trials with PW4460 engines. The fourth will be the first to be delivered to a customer, with American Airlines hoping to put it into trans-Pacific service in early 1991. FAA certification is expected to be received in October 1990 for the GE-powered version, and in November 1990 for the P&W-powered version.

Although to the uninitiated the MD-11 will look much like the DC-10, it will indeed be a very different aircraft as shown by the percentage changes between the DC-10-30 (as originally certificated) and the MD-11 shown below.

The MD-11 N111MD approaching the California coast on its first flight. *(MDC)*

Span	+2.5 per cent
Overall length	+10.3 per cent
Cabin length	+12.2 per cent
Maximum number of seats	+6.6 per cent
Cabin volume (upper and lower decks)	+27.3 per cent
Operating Weight Empty	+4.5 per cent
MGTOW (Maximum Gross Take Off Weight)	+8.5 per cent
Design range	+27.0 per cent

FAA take-off field length	−16.8 per cent
Fuel burn per trip	−20.0 per cent
Fuel burn per seat	−33.0 per cent
Direct operating cost per ton-mile	−18.0 per cent

Note: Range is given for full-passenger loads in typical two-class accommodations. FAA take-off field length is given for sea level, 30°C condition.

In the spring of 1990 MDC was proposing the MD-12, a stretched version of the MD-11, to potential customers, and Japan Air Lines had reserved the right to convert MD-11 options into MD-12 orders. However, the fuselage stretch and the wing design had not been finalised and the MD-12 had not yet been committed to production when this book went to press.

Data for passenger version except as noted:

Span 169 ft 6 in (51.66 m); length 200 ft 10 in (61.21 m); height 57 ft 9 in (17.60 m); wing area 3,648 sq ft (338.91 sq m).

Operating weight empty 277,500 lb (125,872 kg); maximum take-off weight 602,500 lb (273,289 kg); maximum payload 122,500 lb (55,565 kg) for passenger version, 150,900lb (68,447 kg) for combi version, and 205,700 lb (93,304 kg) for freighter version; wing loading 165 kg/sq ft (806 lb/sq ft); power loading 3.3 lb/lb st.

Maximum speed 588 mph at 31,000 ft (946 km/h at 9,450 m); cruising speed 578 mph (930 km/h); range with 293 passengers 8,235 miles (13,250 km); range with maximum cargo load of 205,700 lb (93,304 kg) 4,075 miles (6,555 km).

Northrop/McDonnell Douglas F-23

In answer to an Air Force RFP for conceptual designs of an Advanced Tactical Fighter (ATF) to enter service in the mid-nineties, submissions were made in 1986 by seven US manufacturers (Boeing, General Dynamics, Grumman, Lockheed, McDonnell Douglas, Northrop, and Rockwell). During the summer of that year, five of these companies formed into two groups (Boeing, General Dynamics and Lockheed in one, and McDonnell Douglas and Northrop in the other) and announced agreements to co-operate during the next phase of the programme in the development of whichever team member's design was selected by the Air Force.

On 31 October, 1986, the USAF announced that designs proposed by Northrop and Lockheed had been selected and that a $691-mn contract would be awarded to Northrop Corporation and its partner, McDonnell Douglas Corporation, for the manufacture of two Northrop YF-23As. A similar contract was to be awarded to Lockheed-California Company and its two team partners, General Dynamics' Fort Worth Division and Boeing Military Airplane Company, for the manufacture of two Lockheed YF-22As. The ATF programme schedule then called for the design of the prototypes to be frozen during the spring of 1987, the prototype to fly in October 1989, the Air Force to select either the YF-22A or the YF-23A in late 1990, the first FSD (full scale development) aircraft to begin flight tests in 1993, and the type to achieve IOC (Initial Operational Capability) in 1995. Subsequently delays were incurred as the result of insufficient funding and programme milestones have slipped at least six to 18 months. Further delays are likely to result from the need to incorporate new requirements to counter the greater threat-level which was demonstrated when the Sukhoi Su-27 made its impressive international debut at the 1989 Paris Air Show.

Unlike the McDonnell Douglas F-15 and General Dynamics F-16 which were developed with little apparent concern for security, the YF-22A and YF-23A programmes have been shrouded under a tight security blanket and few details have been made public. Preliminary information indicates that the YF-23A is being designed to operate from relatively short fields and to cruise at supersonic speeds without the use of afterburners. It will be powered by two Pratt & Whitney YF119 or General Electric YF120 turbofans, which have been developed under the Joint Advanced Fighter Engine (JAFE) programme to achieve afterburning thrust of at least 28,000 lb (12,700 kg). It is not yet known, however, whether both YF-23A prototypes will be able to accept either engine, or if one prototype will be powered by YF119s and the other by YF120s. Armament will consist of a mix of AIM-120 advanced medium-range air-to-air missiles (AMRAAMs) and AIM-9 close-range air-to-air missiles as well as an internal gun. Advanced equipment will include the new Air Force/Navy Integrated Communications, Navigation, Identification Avionics (ICNIA), the Integrated Electronic Warfare Systems (INEWS), and a Westinghouse/Texas Instrument active phased-array radar. The YF-23As are expected to use VHSIC (Very-High-Speed Integrated Circuit) common signal processors to communicate with and tie together such avionics elements as radar, infrared search and track, and other passive detection systems. Furthermore, it is expected that new lightweight materials, such as advanced non-metallic composite structures, will be used extensively in the manufacture of the YF-23A and that its design will incorporate advanced low-observable (stealth) technology.

The Air Force has a requirement for at least 750 ATFs to replace its McDonnell Douglas F-15s while the Navy may need up to 620 NATFs (Navy Advanced Tactical Fighter) to replace its Grumman F-14s. Work on the NATF was begun in 1988 when the Northrop/MDC and Lockheed/Boeing/GD teams were awarded $50-mn NAVY contracts to adapt their ATF designs to Navy requirements. The competing contractor teams were to submit NATF design proposals during the summer of 1990. The NATF is expected to be 10,000 to 15,000 lb (4,500 to 6,750 kg) heavier than the ATF, due to the need to strengthen its airframe for carrier operations.

All characteristics and performance remain classified.

McDonnell Douglas C-17 Airlifter

The C-17's gestation period has been unduly protracted but blame for the resulting cost overrun rests squarely with political leaders, particularly members of Congress. For the most part, McDonnell Douglas was able to proceed with engineering without encountering time-consuming or costly technical problems and the Air Force consistently favoured the acquisition of a new military airlifter and lent its full support ever since initiating the C-X (Experimental Cargo) competition in 1980. Yet, the C-17 will fly only in mid-1991, ten years after MDC won the design competition, as project funding was provided on an on again/off again basis as the result of inept political moves.

A draft Request for Proposals for a heavy-lift cargo transport was issued by the Air Force in February 1980 and was followed eight months later by a final RFP. As detailed in the RFP, the new military transport was primarily intended for intertheatre operations, in which it would supplement the C-5s and C-141s in service with the Military Airlift Command and eventually replace the C-141s, but it was also planned to complement MAC's C-130s in intratheatre tactical operations. Primary requirements included (1) a fuselage cross-section sufficient to airlift outsize loads, including the M1 Abrams main battle tank; (2) undercarriage and high-lift devices to enable the CX to operate from runways only

The nose shell of the first C-17 under construction in St Louis. This and other sections and components built in various plants were shipped to Long Beach where final assembly takes place. *(MDC)*

3,000 ft (915 m) long and 90 ft (27 m) wide[1]; and (3) thrust reversers to manoeuvre the aircraft in and out of congested parking areas and to back up slopes with one-in-fifty gradient.

The three traditional United States suppliers of transport aircraft, Boeing, Douglas, and Lockheed, submitted designs. The Boeing proposal was for a three-engined design with two of the engines mounted atop the wings as had been the engine of its YC-14 AMST contender. The proposal submitted by Lockheed looked much like a C-141 with a wider fuselage, and that from Douglas was for a four-engined aircraft with a flap blowing system as used on the YC-15 Advanced Medium STOL Transport. It was the last of these which found favour with the Air Force and on 28 August, 1981, the Department of Defense announced that McDonnell Douglas had been selected as the prime contractor for the proposed C-17A. The decision to proceed with the development of the new transport, however, still required Congressional approval.

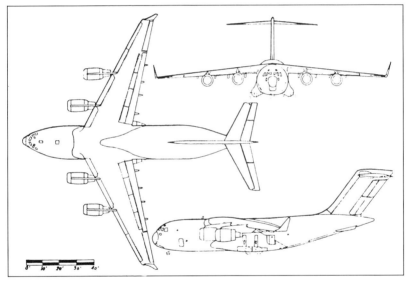

McDonnell Douglas C-17.

In September 1981, immediately after DoD had announced the selection of the McDonnell Douglas design as the winner of the CX competion, Lockheed proposed to the Air Force that forty-four C-5Ns (N for New) should be built in lieu of McDonnell Douglas C-17s as new C-5s could be delivered much sooner and, unlike the C-17s, would not require substantial investments for design, personnel training, and logistic

<hr>

[1] Satisfying this requirement would enable the CX to operate from as many as 436 airfields in Central Europe, whereas the C-5 and the C-141 can only operate from 56 Central European airfields.

support. Although liking the early availability of the proposed C-5N, the Air Force still wanted to go ahead with the C-17A. Congress, on the other hand, liked the lower procurement and operational costs of the C-5N. Accordingly, a compromise was reached in early 1982 whereby the immediate need for additional airlift capability would be filled by ordering 50 Lockheed C-5Bs (the official B suffix replacing the unofficial N) and 44 additional McDonnell Douglas KC-10A tanker/transport aircraft, while long-term needs were to be assessed on the basis of a Congressionally Mandated Mobility Study (CMMS) which had been initiated by DoD in April 1981.

The CMMS study predicted that by 1986 US Armed Forces would require a combined intertheatre airlift capacity of 66 million ton-miles per day (MTM/D, or 96.3 million tonne-km/day) but that aircraft (including the additional KC-10As and C-5Bs) from the active-duty, the Air Force Reserve, the Air National Guard, and the Civil Reserve Air Fleet would only be able to deliver 46 MTM/D (67.1 million tonne-km/day). Notwithstanding this 30 per cent shortfall in airlift capacity, politics continued to plague the C-17 programme as some members of Congress attempted to help US air carriers in their district dispose of older Boeing 747s rendered uneconomic by a traffic slump and rising fuel cost. In the end, sanity prevailed. The Air Force convinced Congress that converted 747s would neither be able to airlift most Army combat and construction vehicles nor operate from 3,000 ft runways. Full-scale development (FSD) work was approved in February 1985, a C-17 prototype was ordered in December 1985, and initial procurement funding was included in the FY87 budget. Funds for the first two production aircraft were provided in the FY88 budget, four C-17As were ordered in FY89, and six more were requested in the FY90 budget. At the end of 1989, procurement plans still called for a total of 210 C-17As, but in April 1990 the Secretary of Defense recommended that only 120 C-17As be procured.

The political shenanigans of the early 'eighties and the small number of aircraft ordered in later years have forced the development of a rather mundane aircraft to take place over a longer period than justified by technical considerations. Consequently, costs rose not only because of inflation but also because the manufacturer and the Air Force had to keep engineering and procurement personnel on the payroll even during periods of reduced activity when insufficient funding prevented the programme from proceeding[2]. Hopefully, when the inevitable hearings into cost overruns take place and attempts made to blame the contractor for gouging the government and the Air Force Systems Command for mismanaging the programme, political editors will remind Congress of its responsibility in this affair.

[2] Had MDC and the Air Force not done so, they would have had to start again from scratch when funding was finally provided, and programme costs would have been even greater.

To be powered by four 37,000 lb (16,783 kg) thrust Pratt & Whitney F117-PW100 turbofans in individual nacelles beneath the wings, the C-17A will have a crew of three (pilot, co-pilot, and loadmaster). It will be able to carry a maximum payload of 172,200 lb (78,110 kg) in a hold having a floor length of 88 ft (26.82 m), a mimimum width of 18ft (5.49 m), and a minimum height of 13 ft 6 in (4.11 m). Cargo will be loaded through a rear ramp and parachute doors will be provided on both sides of the rear fuselage. Typical loads could include oversize items (such as main battle tanks, infantry fighting vehicles, and self-propelled 155-mm guns), helicopters (four UH-60As or two AH-64As and three OH-58C/Ds), or 102 paratroopers. Intended to deliver its load directly to airfields close to FEBA (forward edge of the battle area), the C-17A will be provided with defensive systems not usually associated with transport aircraft (*eg* radar and missile warning systems, and chaff and flare dispensers). It will also be fitted with digital avionics, four CRT displays, and two HUDs.

When the first aircraft (87-0025) was ordered in December 1985, flight trials had been predicted to begin in August 1990. However, due to development problems with the mission computer software and the electronic flight control system, the latter necessitating the replacement of Honeywell by General Electric as system sub-contractor, the start of flight trials has been postponed by at least 10 months. Barring additional delays, Airlifters will be delivered to the 443rd Military Airlift Wing (Training) at Altus AFB, Oklahoma, in late 1992 or early 1993 and IOC (initial operating capability) will be achieved by the 437th MAW at Charleston AFB, North Carolina, in mid 1993.

Span 165 ft (50.29 m); length 175 ft 2 in (53.39 m); height 58 ft (17.68 m); wing area 3,800 sq ft (353.03 sq m).
Empty weight 259,000 lb (117,480 kg); maximum weight 580,000 lb (263,084 kg); wing loading 152.6 lb/sq ft (745 kg/sq m); power loading 3.9 lb/lb st.
Cruising speed 508 mph at 36,000 ft (817 km/h at 10,975 m); maximum tactical speed at low level 472 mph (759 km/h); range with maximum payload 2,765 miles with 172,200 lb (4,450 km with 78,110 kg); range with reduced payload 3,225 miles with 130,000 lb (1,590 km with 58,965 kg); ferry range without air refuelling 5,750 miles (9,250 km).

Artist's rendering of the MDX. *(MDHC)*

McDonnell Douglas MDX

Development of a seven-passenger helicopter, the first all-new commercial rotary-wing aircraft designed by McDonnell Douglas Helicopter Company, was authorized by the MDC Board of Directors on 7 December, 1988. Intended to complement the single-engined, five-passenger MD 520/MD 530 series, the new twin-engined helicopter, tentatively designed MDX, was the result of a lengthy and careful market analysis.

Based on answers to an MDHC questionnaire provided by 177 operators then owning more than a quarter of the turbine helicopters in the free world, the manufacturer began planning a six-passenger helicopter in the 4,000 to 8,000-lb (1,814 to 3,629-kg) class in 1987. At that time, both single- and twin-engined versions were studied as 40 per cent of the initial group of respondents had indicated a definite preference for the single-engine configuration. Seeking and receiving inputs from representatives of major operators, MDHC progressively refined its design. In the autumn of 1988, it reached the conclusion that the new helicopter should accommodate seven passengers and be powered by two turboshaft engines in the 400- to 500-shp class to enable it to fly away from hover with one engine inoperative—a capability which no other light civil helicopter could yet provide. Other design features selected before the project was approved for development included (1) a five-blade flexbeam main rotor as fitted in 1985 to a modified MD 500E as part of the company-funded Helicopter Advanced Rotor Program (HARP); (2) a NOTAR anti-torque system; (3) minimum systems for low operating cost and high availability; and (4) 'glass' cockpit with two

CRT displays. Target price and DOC (direct operating cost) in 1988 dollars were projected at $1.7 million and $200 an hour.

It quickly became apparent that these design parameters were what customers sought as, within a week of announcing at the 40th annual meeting of the Helicopter Association International in January 1989 that it was going ahead with the MDX, McDonnell Douglas Helicopters received more than 100 orders from operators in the Americas, the Orient, and Europe.

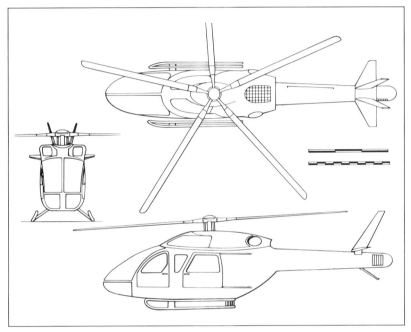

McDonnell Douglas MDX.

Final design was begun in January 1989 under the direction of Project Manager Robert Buffum and full-scale wind-tunnel tests were undertaken later in the year in the 40 by 80 ft tunnel at the NASA Ames Research Center in Moffett, California. In 1989, MDHC also announced that the first 100 MDXs would each be powered by two 450 shp Pratt & Whitney PW206A turboshafts and that customers for subsequent aircraft would be given a choice between PW206As or similarly-rated Turboméca TM319-2s.

Under an agreement signed in February 1989, Hawker de Havilland Pty Ltd in Bankstown, New South Wales, became responsible for final design and production of the MDX airframe and undertook to ship airframes to MDHC for final assembly and installation of engines, transmission, avionics, and other systems in Mesa. First flight of the co-produced MDX is expected to take place in May 1992 with initial customer delivery set for the last quarter of 1993.

Preliminary data:
    Rotor diameter 33 ft 9$^1/_2$ in (10.30 m); overall length 39 ft 3$^1/_2$ in (11.98 m); fuselage length 34 ft 4$^3/_4$ in (10.49 m); height 10 ft 8$^1/_2$ in (3.26 m); rotor disk area 897.27 sq ft (83.32 sq m).
    Empty weight 2,380 lb (1,080 kg); loaded weight 5,400 lb (2,449 kg); maximum weight 6,030 lb (2,735 kg); rotor loading 6 lb/sq ft (29.4 kg/sq m).
    Maximum speed 199 mph (320 km/h) at sea level; cruising speed 173 mph (278 km/h); initial climb rate 1,700 ft/min (8.6 m/sec); hover ceiling out of ground effect 10,000 ft (3,050 m) on a 95°F/35°C day; single-engined hover ceiling 4,000 ft (1,220 m); maximum range 400 miles (645 km).

Artist's rendering of the LHX. *(MDHC)*

McDonnell Douglas/Bell LHX

The US Army began planning for the development of a light rotary-wing aircraft in 1983, with the intention of obtaining a multi-role vehicle to replace Bell AH-1 attack helicopters and Hughes OH-6 and Bell OH-58 scout helicopters in service with active-duty and Army National Guard units. As work on this project proceeded, the Army broadened its operational requirements to add light utility to the scope of missions which were to be assigned to production versions of the LHX (Light Helicopter, Experimental) being developed in the late 'eighties by a McDonnell Douglas/Bell Helicopter team and a Boeing Helicopter/Sikorsky team. Later, however, budget constraints forced the Army to postpone plans for the procurement of 2,400 LHXs in the utility configuration as replacements for UH-1s. Procurement plans for 2,096 LHXs in the scout/attack configuration to replace OH-6s, OH-58s, and AH-1s had been announced, but Congressional support for the programme was fast dwindling at the beginning of 1990. Empty weight and unit cost were then expected not to exceed 7,500 lb (3,402 kg) and $7.5 million, respectively, and the new scout/attack helicopter was planned to enter service in 1996.

Work on the LHX began in 1983 when Hughes Helicopters received four contracts. The first, which was awarded by the Army Aviation Systems Command in July, was for a $205,000 preliminary design study to explore LHX mission-oriented design alternatives. It was followed in September 1983 by two contracts awarded by the Army's Applied Technology Laboratory, a $1.7 million two-year contract to determine the company's 'best technical approach' for the LHX and a $119,000 one-

405

year contract to develop an energy-absorbing retractable undercarriage for application to LHX-class helicopters. A fourth contract, which provided $200,000 to initiate work on Advanced Rotorcraft Technology Integration (ARTI)[1], was awarded to Hughes Helicopters in December

Artist's rendering of the LHX. *(MDHC)*

1983. Concurrently, LHX-related contracts were awarded to other manufacturers including some to Bell Helicopters, MDHC's future partner for the LHX programme.

Subsequent major programme events took place in December 1984 when the Army released an RFP for the development of LHX engines, in March 1985 when the Army stipulated that the LHX would be a conventional helicopter, in September 1985 when MDHC was awarded a $3.8 million contract for wind tunnel testing of an LHX design, in April

---

[1] This was the project which resulted in the fourth YAH-64A (77-23258) being fitted in 1985 with a fly-by-wire digital control system developed jointly by McDonnell Douglas Astronautics Company and Honeywell Inc. Left-hand and right-hand four-axis sidearm controllers and electric foot pedals were installed in the front cockpit to develop an optimum single-pilot configuration for the LHX.

1986 when MDHC, Bell Helicopter Textron, and MCAIR formed a 'Super Team'[2] to work on the LHX, and in October 1986 when the Super Team received a $17.4 million contract to reduce the technological risks of key elements[3] of the LHX programme.

Since its formation, the Super Team has been led by MDHC executives with William R McDonnell becoming the first Super Team Director in April 1986 and Allen C Hagerty being placed in charge of Joint Program Organization in June 1988. Moreover, most of the work has been done in Mesa in facilities provided by MDHC. Work, however, has not been one-sided. The Super Team has decided that the main rotor for its LHX would be based on the Bell 680 all-composite, bearingless and hingeless design and that the anti-torque system would be the MDHC NOTAR.

When the Army received responses to drafts of its Request for Proposals and Required Operating Capabilities in January 1987, it expected to issue a formal RFP and ROC within six months. However, a one-year delay occurred when the Department of Defense requested independent studies of LHX alternatives. Finally, in September 1988, Boeing/Sikorsky and MDHC/Bell submitted proposals in response to the RFP for the DEM/VAL (demonstration/validation) phase of the LHX programme. During the following month, both teams were awarded $166.8 millon, 23-month contracts to construct mock-ups of the cockpit and mission equipment package and to undertake preliminary design work for other LHX components and systems. In the same month, the Light Helicopter Turbine Engine Company (LHTEC), a firm jointly owned by Allison and Garrett, was selected as the winner of the engine competition and was awarded a $207-million contract for initial development of its T800 engine. Following evaluation of work done by MDHC/Bell and Boeing/Sikorsky during the DEM/VAL phase, one of the teams will be selected for the five-year full-scale development (FSD) phase which is expected to begin in late 1990.

As currently envisioned, the LHX will be a two-seat, single-rotor helicopter powered by two 1,200 shp T800 turboshaft engines. It will be fitted with advanced avionics for night and adverse weather operations, nose-mounted FLIR and laser designation systems, and mast-mounted Martin Marietta/Westinghouse Longbow radar for weapon guidance. Armament will consist of Hellfire anti-tank missiles, Stinger air-to-air missiles, and a turret-mounted gun.

[2] The "Super Team" has since been expanded to include AT&T, Eaton Corporation, General Electric, Honeywell, Hughes Aircraft Company, Litton Systems of Canada, Magnavox, Northrop, Sperry, Texas Instruments, and Unisys. Similar LHX teaming arrangements were entered into by Boeing Vertol (Boeing Helicopter Company after September 1987) and Sikorsky for the airframe and by Allison and Garrett and by Textron Lycoming and Pratt & Whitney for engine development.

[3] Principal elements explored under this contract included Very High Speed Integrated Circuits (VHSIC), Electro-Optical Targeting and Designation (EOTADS) systems, and cockpit controls and displays.

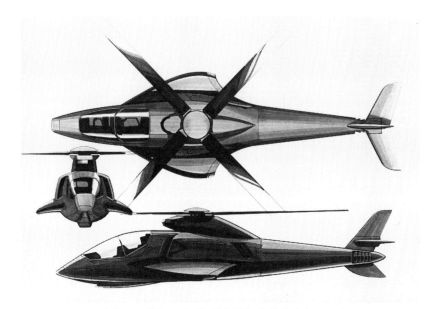

McDonnell Douglas/Bell LHX. *(MDHC drawing)*

First flight of a prototype is scheduled to take place in May 1993 and initial operating capability is to be achieved in 1996. It is to be hoped that this will end the long-drawn out LHX competition.

Preliminary characteristics and performance data have not yet been released as the LHX is still being designed.

McDonnell Douglas/General Dynamics A-12
Avenger II

Since the Navy announcement on 23 December, 1987, that a McDonnell Douglas/General Dynamics team had been selected to develop the Advanced Tactical Aircraft (ATA), the A-12 programme has proceeded under tight security. No details have been revealed but, to be effective in

One of the A-12 cockpit configurations evaluated in a flight simulator. *(MCAIR)*.

its intended role as the replacement for the A-6 carrier-based all-weather medium attack aircraft of the USN and USMC and for the F-111 land-based strike aircraft of the USAF, the A-12 is expected to offer significantly improved performance, particularly in terms of survivability and manoeuvrability.

The two-seat A-12 will be powered by two General Electric F412-GE-400 afterburning turbofans and its structure will incorporate advanced low-observable (stealth) features. It will be fitted with advanced systems including (1) a Westinghouse multi-function air-to-surface and air-to-air radar; (2) a navigation and targeting FLIR (forward-looking infrared) sensor; (3) inertial and global position navigation systems; and (4) advanced electronic surveillance and missile warning systems. More advanced systems currently under development for the Department of Defense's Joint Integrated Avionics Working Group (JIAWIG), including ICNIA (Integrated Communications, Navigation, Identification Avionics), INEWS (Integrated Electronic Warfare Systems), and VHSIC (Very-High-Speed Integrated Circuit) common signal processors, will be incorporated during production, possibly beginning with the 125th A-12, to achieve 90 per cent commonality between the ATA and ATF (YF-22/YF-23) avionics.

Design and development are being done at the McDonnell Aircraft Company in St Louis, and at the General Dynamics Fort Worth Division in Texas. Fort Worth is also the site of the PPO (Principal Program Office) which is staffed by the two companies. Work during the development and initial production phases is being shared equally, with parts and assemblies made in both St Louis and Fort Worth, but the Navy will require MCAIR and GD to compete for the production phase of the programme.

A two-year demonstration/validation phase was begun in late 1989, with the first flight of a prototype to take place in the mid 1990s and IOC (Initial Operational Capability) to be achieved in the late 1990s. The first 25 aircraft will be delivered to the Navy with subsequent aircraft going to the Navy and the Air Force in accordance with a schedule which has not yet been finalized.

All characteristics and performance remain classified.

Appendix A

Selected Projects

The following selection of projects—two helicopters designed by Hughes Tools and Hughes Helicopters, two helicopters from McDonnell Aircraft Company, two combat aircraft proposed by McDonnell Aircraft Company, and three airliner studies from McDonnell Douglas Corporation—provides an overview of the vast number of preliminary designs which originated in Culver City, St Louis, and Long Beach.

Hughes XH-28

Development of a large helicopter was begun in January 1951 to meet an Army requirement for a flying crane capable of transporting combat-loaded military vehicles weighting up to 20 tons (18.1 tonnes). Like the XH-17 which was then about to be flown, the XH-28 was to use a pressure-jet system to drive the four-bladed main rotor, with two Allison XT40-A-8 turbines being geared to a compressor unit and compressed air ducted to burners at the tip of each blade.

Weighing 52,000 lb (23,587 kg) empty and 105,000 lb (47,627 kg) loaded, the XH-28 was to have had enclosed accommodation for two

The XH-28 mock up. *(MDHC)*

411

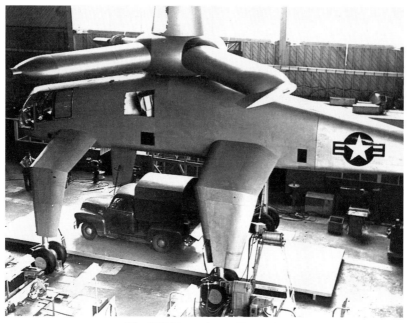

The XH-28 mock-up. *(MDHC)*

pilots. Its four tall undercarriage units, each with dual-wheels would have given it a spider look while providing adequate clearance for outsize loads. These loads were to have been either slung beneath the fuselage or carried on a flat-bed attached between the undercarriage legs and fitted with a ramp for loading and unloading vehicles.

The design was subjected to extensive wind-tunnel tests with various suspended loads, and a full-scale mock-up was constructed. In spite of its promising capability, the XH-28 was not built due to cutbacks in the research and development budget made near the end of the Korean War.

McDonnell XHRH-1

Design of the Model 78 was started in 1950 in answer to a request for proposals for an assault transport helicopter which had been issued by the Navy Department on behalf of the US Marine Corps. Intended to operate from CVE-105 class (uss *Commencement Bay*) carriers, the new helicopter was to fit on 44 ft by 42 ft (13.41 m by 12.80 m) deck elevators. Its primary mission was to carry 30 troops to objectives up to 100 naut miles away and return to the carrier without the need to refuel ashore.

To fulfil what were then most demanding requirements, McDonnell designed a compound helicopter with a three-bladed rotor and short wings on which were mounted two 3,507 shp Allison XT56-A-4 turbines.

An artist's rendering showing the XHRH-1 as it would have appeared in flight.
(MCAIR, courtesy of Dr F. W. Roos)

For vertical flight, air from engine-driven auxiliary compressors was to be ducted to 1,600 lb (726 kg) thrust McDonnell 12JP20 pressure jets, one at the extremity of each rotor. For forward flight, each engine was to drive a three-bladed propeller, with transition from helicopter flight mode to conventional flight being made by transferring power from the auxiliary compressors to the propellers as soon as the forward speed exceeded the stalled speed of the wing. Normal accommodation was to have been provided for a crew of two and 30 fully-equipped troops. Alternatively, accommodation could have been provided for 36 troops or 24 litter patients, or two Jeep-sized vehicles could have been carried internally. Larger loads (up to a maximum weight of 11,518 lb/5,224 kg) could be carried externally. Another noteworthy design feature was the inclusion of a hydraulically-operated loading ramp in the forward fuselage, beneath the cockpit. Folding wings, rotor blades, and tail unit were to have enabled the Model 78 to fit on the deck elevators of CVE-105 carriers.

The Navy selected the McDonnell design on 15 March, 1951, and two and a half months later issued a Letter of Intent for three XHRH-1 prototypes (BuNos 133736/133738) to be built under Contract NOa(s)-51-1201. A full-scale mock-up of the XHRH-1 was inspected on 22 and 23 October, 1952, and construction of the prototypes was begun.

The full-size mock-up of the XHRH-1 showing the nose loading ramp. *(MCAIR, courtesy of Dr. F. W. Roos)*

However, after the Korean War had ended, budget cuts and concern over anticipated developmental problems led to the cancellation of the contract before completion of a single XHRH-1. All work on the project ended in April 1954.

The principal characteristics and calculated performance of the XHRH-1 were as follows: rotor diameter 65 ft (19.81 m); span 45 ft (13.72 m); length 65 ft 11 in (20.09 m); length (rotor blades and tail folded) 53 ft 7 in (16.33 m); height 16 ft 8½ in (5.09 m); rotor disk area 3,320 sq ft (308.22 sq m); wing area 332 sq ft (30.84 sq m); empty weight 19,169 lb (8,695 kg); loaded weight 30,412 lb (13,795 kg); maximum weight 36,000 lb (16,329 kg); maximum speed 276 mph (444 km/h) at sea level; climb rate 2,300 ft/min (12 m/sec); hover ceiling out of ground effect 10,000 ft (3,050 m); combat radius 100 naut miles (185 km).

McDonnell XHCH-1

The McDonnell Model 86 was the first helicopter specially designed for the Navy vert-rep (vertical replenishment) mission—carrying supplies and ammunition between ships—and for the Marine logistic support mission—carrying heavy loads for short distances from ship-to-shore or from marshalling areas ashore to front-line units.

Emphasis was placed during its design on extreme simplicity, ease of maintenance, and good flying characteristics while carrying underslung loads of up to 15,000 lb (6,804 kg) when operating at normal gross weight, or 22,000 lb (9,979 kg) when operating at overload gross weight. The powerplant installation, derived from that developed for the XHRH-1, consisted of two 3,750 eshp Allison XT56-A-2 turbines mounted atop the

The full-size mock-up of the XHCH-1. *(MCAIR, courtesy of Dr F. W. Roos)*

fuselage and providing compressed-air to the 1,600 lb (726 kg) thrust McDonnell 12JP20 pressure jet at the extremity of each rotor blade. The crew of two consisted of a pilot on the starboard side and an aft-facing winch operator to port. There was no provision for carrying loads internally. Loads were to be carried externally on a sling, in a net, or in a specially-developed pod. This pod was to be fitted with a detachable tail unit to stabilize the load in flight and with large wheels to enable it to be towed on uneven ground after it had been delivered to forward bases. Consideration was also given to using the Fairchild pod which had been designed for the XC-120 twin-engined cargo aircraft.

Three XHCH-1 prototypes (BuNos 138654/138656) were ordered on 11 April, 1952, under Contract NOa(s)52-947 and a mock-up was inspected on 22 and 23 May, 1953. However, the programme was later cut back due to lack of funds. No prototypes were completed but a much revised mock-up was inspected on 15 and 16 November, 1956, and a full-scale rotor was tested on a hot-whirling bench beginning in December 1957. Additional budget cuts forced the Navy to terminate the contract on 18 January, 1959, before completion of a prototype. Nevertheless, McDonnell kept working on the Model 86 sky crane until June 1961.

The principal characteristics and calculated performance of the XHCH-1 were as follows: rotor diameter 65 ft (19.81 m); length 37 ft 6³/₄ in (11.45 m); height 16 ft 7¹/₂ in (5.07 m); rotor disk area 3,320 sq ft (308.22 sq m); empty weight 14,878 lb (6,749 kg); loaded weight 35,332 lb (16,026 kg); maximum weight 42,000 lb (19,051 kg); maximum speed 115 mph (185 km/h) at sea level; climb rate 3,200 ft/min (16 m/sec); hover ceiling out of ground effect 7,500 ft (2,285 m); combat radius 20 naut miles (37 km).

McDonnell F-4 (FV)S

Towards the end of 1965, after it became evident that Grumman and General Dynamics would be unable to keep the loaded weight of their F-111B variable geometry carrier-based fighter within the upper limit of 55,000 lb (24,947 kg) as required by the Navy, McDonnell began work on a variable sweep wing modification of the F-4J. This privately-funded study led to the submission of an unrequested proposal for the F-4 (FVS) in August 1966. In response to comments from NAVAIR (Naval Air Systems Command), additional studies were undertaken in the autumn and winter of 1966 in attempts to reduce approach speed by about 10 knots and improve manoeuvrability at high altitude. The resulting design, with a subtle change in designation from F-4 (FVS) to F-4 (FV)S, was described in a report dated 20 February, 1967.

Essentially, the F-4 (FV)S retained the fuselage, vertical tail surfaces, and powerplant installation of the F-4J and was to have been fitted with two-pivot variable-geometry wings which could be swept from a minimum of 19 deg to a maximum of 70 deg. Other major airframe differences included the use of horizontal tail surfaces without the characteristic anhedral of the Phantom II's stabilizer and a new main undercarriage retracting in the fuselage alongside the engines. For its primary mission, FAD (Fleet Air Defense), the F-4 (FV)S was to have been fitted with an AN/AWG-10 Airborne Missile Control System modified to provide multi-shot capability and armed with four AIM-7F Sparrow air-to-air missiles. For its secondary air-to-ground mission, it was to have been equipped with an inertial nav-bomb system, lead computing sight, and other updated avionics.

Although the F-4 (FV)S promised to be substantially more capable than the F-4J, it was no match for what could be achieved with a new design such as the Grumman G-303 variable-geometry fighter (the future F-14 Tomcat). In particular, the modified AN/AWG-10 radar and AIM-7F Sparrow medium-range missiles did not provide the same level of simultaneous multiple-target intercept capability as that made possible by the AN/AWG-9 radar and AIM-54 Phoenix long-range missiles as developed for the F-111B and later incorporated in the F-14. Accordingly, the Navy did not show much interest in the F-4 (FV)S proposal and issued an RFP for a new carrier-based fighter in June 1968.

The principal characteristics and calculated performance of the F-4 (FV)S were as follows: span (wings swept forward) 59 ft 11³/₄ in (18.28 m); span (wings swept back) 38 ft 1 in (11.61 m); length 60 ft 11¹/₂ in (18.58 m); height 18 ft 1¹/₄ in (5.52 m); wing area (wings swept forward) 680 sq ft (63.17 sq m); wing area (wings swept back) 617 sq ft (57.32 sq m); empty weight 33,229 lb (15,072 kg); loaded weight 50,910 lb (23,092 kg); maximum weight 68,710 lb (31,166 kg); maximum Mach 2.27 (with afterburners) and 1.05 (without afterburners); combat ceiling 58,000 ft (17,680 m); endurance 5 hr on CAP at 150-naut mile (280-km) from the carrier; ferry range 3,035 miles (4,885 km).

McDonnell Douglas Model 210

In addition to planning the Model 188, a direct derivative of the Breguet 941 STOL transport as described on page 270, in 1967-68 MCAIR worked on preliminary design studies for several versions of its Model 210 propeller-turbine airliner. Like the Breguet 941 and McDonnell Douglas Model 188, the Model 210 was proposed as a high-wing aircraft relying on the deflected-slipstream principle to achieve outstanding STOL performance. Its four 3,300 shp General Electric CT64-630-3 turboshafts were to be interconnected through a Breguet-patented flexible transmission shaft so that all propellers would remain operative in the event of an engine failure.

The two most promising versions each had a fuselage of different diameters and lengths. The Model 210E provided six-abreast accommodation for 90 passengers with a single aisle and three-three seating and the Model 210G accommodated 112 passengers with two aisles and two-two-two seating. Fitted with special avionics and navigation equipment, Model 210s were intended to operate along separate tracks instead of competing with other airliners for slots in congested airways and terminal areas. As they were endowed with sprightly performance, they were expected to find a ready market among airlines operating in busy corridors such as between Washington, New York, and Boston, and between San Diego, Los Angeles, and San Francisco. However, in the late sixties, the travelling public expected to fly in jet transports even on short routes and the airlines could not risk going against this trend.

Principal characteristics and calculated performance were as follows (Model 210E/Model 210G): span 89 ft 9¹/₂ in/97 ft 8¹/₂ in(27.37/29.78 m); length 100 ft 7¹/₂ in/118 ft 9¹/₂ in (30.67/36.21 m); height 34 ft 11in/35 ft 10³/₄ in (10.64/10.94 m); wing area 1,240/1,520 sq ft (115.2/141.2 sq m); empty weight 42,816/51,081 lb (19,421/23,170 kg); loaded weight 70,876/84,500 lb (32,149/38,329 kg); cruising speed 401/372 mph (645/603 km/h); range with full passenger load 690/650 miles (1,110/1,045 km); take-off field length to clear 35-ft/10-m obstacle 1,160/1,380 ft (355/420 m).

McDonnell Model 225 (VFX)

In answer to a Navy Request for Proposals dated 21 June, 1968, MCAIR submitted VFX (experimental carrier-based fighter) proposals for a version to be powered by existing 20,900 lb (9,480 kg) thrust Pratt & Whitney TF30 turbofans, the Model 225A (VFX-1), and a version to be powered by 28,000 lb (12,700 kg) thrust General Electric GE1/10F10B2 turbofans then under development, the Model 225B (VFX-2). In both cases, engines were to be separated by large main fuel tanks to reduce vulnerability and provide a large undersurface area for low-drag weapons carriage.

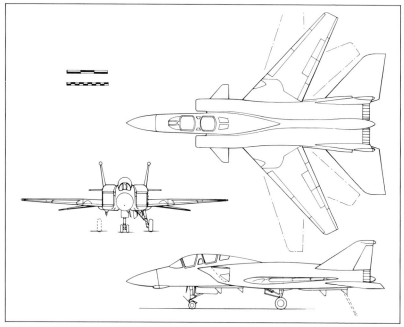

McDonnell Model 225A (VFX-1)

The Model 225A was characterized by twin canted vertical tail surfaces, downward-folding canard surfaces, and variable-geometry wings. Sweep was to be set at 19 deg for take-off, landing, loiter, and ferry; 45 deg for high-speed cruise and transonic combat; 70 deg for acceleration and supersonic operation; and 80 deg for carrier stowage.

For the Fleet air defence mission, the Model 225A was to be armed with six AIM-54 Phoenix long-range missiles or six AIM-7E/F Sparrow medium-range missiles semi-submerged beneath the fuselage. For the air superiority mission, it was to carry four AIM-7E/F Sparrows and four AIM-9D short-range missiles. For the fighter-attack mission, it could have carried 13 Mk 83 1,000-lb (454-kg) bombs. In all cases, a 20-mm cannon was to be carried internally and an AN/AWG-9 radar fitted in the nose.

The McDonnell Model 225A and Grumman Design 303E were short-listed by NAVAIR on 15 December, 1968, and on 14 January, 1960, Grumman was announced the winner of the VFX competition.

The principal characteristics and calculated performance of the Model 225A (VFX-1) were as follows: span (19-deg sweep) 57 ft 9½ in (17.62 m), (45-deg sweep) 50 ft 3½ in (15.33 m), (70-deg sweep) 36 ft 9½ in (11.22 m), (80-deg sweep) 30 ft 2½ in (9.20 m); length 62 ft 8½ in (19.11 m); height 15 ft 7¼ in (4.75 m); wing area 500 sq ft (46.45 sq m); empty weight 34,643 lb (15,714 kg); loaded weight 52,900 lb (23,995 kg); maximum weight 62,216 lb (28,221 kg); maximum Mach 2.4; combat ceiling 58,300 ft (17,770 m); endurance 3 hr on CAP at 150-naut mile (280-km) from the carrier; ferry range 2,680 miles (4,310 km).

McDonnell Douglas DC-X-200

In 1967, when Douglas decided to proceed with the three-engined DC-10 rather than with the twin-engined aircraft originally designed to meet an American Airlines' requirement (see Douglas D-966 in Volume I, page 615), company planners had advised their management that the world's

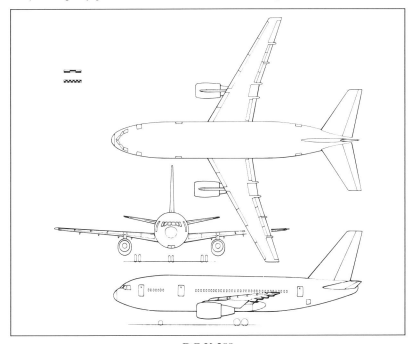

DC-X-200

airlines would need twin-engined, wide-body jetliners by the mid-seventies. Accordingly, DAC proposed a twin-engined DC-10 derivative (with shortened forward fuselage to offset the removal of the centre engine) in 1972 but was unsuccessful in its attempt to secure launch orders before the 1973 energy crisis brought about a slowdown in airline activities. DAC next studied a series of more fuel efficient Advanced Medium Range Aircraft (AMRA) projects, some all-new and some derived from the DC-10, before proposing its DC-X-200 in mid-1975. This project was to have used the cockpit and major portions of the DC-10 fuselage, the wing-mounted General Electric CF6-50 installation of the DC-10-30, and many common systems, but was to have been fitted with new wing and tail surfaces. However, in the mid-seventies the Airbus A300 had a commanding lead and, unlike Boeing which persisted with the development of wide-body twins culminating with the launching of the 767, in the end McDonnell Douglas decided that a direct challenge to the A300 would not be profitable.

The principal characteristics and calculated performance of the DC-X-200 were as follows: span 133 ft 7¹/₄ in (40.72 m); length 143 ft 4 in (43.69 m); height 52 ft (15.85 m); wing area 2,100 sq ft (195.1 sq m); empty weight 163,850 lb (74,321 kg); loaded weight 283,400 lb (128,548 kg); cruising speed Mach 0.82; range 2,935 miles (4,720 km) with 206 passengers and baggage; accommodation for 206 passengers in mixed-class configuration or 278 passengers in all-coach configuration.

McDonnell Douglas ATMR and DC-XX

Having decided not to challenge the A300, DAC switched its developmental activities from the design of wide-body twins with 200 to 300 seats to that of narrow-body twins with 160 to 250 seats. The company also decided to seek foreign partners with which to share work and risks. Thus, in the summer of 1976, Douglas and Dassault-Breguet announced that they would explore the feasibility of developing the French-designed Mercure 200 twinjet as the 160- to 186-seat ASMR (Advanced Short-Medium Range) aircraft. Joint work, however, was terminated in October 1977 when Douglas went ahead with the development of the DC-9-80.

Under the acronym of ATMR (Advanced Technology Medium Range), Douglas next studied a series of twin-aisle narrow-body aircraft to fill the seating gap between the DC-9-80 and the A300. As offered to airlines in early 1980, the ATMR-II version was to have been powered by two 32,000 lb (14,515 kg) thrust Pratt & Whitney JT10D-232 turbofans in underwing nacelles and was to have carried between 180 and 200 passengers, with two-two-two seating in coach class and two-one-two seating in first class, in a twin-aisle cabin. This project evolved into the DC-XX which was offered later in 1980 and was to have been powered by two 35,000 to 37,500 lb (15,876 to 17,010 kg) thrust turbofans (General

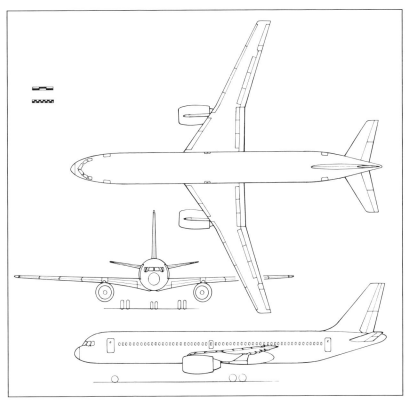

DC-XX

Electric CF6-32C1s, Pratt & Whitney JT10D-234s, or Rolls-Royce RB.211-535C2As). The DC-XX was to have had a slightly wider fuselage than the ATMR-II to provide two-three-two seating in high-density configuration and increased underfloor cargo capacity. However, Douglas was again unsuccessful in its attempt to launch a new jetliner.

The principal characteristics and calculated performance of the DC-XX were as follows: span 131 ft 5 in (40.06 m); length 148 ft 5 in (45.24 m); height 44 ft 4 in (13.51 m); empty weight 127,700 lb (57,924 kg); loaded weight 213,500 lb (96,842 kg); cruising speed Mach 0.82; range 2,645 miles (4,255 km) with 180 passengers and bags; accommodation for 180 passengers in mixed-class configuration or 255 passengers in high-density configuration.

Hughes 600X

Seeking to expand its family of civil helicopters by adding a six-seat aircraft to its two-/three-seat Model 269/300 series and four-/five seat Model 500 series without having to make a major investment of capital, in

421

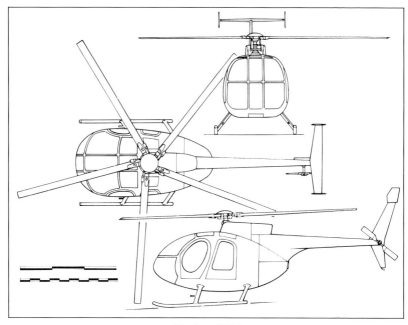

Hughes 600X

mid-1981 Hughes proposed a 'wide-body' version of the Model 500. The new model was to have a 15-in (38 cm) longitudinal plug inserted in the fuselage but was to retain the powerplant installation, rotor system, tail boom and T-tail surfaces, and most of the fuselage of the Model 500D virtually unchanged.

Market conditions were not favourable in late 1981 and early 1982 for the launch of a new helicopter. Moreover, the corporate re-organization and the decision of the parent organization, The Hughes Corporation, to divest itself of Hughes Helicopters, Inc, also made the development of a new product ill advisable. Consequently, all work on the Model 600X was terminated before Hughes Helicopters was acquired by McDonnell Douglas Corporation.

The principal characteristics and calculated performance of the 600X were as follows: rotor diameter 26 ft 6 in (8.08 m); length 30 ft 6 in (9.30 m); height 8 ft 6 in (2.59 m); rotor disc area 551.5 sq ft (51.3 sq m); empty weight 1,436 lb (651 kg); loaded weight 3,000 lb (1,361 kg); cruising speed 157 mph (253 km/h); hover ceiling out of ground effect 7,400 ft (2,255 m); maximum range 490 miles (790 km).

Gemini VII photographed from *Gemini VIA* during station keeping at an altitude of approximately 160 miles on 16 December, 1965. *(NASA)*

Manned Space Vehicles

'Ahh, Roger; lift-off and the clock is started... Yes, sir, reading you loud and clear. This is Freedom 7. The fuel is go; 1.2 g; cabin at 14 psi; oxygen is go... Freedom 7 is still go!'—Cdr Alan B Shepard talking to Mercury Control 2.3 seconds after the launch of *Mercury-Redstone 3* from Cape Canaveral, Florida, on 5 May, 1961.

In keeping with the precedent set with other titles in the Putnam Aeronautical Series, the history of missiles and space launch vehicles designed and built by McDonnell Douglas and its forebears has been excluded. However, the Mercury manned space capsule, the Gemini manned spacecraft, the MOL manned orbiting laboratory, and the Skylab space station rightfully belong in a book on piloted aircraft.

Project Mercury

In March 1946, General of the Air Force H H Arnold asked Douglas to house and operate Project RAND (for research and development), a 'think tank' funded by the Army Air Forces to undertake national security research projects. Douglas agreed and one of the reports completed later in that year under Project RAND[1] was entitled *Preliminary Design of an Experimental World-Circling Spaceship*. Studies on the feasibility and military applicability of instrumented Earth satellites were also undertaken by the Navy Bureau of Aeronautics in the immediate postwar years. However, there was then little incentive for undertaking ventures as ambitious as putting either instrumented or manned satellites in Earth orbit and the United States did not seriously consider a manned space programme until national pride and military preparedness were challenged by a string of Soviet missile and space successes during the second half of 1957. The announcement on 26 August that the USSR had successfully launched an intercontinental ballistic missile and the placing into Earth orbit of the instrumented *Sputnik 1* on 4 October and the dog-carrying *Sputnik 2* on 3 November clearly showed that the USSR would soon have the capability of placing a man in Earth orbit.

Although military and other government officials keenly felt the urgency of developing reliable intercontinental missiles and space launchers and Congress and the American public clamoured for matching Soviet achievements at once and for taking the lead as soon as possible, the United States was ill-prepared to do so. The first test of a US intercontinental ballistic missile, the Atlas 4A, ended in failure on 11 June, 1957, when it had to be destroyed prematurely by a range safety officer, and the first attempt at launching an instrumented satellite, the diminutive *Vanguard I* developed by the Naval Research Laboratory, ended dismally on 6 December, 1957, when the first stage exploded. Even after the first US satellite, *Explorer I*, was put into orbit on 31 January, 1958, it was painfully clear that the Soviet Union had a commanding lead in space as *Sputnik 2* weighed 1,121 lb (508 kg) whereas *Explorer I* weighed only 31 lb (14 kg). Moreover, in the militarily more important field of intercontinental ballistic missiles, the United States appeared to be lagging even further behind as the Convair Atlas achieved its design range only in November 1958.

Low-priority contract feasibility studies of manned satellites had been funded by the Air Research and Development Command beginning during the spring of 1956 in pre-*Sputnik* days. On the strength of this work, in March 1958 the Air Force proposed an ambitious multi-step programme for instrumented and manned Earth satellites and for a manned landing on the surface of the Moon. The first phase of this

[1] In November 1948, after the Ford Foundation provided initial funding for a complete reorganization, the project evolved into RAND Corporation, an entirely separate, non-profit research organization. Still with its headquarters in Santa Monica, California, RAND Corporation is one of the principal consulting firms currently undertaking research studies under USAF contracts.

programme was called 'Man-in-Space-Soonest' and was predicted to result in a manned orbital flight in October 1960.

Within the National Advisory Committee for Aeronautics (NACA),

A Mercury capsule being raised atop the launch gantry at Cape Canaveral. *(MDC)*

limited research work on manned and unmanned upper atmosphere vehicles had begun in mid-1952 at the Langley Aeronautical Laboratory in Hampton, Virginia, and at the Pilotless Aircraft Research Division on Wallops Island, off the coast of Virginia, in support of work undertaken by other agencies. Thus, six years later, NACA agreed to collaborate with the Air Force in drawing up plans for a manned orbital project. However, this March 1958 agreement was short-lived. On 14 April, 1958, President Eisenhower sent a bill to Congress to expand NACA into an agency with research, development, managerial, and flight operational capabilities extending to space projects. The outcome was the passing by

425

Congress on 16 July of the National Aeronautics and Space Act of 1958 creating the National Aeronautics and Space Administration (NASA). In addition to other duties, the newly created NASA was to take responsibility for the US manned space project. The Air Force would drop its 'Man-in-Space-Soonest' project but would continue to sponsor military manned space projects such as the Dyna-Soar.

Under the direction of Robert R Gilruth and his Space Task Group, NASA immediately undertook work on the manned space project. Preliminary specifications for capsule and subsystems were sent to prospective bidders on 23 October, 1958, and formal specifications and a request for bids were issued on 14 November. The name Mercury was selected for the project on 26 November, an initial order for a first Convair Atlas space booster was placed on 8 December, and bids for the capsule and associated systems were submitted by eleven companies on

Astronaut John H Glenn Jr being suited up before becoming the first US astronaut to fly in orbit. He did so in capsule No. 7, *Friendship 7*, on 5 May, 1961. *(NASA)*

11 December. Among the bidders[2] were the Douglas Aircraft Company and the McDonnell Aircraft Corporation.

In anticipation of requests to bid for space systems, a McDonnell team led by Raymond A Pepping, Albert Utsch, Lawrence M Weeks, and John F Yardley had begun preliminary design work on a manned space capsule during the spring of 1958 and had completed a large report on the subject by mid-October. That report served as the basis for the proposal submitted on 11 December, 1958, in answer to the NASA request for bids and led to McDonnell being selected as the prime contractor[3] for the Mercury capsule on 12 January, 1959. The 'Research and Development Contract for Designing and Furnishing Manned Satellite Capsule' was signed on 5 February and the mock-up of the capsule was inspected in St Louis on 17/18 March. The first seven astronauts—Lt M Scott Carpenter, USN; Capt L Gordon Cooper Jr, USAF; Lt Col John H Glenn Jr, USMC; Capt Virgil I Grissom, USAF; LCdr Walter M Schirra Jr, USN; LCdr. Alan B Shepard, USN; and Capt Donald K Slayton, USAF—were introduced to the public on 9 April. Project Mercury was 'go'.

Initially, McDonnell was to have supplied 12 identical capsules but soon after the mock-up review it was decided to procure 20 capsules, each tailored to a specific mission. In addition, NASA was to fabricate 'boilerplate' capsule replicas (BPs) in its own facilities for use in various unmanned tests. BPs and Mercury capsules were to be used in five unmanned ballistic flights atop NASA Little Joe[4] boosters, two balloon ascents (later cancelled), 10 unmanned or manned ballistic flights atop Army Redstone or Jupiter missiles, and 10 unmanned or manned orbital flights launched by Air Force Atlas booster. The first manned suborbital flight of a Mercury-Redstone was scheduled for 26 April, 1960, and the first manned orbital flight of a Mercury-Atlas for 1 September, 1960. Not surprisingly, this overly ambitious schedule slipped, with delays stemming mainly from concern for astronaut safety, slippage with the Redstone rocket, and difficulties with Mercury capsule systems integration.

From the retrograde package at the bottom of the frustrum-shaped capsule to the tip of the aerodynamic spike, the entire capsule measured 24 ft (7.31 m) in length and, when mounted atop the Redstone booster, overall length was 83 ft (25.30 m). When placed atop the Atlas booster, the spacecraft had an overall length of 95 ft 4 in (29.06 m). The Mercury capsule was comprised of (1) a truncated conical antenna and drogue-chute housing; (2) a cylindrical compartment of greater diameter housing

[2] The other bidders were Avco, Convair/Astronautics, Lockheed, Martin, North American, Northrop, Republic, and Winzen Research.

[3] McDonnell was apparently selected because the engineering personnel of the other finalist, Grumman Aircraft, were already quite busy with the development of several Navy aircraft.

[4] Little Joe was a booster specially developed by the Pilotless Aircraft Research Division to launch full-scale and full-weight capsules to a maximum altitude of 100 miles (161 km).

Friendship 7, the seventh Mercury capsule fitted with its escape rocket. *(MDC)*

428

the main and reserve parachutes, beacons, and other recovery aids; (3) the conical pressurized compartment with the fibreglass couch cast to the contour of each astronaut, instrumentation, communications, navigation aids, electrical power, environmental control, and stabilisation and control systems; and (4) the pneumatic landing bag, ablative heat-shield, and retro-rockets. An escape rocket, which was attached on top of the capsule by means of a tubular fitting, was intended to be jettisoned after launch.

After initial parachute drop tests of boilerplate capsules from a Lockheed C-130, assorted wind-tunnel tests, and other experiments, the first major step in the Mercury programme was the first launch of a Little Joe (LJ-1) carrying a boilerplate capsule and the complete escape system. Unfortunately, this test failed on 21 August, 1959, when the Grand Central escape rocket fired prematurely while the booster was still on the launch pad at Wallops Island. The next launch, that of Big Joe, an Atlas D carrying a BP capsule, which was intended to prove that the ablation shield would safely protect the Mercury astronauts during re-entry into

The future partners at work: A Mercury capsule being loaded at the McDonnell plant in St Louis aboard a Douglas C-124C of the 1607th Air Transport Wing. *(MDC)*

the Earth atmosphere, took place at Cape Canaveral on 9 September. It was classified as a partial failure because velocity was less than desired (but still an impressive 14,857 mph, 23,905 km/h) due to the failure of the outboard booster engines to separate. Nevertheless the test accomplished its principal purpose as the ablation shield fully protected the BP during re-entry. The boilerplate capsule was recovered in the Atlantic, 675 naut miles (1,250 km) down range from Cape Canaveral.

Four additional boilerplate capsules were launched from Wallops Island atop Little Joe boosters before the first test of a McDonnell Mercury capsule could take place. LJ-6, on 4 October, and LJ-1A, on 4 November, were considered partial failures but two tests with BP capsules carrying rhesus monkeys were successful. 'Sam' survived his ride in LJ-2 on 4 December, 1959, and 'Miss Sam' endured safely the intentional firing of the escape system after LJ-1B was launched on 21 January, 1960.

Stripped of most of its subsystems, Capsule No 1 was used at Wallops Island for a test of the escape rocket, parachute recovery, and landing system. This was successfully accomplished on 9 May, 1960, when the escape rocket propelled the capsule half a mile up and one mile down range, and Capsule No. 1 was recovered. It was later refurbished and renumbered Capsule No. 2A when the failure of MR-1, the first Mercury-Redstone unmanned flight, necessitated a replacement to qualify the capsule before a manned flight. Other capsules used in unmanned tests

Capsule No. 2 being hoisted atop MR-1 at Cape Canaveral. The capsule was destroyed when MR-1 failed two seconds after being launched on 21 November, 1960. *(NASA)*

during the second half of 1960 were No. 2, which was lost in the failure of MR-1 on 21 November; No. 3, the first production standard capsule, which was lost in the LJ-5 failure on 8 November; and No. 4 which was lost on 29 July when the first Mercury-Atlas blew up one minute after lift-off from Cape Canaveral. Although 1960 ended without NASA, McDonnell, and their sub-contractors being able to accomplish the manned suborbital and orbital flights as had been optimistically predicted less than two years earlier, the last Mercury event of the year was a success. On 19 December, 1960, the refurbished Capsule No. 2A was recovered at the end of the *Mercury-Redstone 1A* suborbital flight. Moreover, national pride had yet to be hurt further by the failure to place an astronaut in Earth orbit ahead of a Soviet cosmonaut.

The first three months of 1961 were much more satisfactory for the Project Mercury team: on 31 January, the chimpanzee 'Ham' came back safe and sound after a suborbital flight in Capsule No. 5; on 21 February, Capsule No. 6 was recovered after a suborbital flight to qualify the Mercury-Atlas combination; and on 18 March, Capsule No. 14 was reusable after the escape rocket fired prematurely during the test of Little Joe 5A at Wallops Island. The month of April, conversely, held more than its fair share of bad news for the Mercury people. On the 12th, Yuri Gagarin became the first man to orbit the Earth, on the 25th, the first attempt at placing a Mercury capsule in orbit failed when *Mercury-Atlas 3* (MA-3) had to be destroyed by the range safety officer 40 seconds after it had been launched from Cape Canaveral, and finally on the 28th, testing of the escape system at Wallops Island was once again only partially successful as LJ-5B failed to achieve the desired speed. Notwithstanding these new difficulties, NASA decided to proceed with the first US suborbital manned flight without further delay. That momentous event took place on 5 May, 1961.

Capsule No. 7 had been selected during the summer of 1960 to be used for the first manned flight and had been delivered to Cape Canaveral in December of that year. Mounted atop the seventh Redstone booster procured by NASA and named *Freedom 7*, this capsule was carefully prepared to take Alan Shepard on his suborbital flight. The launch, which was to have taken place on 2 May, was cancelled twice due to weather and the countdown, which started at 8:30 pm on 4 May, was held several times for weather and technical reasons even after Shepard had been secured on his couch in *Freedom 7*. Finally, the capsule and astronaut were launched atop *Mercury-Redstone 3* without a flaw. The Redstone's engine shut down 142 seconds after lift-off and the escape rocket separated as planned. Safe in the smoothly working *Freedom 7*, Shepard reached a top altitude of 116.5 naut miles (215.8 km) and a top speed of 5,134 mph (8,261 km/h). During his flight, Shepard switched from automatic to manual controls, thus acting as a true pilot instead of being just 'spam in the can' as critics of the manned spaced flight programme had claimed would be the case. Retro-Rockets fired on cue and during the

A Mercury capsule being launched atop a Redstone booster. *(MDC)*

deceleration the astronaut was subjected to a maximum of 11.6 g. Following deployment of the 63-ft (19.20-m) diameter main parachute at an altitude of 10,000 ft (3,050 m), *Freedom 7* splashed into the water 303 naut miles (561 km) down range from Cape Canaveral. Astronaut and capsule were recovered by a Sikorsky HUS-1 Seahorse helicopter from Marine Squadron HMR(L)-262 and taken to the prime recovery ship, the carrier USS *Lake Champlain* (CVS-39).

Project Mercury's first major success encouraged President Kennedy to suggest to Congress on 25 May that the 'Nation should commit itself to achieving the goal, before this decade is out, of landing a man on the Moon and returning him safely to Earth.' However, much work remained

432

to be done before this goal could be accomplished and, before NASA could go on to Gemini and Apollo, Mercury had to prove itself once more in a suborbital manned flight and to place the first US astronauts in Earth orbit.

Capsule No. 11 differed from that used by Shepard in having (1) the two small side ports replaced by a larger, centrally-mounted, trapezoidal

The seven Mercury astronauts at the St Louis plant on 27 July, 1961. Flanking 'Old Mac,' James S McDonnell, are Virgil I Grissom and Alan B Shepard, the astronauts who made suborbital flights respectively on 21 July and 5 May, 1961. *(MDC)*

window; (2) modified manual controls; and (3) an explosive egress hatch cover instead of a latched cover. Named *Liberty Bell 7* by Virgil Grissom and mounted atop MR-4, the fourth Mercury-Redstone, it was launched from Cape Canaveral on 21 July for what was essentially a repeat of *Freedom 7*'s suborbital flight. The 302 naut mile (559-km) flight down the Atlantic Missile Range was without significant problems and Grissom was recovered by a helicopter from HMR(L)-262. Unfortunately, as its weight exceeded the lifting capability of the Sikorsky HUS-1 after water poured in when the egress hatch was blow out accidentally, *Liberty Bell 7* could not be recovered.

According to the original and overly sanguine schedule, the first orbital flight was to have occurred just over four months after the first manned suborbital flight. However, the failure of the robot-carrying MA-3 flight in April 1961, various delays in the completion and delivery of boosters and capsules, and deliberate slowdown to enhance safety all combined to increase the gap between suborbital and orbital US manned flights to more than nine months. Before this could take place, a second cosmonaut, Gherman Titov, made a 17-orbit flight on 6 August, 1961. Five weeks later, NASA was encouraged by the success of MA-4 which ended with the recovery of the robot-carrying Capsule No 8A, the refurbished No. 8 saved from the unsuccessful MA-3 flight, after a single-orbit. Confidence increased further when on 29 November Capsule No. 9 was recovered after safely carrying the chimpanzee 'Enos' on a two-orbit flight.

Following numerous schedule slippages and postponements, Capsule No 13 and its Atlas booster were ready for launch as MA-6 from Cape Canaveral in early 1962. Named *Friendship 7* by the family of John

The launch of Mercury-Atlas 6 at Cape Canaveral on 20 February, 1962. *(NASA)*

A Mercury capsule being launched atop an Atlas booster. *(MDC)*

Glenn, the first man-rated orbital US capsule was delivered by McDonnell in August 1961 and afterwards was carefully checked by personnel from the contractor and NASA Space Task Group. A first attempt at launching the first US orbital flight had to be aborted at T minus 20 minutes on 27 January, 1962, due to weather after Glenn had spent over five hours atop the fuelled Atlas booster. More postponements followed and during the night and early morning hours of 20 February, 1962, sundry difficulties delayed the launch. At last, at 9:47 AM, Eastern Standard Time, MA-6 lifted off the pad carrying John Glenn and

Friendship 7 on their historical flight. Although problems with the attitude control system forced Glenn to take over manual control and a faulty telemetry signal indicated possible detachment of the ablation heat-shield, thus apparently placing the astronaut's life in serious jeopardy, *Friendship 7* came back down safely in the Atlantic at the end of the third orbit with the heat-shield firmly attached. John Glenn and his Mercury capsule[5] were hoisted aboard the destroyer USS *Noa* (DD-841) some 5 hr 15 min after lift-off. Of that time, 4 hr 48 min 27 sec had been spent in weightlessness.

Three months elapsed before a second astronaut orbited the Earth; this time it was Scott Carpenter who made a three-orbit flight in *Aurora 7* on 24 May, 1962. While the duration of Carpenter's flight was almost identical to that of Glenn's flight in February, it was different in a number of respects. In particular, whereas Glenn's MA-6 had been undertaken primarily to gather test data, Carpenter's MA-7 was used for several scientific experiments. Following minimum pre-launch holds, the orbital flight itself was almost uneventful until Carpenter began aligning the capsule for re-entry. A malfunctioning automatic stabilization system and the astronaut's failure to switch off the manual system when using the fly-by-wire control mode contributed to the capsule being slightly misaligned at the time of retro-rocket firing. Consequently, *Aurora 7* dropped into the Atlantic 200 naut miles (370 km) from the predicted impact point, too far for the primary recovery team to be able to help the astronaut. Carpenter was forced to exit *Aurora 7* on his own. He remained in his life raft for three hours before being picked up by a Sikorsky HSS-2 from the USS *Intrepid* (CVS-11) and returned safely to the carrier.

Following the second three-orbit US flight, pressure increased within and without NASA to undertake a flight matching, or even exceeding, the 17-orbit flight of cosmonaut Titov. However, as Mercury capsules had been initially designed for three-orbit flights, a flight of such duration could not be undertaken without much additional planning and some equipment modifications. While this was taking place, cosmonaut Andrian Nikolayev flew a 64-orbit flight on 11/15 August, 1962. Clearly, a flight of this duration could not be accomplished with existing US spacecraft. Nevertheless NASA and McDonnell went on preparing for Mercury flights of longer duration than planned at the onset.

For the flight of *Sigma 7* (Capsule No. 16 on MA-8), the number of experiments requiring control fuel and electrical power was deliberately minimized to extend duration. In addition, the capsule was modified at Cape Canaveral to give it a six-orbit capability through weight reduction, deletion of equipment not absolutely necessary, and provision for carrying extra supplies. In addition to procedural changes and hardware

---

[5] One year after its epic flight *Friendship 7* was donated to the Smithsonian Institution. Since then, it has been on display at the National Air Space Museum in Washington, DC.

modifications, the longer flight also required shifting the primary recovery area from the Atlantic to the Pacific. All the additional planning that went into the preparation of the *Sigma 7* flight was time and effort

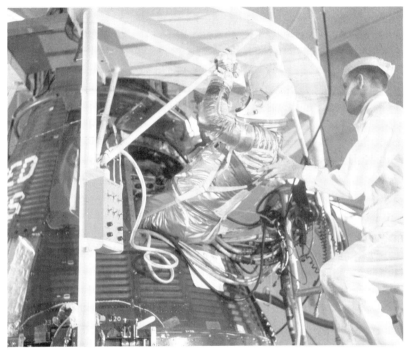

Astronaut Walter M 'Wally' Schirra Jr boarding capsule No. 16, *Sigma 7,* at the start of his six-orbit flight on 3 October, 1982. *(NASA)*

well spent; only a 15-minute hold was required before the launch of MA-8 on 3 October, 1962, and the 9 hr 13 min flight was near perfect. The capsule splashed into the Pacific only 4.5 naut miles (8.3 km) from the primary recovery ship, the uss *Kearsarge* (CVS-33), and Walter Schirra and his *Sigma 7* were quickly hoisted aboard the carrier.

Contemplated on several earlier occasions, notably to fill the gap between the originally scheduled three-orbit Mercury flights and the two-man Project Gemini, a one-day 18- or more orbit Mercury flight was planned by NASA to take place as soon as a capsule could be modified. The capsule eventually selected for the Manned One-Day Mission (MODM) Project was Capsule No. 20 which was prepared for the last Mercury flight during the first four months of 1963. Named *Faith 7* and mated to MA-9, this capsule carried Gordon Cooper into space on 15

May. Splashdown came 34 hr 20 min after lift-off, just 4 naut miles (7.4 km) from the primary recovery ship in the Pacific the USS *Kearsarge* (CVS-33), and Cooper and *Faith 7* were taken aboard at the end of the last Mercury flight. Five of the capsules (Nos. 10, 12, 15, 17, and 19) had not been used as all programme goals had been met in the course of two suborbital and four orbital manned flights. All unmanned and manned flights are summarized in the table on page 455 entitled Mercury Flights.

Although Project Mercury had been marred by numerous disappointments and quite a few complete or partial failures, McDonnell had good reason to be satisfied as none of the failures were due to the capsule and

Mercury capsules being assembled in a clean room at St Louis in April 1960. Capsule No. 2, in the foreground, was lost in the failure of MR-2; No. 5 carried the chimpanzee 'Ham' into space; No 6 was used for a suborbital qualification flight; and No 7 carried Alan B Shepard, the first American astronaut, on a suborbital flight. *(MDC)*

NASA could justly derive much satisfaction from the successful completion of Project Mercury. However, the United States still trailed behind the Soviet Union in the space race. Between 12 April, 1961, when Yuri Gagarin had become the first man to fly in space, and 19 June, 1963, when Valentina Tereshkova safely returned to Earth, the six Vostok cosmonauts had logged more than seven times as much time in orbital flights as had the four Mercury astronauts (381 hr 31 min versus 53 hr 24 min). Project Gemini, which had been announced in January 1962, would see astronauts overtake cosmonauts in term of mission duration and numerous technical achievements (notably the development of the space rendezvous technique).

According to published NASA information, the cost of Project Mercury came to a total of $400,658,000, of which $143,413,000 was for the procurement of capsules and $82,847,000 for the procurement of launch vehicles. Quite remarkably, if inflation and the devalued dollar are not taken into consideration, the total cost of Project Mercury equates to about four-fifths of the cost of a single Northrop B-2! Even if inflation is considered, the total programme cost for Project Mercury comes to the equivalent of the purchase price of only five B-2s. One can only wonder whether, to justify such a high price tag, the developers of the B-2 can rightly claim that their project requires a greater advance in the state-of-the-art than did Project Mercury more than a quarter of a century earlier.

Edward H. White II during his 21-min extra vehicular activity (EVA) on 3 June, 1965. *(NASA)*

Project Gemini

Appearing to the uninitiated merely to be a two-seat version of the Mercury capsule, Gemini was in fact a much more complex machine which was designed to manoeuvre in space and thus fully deserved the designation of spacecraft. Origins of the project can be traced to the spring of 1959, when various NASA groups began planning for Mercury follow-on activities, and to the summer of that year, when McDonnell

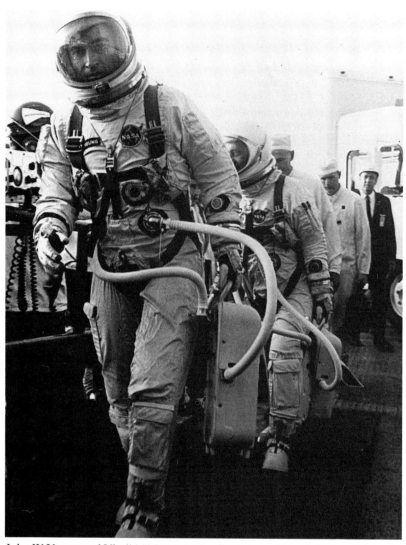

John W Young and Virgil I Grissom preparing to board *Gemini III* on 23 March, 1965. *(NASA)*

worked on a report titled *Follow On Experiments, Project Mercury Capsules*. Additional government and industry studies during the following 18 months led to the award of a study contract to McDonnell on 14 April, 1961. Intended to identify improvements which could be incorporated in Mercury to ease equipment accessibility and transform the experimental capsule into an operational vehicle, this study brought McDonnell to consider three configurations: (1) a minimum-change capsule capable of sustaining one man for 18 orbits; (2) a reconfigured one-man capsule with an ejection seat for the astronaut and most of the equipment relocated from inside the pressure vessel to highly accessible pallets; and (3) a two-man capsule similar to the reconfigured one-man capsule. The first option provided the basis for modifications later incorporated in Capsule No.20, *Faith 7*, in which Gordon Cooper flew the Manned One-Day-Mission in May 1963, whereas the third option was developed into the Mercury Mark II spacecraft (the name being changed to Gemini on 3 January, 1962).

During the Mercury Mark II/Gemini project definition and preliminary design phases, the objectives of the programme were refined and eventually included: (1) subjecting two-man crews to flights of up to two-weeks' duration; (2) developing space rendezvous and docking techniques; (3) using the target vehicle propulsion system to manoeuvre the spacecraft into new orbits; (4) performing extravehicular activities (EVAs); (5) developing a controlled re-entry capability to bring the spacecraft to a specific landing area; (6) training crews for the Apollo programme; and (7) conducting engineering and scientific experiments. In support of this programme, NASA arranged to procure through Air Force channels Martin Titan II boosters to launch the spacecraft and Convair Atlas boosters to launch the target vehicles. It also placed contracts directly with Lockheed for Agena B boosters and target vehicles and with McDonnell for the spacecraft. Letter Contract NAS 9-170 covering the design and manufacture of 12 spacecraft, 15 launch vehicle adapters, and 11 target vehicle adapters was accepted by McDonnell on 22 December, 1961.

While the prime contractors and their sub-contractors designed spacecraft, boosters, and target vehicles, NASA and the Department of Defense selected additional astronauts for the Gemini and Apollo programmes. The selection of nine astronauts—Neil A Armstrong, NASA; Maj Frank Borman, USAF; Lt Charles Conrad Jr, USN; LCdr James A Lovell Jr, USN; Capt James A McDivitt, USAF; Elliot M See Jr, NASA; Capt Thomas P Stafford, USAF; LCdr John W Young, USN; Capt Edward H White II, USAF—was announced on 17 September 1962. Fourteen additional astronauts—Maj Edwin E Aldrin Jr, USAF; Capt William A Anders, USAF; Capt Charles A Bassett II, USAF; Lt Alan L Bean, USN; Lt Eugene A Cernan, USN; Lt Roger B Chaffee, USN; Capt Michael Collins, USAF; R Walter Cunningham, NASA; Capt Donn F Eisele, USAF; Capt Theodore C Freeman, USAF; LCdr Richard F Gordon Jr, USN; Russell L Schweikart, NASA; Capt David R Scott, USAF; and Capt Clifton C Williams Jr, USMC—were added on 18 October, 1963. With the exception of Elliot See who was killed with Charles Bassett in the crash of a Northrop T-38 at St Louis on 28 February, 1966, all astronauts from the first group went on at least one Gemini flight. Five astronauts from the second group flew Gemini missions as did three of the original Mercury astronauts.

Mock-up of the North American Paraglide Landing System. *(NASA)*

In May 1961, during the feasibility phase of what became Project Gemini, NASA issued a Statement of Work for a Design Study of a Paraglide Landing System with the intention of having a paraglider used to provide spacecraft manoeuvrability and controlled energy descent and landing by aerodynamic lift. A contract for the development of the paraglider was awarded to North American in November 1961 with the intention of using this system to make controlled landings on hard surfaces the primary recovery mode for Gemini. However, due to lack of funds, development of the paraglider system had to be terminated in December 1964 and Gemini was designed for recovery at sea using a conventional parachute system. Conversely, it was decided to substitute individual ejection seats for the rocket escape system of Mercury, the seats being intended for use before launch (off-the-pad abort) or during the first phase of powered flight (to about 60,000 ft/18,300 m).

From the adapter and equipment storage section at its base to the tip of the radar cover, the entire spacecraft measured 19 ft (5.79 m) in length and, when mounted atop the two-stage Titan launch vehicle, overall length was 109 ft (33.22 m). The Gemini spacecraft was comprised of (1) a frustrum-shaped rendezvous and recovery section; (2) a cylindrical reaction control system section housing 25-lb (11.3-kg) thrusters; (3) a frustrum-shaped cabin with side-by-side contour-shaped ejection seats for the astronauts, incorporated a re-entry heat-shield at its base; (4) a frustrum-shaped retrograde section; and (5) a frustrum-shaped adapter and equipment storage section.

The first Gemini spacecraft and launch vehicle were delivered to the Atlantic Missile Range at Cape Canaveral in October 1963 and, after four months of careful testing, were mated on 5 March, 1964, in preparation

Gemini spacecraft and adapter section. *(NASA)*

for an unmanned qualification flight. *Gemini-Titan 1* (GT-1) was successfully launched on 8 April and, as mission plans did not call for separation of the spacecraft from the second stage of the launch vehicle, both were placed in orbit. No recovery had been planned for this mission and GT-1 disintegrated when re-entering the atmosphere on 12 April.

As the GT-1 mission had been a success, NASA still hoped to fly GT-3, the first Gemini manned mission, before the end of 1964 (optimistically, the initial Mercury Mark II schedule had called for the first manned mission to be flown in July 1963). However, on 17 August some GT-2 equipment was damaged by a nearby lightning strike while the spacecraft and launch vehicle were being prepared for an unmanned test. During the

Gemini III being hoisted aboard the USS *Intrepid* (CVS-11) on 23 March, 1965. *(NASA)*

next four weeks, three approaching hurricanes forced NASA to deerect[6]

[6]   In addition to their many worthwhile achievements, people associated with the US space programme made a deleterious contribution to the English language by creating (or, at the very least, rendering more familiar) new words instead of using correct and precise words already in common usage. This was notably the case of the verbs 'to deerect' instead of to take down and 'to rendezvous'—particularly atrocious in its past tense, rendezvoused—when to meet, to join, or to muster would have been adequate.

The launch of *Gemini-Titan* 4 at Cape Kennedy on 3 June, 1965. *(NASA)*

and store the launch vehicle. Various minor technical problems then caused additional delays, but it was the loss of hydraulic pressure one second after engine ignition which definitely ended the chance of a manned Gemini mission before 1965 by forcing the GT-2 launch to be aborted on 9 December. The GT-2 unmanned suborbital mission was finally flown on 19 January, 1965, and the successful recovery of Spacecraft No.2 by the uss *Lake Champlain* (CVS-39) demonstrated the adequacy of the re-entry heat-shield, as well as structural integrity of the spacecraft, and checkout and launch procedures. Meanwhile all other required tests, such as that of the ejection seat and the parachute recovery system, had been completed and NASA was at last ready to proceed with manned Gemini missions.

Gemini-Titan 3, the first two-man US space flight, saw Virgil Grissom and John Young go on three orbits on 23 March, 1965, to evaluate spacecraft and launch vehicle systems and to demonstrate the capability to manoeuvre the spacecraft in orbit using the Orbit Attitude and Maneuver System (OAMS). The mission went as planned, and astronauts and spacecraft were recovered east of Bermuda by a helicopter from the USS *Intrepid* (CVS-11). The only significant disappointment was provided by the inaccuracy of the re-entry system which resulted in the capsule splashing down some 60 naut miles (111 km) from the primary recovery carrier.

The first mission to be controlled from the new Mission Control Center in Houston, Texas, *Gemini-Titan 4* on 3/7 June, 1965, considerably narrowed the gap between the US and Soviet space programmes as its duration of 97 hr 56 min was exceeded only by that of *Vostok 5*, the longest Soviet mission (118 hr 57 min on 14/18 June, 1963) and as Ed White became the second man to 'walk' in space, doing so only 77 days after that feat had first been achieved by Alexei Leonov. James McDivitt, Ed White, and their *Gemini IV* spacecraft splashed into the Atlantic 44 naut miles (81 km) off target and were taken by helicopter to the USS *Wasp* (CVS-18).

Gemini V, carrying Gordon Cooper and 'Pete' Conrad, was launched atop GT-5 on 21 August, 1965, at the start of a record duration mission during which the rendezvous guidance and navigation system was evaluated. In spite of falling pressure in the oxygen supply tank, the astronauts were able to accomplish most tasks as scheduled. Notably, using the Orbit and Maneuver System (OAMS), they conducted a simulated Agena rendezvous during which they adjusted the spacecraft's apogee and phase, changed its plane, and performed coelliptical manoeuvres. On 29 August, after 190 hr 55 min in orbit, *Gemini V* splashed into the Atlantic 91 naut miles (169 km) from the primary recovery ship, the USS *Lake Champlain* (CVS-39). Astronauts and spacecraft were safely recovered by helicopter.

The space programme suffered a setback on 25 October when the Gemini Agena Target Vehicle (GATV), with which *Gemini VI* was to have rendezvoused, suffered what appeared to be a catastrophic failure shortly after separating from the Atlas launch vehicle on 25 October, 1965. The *Gemini VI* mission was cancelled and, as waiting for a new Gemini Agena Target Vehicle would have resulted in an excessive delay, NASA decided to attempt launching *Gemini VIA* while *Gemini VII* was in orbit and to have the two spacecraft practise rendezvous operations.

446

Gemini VII, the fourth manned mission of the Gemini programme, was launched on 4 December, 1965. Primary objectives were to demonstrate long-duration manned orbital flights and to evaluate their physiological effects on the crew. As initially planned, secondary objectives were to perform stationkeeping with the second stage of the launch vehicle and to

Gemini VII on 15 December, 1965. The white adapter section was designed to burn in space after separation from the spacecraft during recovery. *(NASA)*

conduct 20 experiments during which Frank Borman and Jim Lovell were notably to demonstrate the feasibility of removing their pressure suits, working in a 'shirt sleeve' environment, and putting their suits on again. As indicated, following the failure of the first GATV, *Gemini VII* was to serve as a passive target for *Gemini VIA*. Accordingly, *Gemini VIA* was launched on 15 December and, at 5 hr 56 min into the flight, Wally Schirra and Tom Stafford successfully accomplished the rendezvous with the other spacecraft. For the next 20 hours the two spacecraft remained in formation and at times came within a few feet of each other before preparing for re-entry. After making precise splash-downs in the West Atlantic, *Gemini VIA* and *Gemini VII* coming down 7 and 6.4 naut miles (13 and 12 km) from the uss *Wasp* (CVS-18), the two spacecraft and the four astronauts were quickly recovered, Borman and Lovell being brought aboard by helicopter and Schirra and Stafford remaining in *Gemini VIA* to be hoisted aboard the carrier. With 206 orbits and flight time of 330 hr 35 min, the *Gemini VII* astronauts had become the new holders of the space duration record.

US Navy frogmen assisting in the recovery of *Gemini VIA* in the western Atlantic on 16 December, 1965. *(NASA)*

The first docking mission began on 16 March, 1966, with the launch of a GATV and, 101 minutes later, of GT-7 with *Gemini VIII* carrying Neil Armstrong and Dave Scott into space. The mission progressed as scheduled with *Gemini VIII* first manoeuvring from its 161-naut mile (298-km) circular orbit to complete six rendezvous with the GATV which was on a 220-naut mile (407-km) circular orbit. Docking was achieved 6 hr 33 min after the launch of *Gemini VIII*. Unfortunately, a spacecraft thruster malfunctioned and Neil Armstrong was forced to separate *Gemini VIII* from the GATV with some urgency and to use the Reentry Control System (RCS) to reduce the spacecraft's rapid rotation. Although successful, this manoeuvre consumed nearly 75 per cent of the re-entry fuel and created a new emergency. Accordingly, the retrofire sequence was initiated in the seventh orbit, followed by nominal re-entry and splashdown 1.1 naut miles (2 km) from a destroyer in the secondary recovery area in the western Pacific, some 500 miles (925 km) east of Okinawa. Neil Armstrong, Dave Scott, and *Gemini VIII* were safely recovered by the USS *Leonard F Mason* (DE-529) after a space flight lasting only 10 hr 41 min.

The failure of a GATV to achieve orbit on 17 May, 1966, led to postponing the launch of *Gemini IX* until a hastily developed Augmented Target Docking Adapter (ATDA) could be readied for another docking mission. Carrying Tom Stafford and Gene Cernan and redesignated

The damaged Augmented Target Docking Adapter as seen from *Gemini IX* on 3 June, 1966. *(NASA)*

Gemini IXA, the spacecraft was placed in orbit on 3 June, 1966. As the ATDA shroud failed to separate, the astronauts were unable to achieve their primary objective, docking with the ATDA. Nevertheless, they practiced rendezvousing under different conditions. In addition, Gene Cernan made the second US EVA but was unable to test the Astronaut Maneuvering Unit (AMU) due to excessive fogging of his visor while he was floating in space. The GT-9 mission ended after 45 orbits with *Gemini IXA* splashing down a mere 0.38 naut miles (0.70 km) from the primary recovery ship in the Atlantic. Remaining in the spacecraft, the astronauts were quickly hoisted aboard the USS *Wasp* (CVS-18).

On 18 July, 1966, barely six weeks after the Stafford-Cernan mission, John Young and Mike Collins were sent on the 12th US orbital flight aboard *Gemini X*. Docking with the GATV which had been launched earlier in the day and placed in an orbit at a slant range of 1,000 naut miles (1,850 km) from that of *Gemini X* was achieved less than six hours after launch but required more spacecraft propellant than predicted. Hence, to conserve propellant, activities during the remainder of the three-day mission were somewhat curtailed. Notwithstanding this change, most objectives were accomplished. Notably, Mike Collins made two EVAs and 'space walked' to recover a micrometeoroid detector pack from an Agena target vehicle before *Gemini X* returned to Earth at the end of the 43rd revolution. The spacecraft landed within sight of the primary recovery ship, the USS *Guadalcanal* (LPH-7), and the astronauts were quickly taken on board the amphibious assault ship.

449

Launched on 12 September, 1966, *Gemini XI* took Pete Conrad and Dick Gordon on a three-day, 44-orbit flight during which the astronauts rendezvoused with a GATV and achieved docking only 1 hr 34 min into the flight at the end of the first orbit. During the second day in orbit, after Dick Gordon had made the first of two EVAs, the GATV propulsion system was fired to raise the apogee of the docked *Gemini XI* -GATV to a new record of 739.2 naut miles (1,369 km). At the end of the penultimate Gemini mission, Conrad and Gordon were recovered by a helicopter of HS-3 operating from the USS *Guam* (LPH-9) some 700 naut miles (1,295 km) off Cape Kennedy.

The last Gemini mission, between 11 and 15 November, 1966, saw Jim Lovell and Edwin Aldrin fly 59 orbits in *Gemini XII* and dock with a

Edwin Aldrin during EVA from *Gemini XII. (NASA)*

GATV. Aldrin undertook two EVAs, one lasting 2 hr 29 min and the other 55 min, during which he performed various tasks requiring physical exertion in order to validate space suit modifications and demonstrate the astronauts' ability to work in space. Automatic re-entry brought *Gemini XII* within 2.6 naut miles (4.8 km) of the USS *Wasp* (CVS-18) in the Atlantic, thus bringing to an end the very successful Gemini programme. With Gemini, the United States had gained the lead into space. At the end of 1966, eighteen astronauts had spent 1,023 hr 45 min in space during the course of 14 Mercury and Gemini orbital missions whereas 11 cosmonauts had spent 431 hr 50 min in eight Vostok and Voshkod orbital missions.

According to published NASA information, the cost of Project Gemini came to a total of $1,290,100,000, of which $790,400,000 was for the procurement of capsules and $417,400,000 for the procurement of launch vehicles.

The Manned Orbiting Laboratory

Although most of the astronauts came from the Armed Forces and much support was provided to NASA by the Department of Defense, the Mercury and Gemini programmes had been undertaken for non-military purposes. Nevertheless, they provided much useful data as well as a modified Gemini spacecraft to the Air Force's Manned Orbiting Laboratory (MOL). The selection of the Missile & Space Systems Group, Douglas Aircraft Company, as prime contractor for the MOL was announced by President Lyndon B Johnson on 25 August, 1965.

Other major MOL contractors were McDonnell which was to supply specially-modified Gemini B capsules for the two-man crew, Martin Marietta which was to design and build Titan IIIM launch vehicles, and General Electric which was to plan and develop the experiments to be performed by the military crew. The Gemini B capsule was to incorporate an air-lock in its heat-shield to enable the crew access to the laboratory. The cylindrical laboratory, 10 feet (3.05 m) in diameter and 40 feet (12.19 m) long, was designed to enable the crew to work in a shirt-sleeve environment for periods of up to 30 days before returning to earth in the Gemini B.

Plans called for the launching of 10 Titan IIIMs to qualify their new boosters before two MOL unmanned flights were made to test launch, tracking, and recovery procedures. Five MOL operational missions were planned with the first scheduled for late 1969. This, however, was not to be as the MOL programme had to be cancelled.

In their report to stockholders published in the 1965 Annual Report, Donald W Douglas and Donald W Douglas, Jr hailed the award of the MOL contract as the highlight of the year's activities and glossed over the loss of the C-5A contract. They confidently stated: 'While annual appropriations may fluctuate somewhat, we believe the nation's commitment to the space program to be firm and to augur well for the future of our Missile & Space Systems Group.' Unfortunately, the mounting cost of the war in Southeast Asia forced the Department of Defense to re-allocate funds from its space programme to other more urgent needs. Accordingly, while Lockheed was able to continue work on the C-5A, McDonnell Douglas was instructed to terminate work on the Manned Orbiting Laboratory in June 1969.

The Skylab space station

Whereas Mercury and Gemini missions were flown primarily to conduct basic space exploration and to substantiate the principle that man can survive and perform useful work in the space environment, Apollo missions were undertaken to take astronauts to the Moon and return them safely to Earth. Capitalizing on this experience, the Skylab space station was developed as a research facility in which experimental and operational tasks would be performed in near-Earth orbit. It was to be capable of prolonged manned missions and was to be used to conduct experiments falling into five categories: (1) Earth resources, (2) solar observations, (3) physical sciences, (4) life sciences, and (5) technology and operations.

The basic concept called for Skylab to be outfitted and provisioned on the ground and to be launched unmanned atop a two-stage Saturn V launch vehicle. Later, the Apollo Command and Service Module was to be launched with a three-astronaut crew by a Saturn IB vehicle. The module was then to rendezvous and dock with the Skylab to complete the space station assembly and to initiate the manned mission phases. At the end of the mission, the astronauts were to return to earth aboard the Apollo module. Two other manned missions, again using Apollo Command and Service Modules and Saturn IB launch vehicles, were to be flown before the space station would disintegrate upon return to Earth.

With NASA's Office of Manned Space Flight being responsible for directing, integrating, and evaluating all phases of Skylab, the management and development of the programme involved a broad segment of the US aerospace industry. Notably, Boeing Company and Chrysler Corporation respectively produced the first stage of the Saturn V and Saturn IB launch vehicles. Martin Marietta Corporation was responsible for Skylab cluster systems engineering, payload systems integration, design and development of the control and display panel for the earth resources experiments, and monitoring the development and design of the Apollo Telescope Mount (ATM) by The Bendix Corporation. Finally, North American Rockwell Corporation manufactured the second stage of the Saturn V and modified the Apollo Command and Service Module to meet the requirements of the Skylab programme. However, the largest share of the project went to the McDonnell Douglas Astronautics Company (MDAC) in Huntington Beach, California.

In addition to its role as prime contractor, MDAC was responsible for the design, development, fabrication, equipment installation, testing, and checkout of the Orbital Workshop and the Airlock Module. MDAC was also responsible for providing living quarters for the astronauts in the Orbital Workshop and for producing the upper stage for both the Saturn V and Saturn IB launch vehicles.

As shown in the drawing on page 453, Skylab consisted of five major elements: (1) a Multiple Docking Adapter, which provided the docking interface for the Apollo Command and Service Module and supported the majority of the Earth resources experiments; (2) an Airlock Module, providing an airlock to space and housing controls and

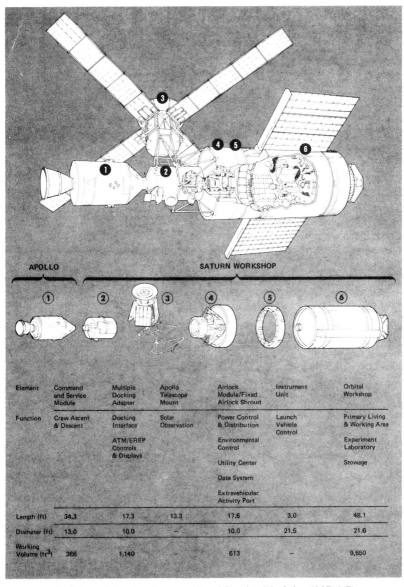

Element	Command and Service Module	Multiple Docking Adapter	Apollo Telescope Mount	Airlock Module/Fixed Airlock Shroud	Instrument Unit	Orbital Workshop
Function	Crew Ascent & Descent	Docking Interface ATM/EREP Controls & Displays	Solar Observation	Power Control & Distribution Environmental Control Utility Center Data System Extravehicular Activity Port	Launch Vehicle Control	Primary Living & Working Area Experiment Laboratory Stowage
Length (ft)	34.3	17.3	13.3	17.6	3.0	48.1
Diameter (ft)	13.0	10.0	—	10.0	21.5	21.6
Working Volume (ft³)	366	1,140	—	613	—	9,550

Skylab and Apollo Command and Service Module. *(MDAC)*

displays; (3) an Apollo Telescope Mount, containing the United States' first manned telescope in space; (4) an Orbital Workshop, which was modified from an empty Saturn S-IVB hydrogen tank to house crew

453

quarters and experiment facilities; and (5) a Saturn V Instrument Unit, used only during launch and initial deployment.

NASA had wanted to launch the space station in 1970, but funding constraints necessitated a slowdown. In accordance with the revised schedule, the Orbital Workshop, built in Huntington Beach, and the Airlock Module, manufactured in St Louis, were delivered in mid-1972. Following checkout and mating at the Kennedy Space Center, Cape Canaveral, Florida, the unmanned *Skylab I* space station was launched into orbit on 14 May, 1973, by a two-stage Saturn V. However, as *Skylab I's* meteoroid shield and solar array system were damaged during launch, the launch of *Skylab II* with astronauts Charles 'Pete' Conrad Jr, Paul J Weitz, and Joseph P Kerwin had to be postponed 11 days while NASA devised a plan to have the astronauts repair the damaged equipment. Finally, *Skylab II* was launched on 25 May and quickly met and docked with the earth-orbiting *Skylab I* workshop, then approximately 235 naut miles (435 km) above the Earth. The crew boarded the space station and, after repairing the damaged equipment, proceeded with activities which had been planned for their 28-day, 404-orbit mission. These activities included a series of medical experiments for the evaluation of astronaut activity and physical condition during the conducting of experiments, solar astronomy, and Earth resources and other technical experiments. At completion of the scheduled mission, Conrad, Weitz, and Kerwin prepared *Skylab I* for its unmanned orbital phase and boarded the Apollo Command and Service Module for their return to Earth. The Apollo spacecraft splashed down in the Pacific,

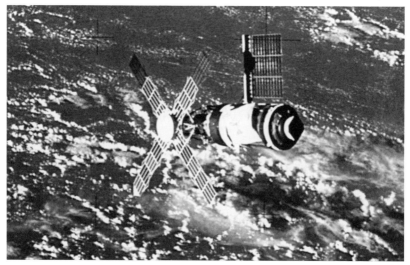

The Skylab space station seen from the Apollo Command and Service Module.
(NASA, courtesy of MDAC)

southwest of San Diego on 22 June, 1973, and the astronauts were recovered by the crew of a Sikorsky SH-3A from Helicopter Combat Support Squadron One (HC-1) and taken aboard the USS *Ticonderoga* (CVA-14) after their 28 days 49 minutes mission.

Astronauts Alan L Bean, Jack R Lousma, and Owen K Garriott were taken into space aboard *Skylab III* on 28 July, 1973, at the start of a mission during which they resupplied specific items, continued specific experiments, and initiated new experiments. Splashdown southwest of San Diego occurred on 25 September, after 59 days 11 hours and 9 minutes in space (858 orbits), with recovery by a helicopter of HC-1 operating from the USS *New Orleans* (LPH-11). The third and final mission to the space station began on 16 November, 1973, with the launch of *Skylab IV* with astronauts Gerald P Carr, William R Rogue, and Edward C Gibson. The mission, which was to last at least 56 days but was 'open-ended,' set a new duration record as the astronauts were recovered by HC-1 and the USS *New Orleans* on 8 February, 1974, after 84 days 1 hour and 16 minutes in space (1,214 orbits).

In the course of the three missions, the astronauts had made EVAs totalling 41 hours and 44 minutes and their laboratory experiments nearly doubled scientific knowledge about the sun and its influence upon all terrestrial life forms. The astronauts also recorded data useful in locating oil and mineral resources, mapped air and water pollution sources, determined flood danger areas, and helped assess arable land. Moreover, they took part in important scientific experiments during which they formed crystalline materials free of gravitational effects that had so far prevented the achievement of theoretically efficient properties.

455

Mercury Flights

Mercury	Dates	Astronauts	Highlights
Capsule No.1	9 May, 1960	Unmanned	Successful test of escape rocket, parachute recovery, and landing system at Wallops Island, Virginia.
Capsule No.4 MA-1	29 July, 1960	Unmanned	Qualification flight for Mercury-Atlas combination. Failed after 3 min 18 sec.
Capsule No.3 LJ-5	8 November, 1960	Unmanned	First qualification flight of a production capsule. Failed 2 min 22 sec after launch from Wallops Island.
Capsule No.2 MR-1	21 November, 1960	Unmanned	Qualification flight for Mercury-Redstone combination. Failed 2 sec after attempted launch from Cape Canaveral.
Capsule No.2A MR-1A	19 December, 1960	Unmanned	Successful suborbital flight to qualify Mercury-Redstone combination. Duration, 15 min 45 sec; apogee, 130.7 n m/242.1 km; range 235 n m/435 km.
Capsule No.5 MR-2	31 January, 1961	Chimpanzee 'Ham'	Successful suborbital flight ending with safe recovery of 'Ham.' Duration, 16 min 39 sec; apogee, 157 n m/291 km; range, 422 n m/782 km.
Capsule No.6 MA-2	21 February, 1961	Unmanned	Successful suborbital flight to qualify Mercury-Atlas combination. Duration, 17 min 56 sec; apogee, 114 n m/211 km; range, 1,432 n m/2,652 km.
Capsule No.14 LJ-5A	18 March, 1961	Unmanned	Partial failure due to premature firing of escape rocket during test at Wallops Island. Capsule was recovered and used for repeat test on 28 April 1961.
Capsule No.8 MA-3	25 April, 1961	Robot	First attempt to place a Mercury capsule in orbit. Failed when MA-3 had to be destroyed 40 seconds after being launched from Cape Canaveral. The capsule successfully aborted and was recovered; it was refurbished and used for repeat test on 13 September, 1961.
Capsule No.14A LJ-5B	28 April, 1961	Unmanned	Partially successful demonstration of escape systems. Capsule recovered in good condition after launch of LJ-5B from Wallops Island.

Mercury	Dates	Astronauts	Highlights
Capsule No.7 *Freedom 7* MR-3	5 May, 1961	Alan B Shepard	First US suborbital manned flight. Duration, 15 min 28 sec; apogee, 116.5 n m/215.8 km; range, 303 n m/561 km. Astronaut and capsule safely recovered.
Capsule No.11 *Liberty Bell 7* MR-4	21 July, 1961	Virgil I Grissom	Partially successful suborbital manned flight. Duration, 15 min 37 sec; apogee, 118.3 n m/219.1 km; range, 302 n m/559 km. Astronaut recovered, capsule sank.
Capsule No.8A MA-4	13 September, 1961	Robot	First orbital flight by Mercury capsule. One orbit; duration, 1 hr 49 min 20 sec; apogee/perigee, 142.1 n m/263.2 km; perigee, 98.9 n m/183.2 km. Capsule recovered.
Capsule No.9	29 November, 1961	Chimpanzee 'Enos'	Successful orbital flight ending with safe recovery of chimpanzee and capsule. Two orbits; duration, 3 hr 20 min 59 sec; apogee, 147.4 n m/273.0 km; perigee, 99.5 n m/184.3 km.
Capsule No.13 *Friendship 7* MA-6	20 February, 1962	John H Glenn Jr	First US orbital manned flight. Three orbits; duration, 4 hr 55 min 23 sec; apogee, 162.2 n m/300.4 km; perigee, 100 n m/185.2 km. Astronaut and capsule safely recovered.
Capsule No.18 *Aurora 7* MA-7	24 May, 1962	M Scott Carpenter	Second US orbital manned flight. Three orbits; duration, 4 hr 56 min 5 sec; apogee, 166.8 m/308.9 km; perigee, 99.9 n m/185.0 km. Astronaut and capsule safely recovered.
Capsule No.16 *Sigma 7* MA-8	3 October, 1962	Walter M Schirra Jr	Third US orbital manned flight. Six orbits; duration, 9 hr 13 min 11 sec; apogee, 175.8 n m/325.6 km; perigee, 100 n m/185.2 km. Astronaut and capsule safely recovered.
Capsule No.20 *Faith 7* MA-9	15/16 May, 1963	L Gordon Cooper Jr	Fourth US orbital manned flight. Twenty-two and one half orbits; duration, 34 hr 19 min 49 sec; apogee, 165.9 n m/307.2 km; perigee, 100.3 n m/185.8 km. Astronaut and capsule safely recovered.

SOURCE: Appendix D, Flight Data Summary, in L S Swenson Jr, J M Grimwood, and C C Alexander *This New Ocean, a History of Project Mercury*, National Aeronautics and Space Administration, Washington, DC, 1966.

Gemini Flights

Gemini	Dates	Astronauts	Highlights
Spacecraft No.1 *Gemini I* GT-1	8 April, 1964	Unmanned	Successful qualification orbital flight. Neither spacecraft separation nor recovery was planned and GT-1 disintegrated on re-entry during the 64th orbit.
Spacecraft No.2 *Gemini II* GT-2	19 January, 1965	Unmanned	Successful suborbital flight. Duration, 18 min 16 sec; apogee, 92.4 n m/171.1 km; range, 1,848 n m/3,422 km. Capsule recovered.
Spacecraft No.3 *Gemini III* GT-3	23 March, 1965	Virgil I Grissom John W Young	First two-man US orbital flight. Three orbits; duration, 4 hr 52 min 31 sec; highest apogee, 121.0 n m/224.1 km; lowest perigee, 85.6 n m/158.5 km. Astronauts and spacecraft safely recovered.
Spacecraft No.4 *Gemini IV* GT-4	3/7 June, 1965	James A McDivitt Edward H White	First long-duration mission and first EVA. Orbits, 62; duration, 97 hr 56 min 12 sec; highest apogee, 159.9 n m/296.1 km; lowest perigee, 86.1 n m/159.5 km. Astronauts and spacecraft safely recovered.
Spacecraft No.5 *Gemini V* GT-5	21/29 August, 1965	L Gordon Cooper Jr Charles Conrad Jr	Evaluation of the rendezvous guidance and navigation system. Orbits, 120; duration, 190 hr 55 min 14 sec; highest apogee, 188.9 n m/349.8 km; lowest perigee, 87.4 n m/1461.9 km. Astronauts and spacecraft safely recovered.
Spacecraft No.6 *Gemini VI-A* GT-6	15/16 December, 1965	Walter M Schirra Jr Thomas P Stafford	First rendezvous mission. Orbits, 16; duration, 25 hr 51 min 24 sec; highest apogee, 168.1 n m/311.3 km; lowest perigee, 86.9 n m/160.9 km. Astronauts and spacecraft safely recovered.
Spacecraft No.7 *Gemini VII* GT-7	4/18 December, 1965	Frank Borman James A Lovell Jr	Target spacecraft for first rendezvous mission with Gemini VI-A. Longest Gemini mission. Orbits, 206; duration, 330 hr 35 min 1 sec; highest apogee, 177.1 n m/328.0 km; lowest perigee, 87.2 n m/161.5 km. Astronauts and spacecraft safely recovered.
Spacecraft No.8 *Gemini VIII* GT-8	16/17 March, 1966	Neil A Armstrong David R Scott	First docking mission with Gemini Agena Target Vehicle. Orbits, 7; duration, 10 hr 41 min 26 sec; highest apogee, 161.3 n m/298.7 km; lowest perigee, 86.3 n m/159.8 km. Astronauts and spacecraft safely recovered.

Gemini	Dates	Astronauts	Highlights
Spacecraft No.9 *Gemini IX-A* GT-9	3/6 June, 1966	Thomas P Stafford Eugene A Cernan	Uncompleted docking with Augmented Target Docking Adapter and second US EVA. Orbits, 45; duration, 72 hr 50 min 20 sec; highest apogee, 168.2 n m/311.5 km; lowest perigee, 85.7 n m/158.7 km. Astronauts and spacecraft safely recovered.
Spacecraft No.10 *Gemini X* GT-10	18/21 July, 1966	John W Young Michael Collins	Successful docking with GATV and third US EVA. Orbits, 43; duration, 70 hr 46 min 39 sec; highest apogee, 412.2 n m/763.4 km; lowest perigee, 86.3 n m/159.8 km. Astronauts and spacecraft safely recovered.
Spacecraft No.11 *Gemini XI* GT-11	12/15 September, 1966	Charles Conrad Jr Richard F Gordon Jr	Docking with GATV achieved during first revolution and fourth US EVA. Orbits, 44; duration, 71 hr 17 min 8 sec; highest apogee, 739.2 n m/1,369.0 km; lowest perigee, 86.6 n m/160.4 km. Astronauts and spacecraft safely recovered.
Spacecraft No.12 *Gemini XII* GT-12	11/15 November, 1966	James A Lovell Jr Edwin E Aldrin Jr	Last Gemini mission with GATV docking and longest US EVA. Orbits, 59; duration, 94 hr 34 min 31 sec; highest apogee, 162.7 n m/301.3 km; lowest perigee, 86.8 n m/160.8 km. Astronauts and spacecraft safely recovered.

SOURCE: Appendix 1, Gemini Program Flight Summary Data, J M Grimwood, B C Hacker, and P J Vorzimmer *Project Gemini, A Chronology*, National Aeronautics and Space Administration, Washington, DC, 1969.

Production Details and Serial Numbers

McDONNELL DOODLEBUG (Number built: 1)

Doodlebug	Co owned	X157N	1

HUGHES 1B RACER (Number built: 1)

1B	Howard Hughes	NR258Y	1

PLATT-LePAGE XR-1 (Number built: 2)

XR-1	USAAC	41-001	1
XR-1A	USAAF	42-6581	1

FAIRCHILD AT-21 GUNNER (Number built by McDonnell: 30)

AT-21-MM	USAAF	42-48412/42-48441	30

HUGHES D-2 (Number built: 1)

D-2	Co owned	Not Known	1

McDONNELL XP-67 (Number built: 1)

XP-67	USAAF	42-11677	1

McDONNELL FH-1 PHANTOM (Number built: 62)

XFD-1	USN	48235/48236	2
FH-1	USN	111749/111808	60

McDONNELL XHJD-1 WHIRLAWAY (Number built: 1)

XHJD-1	USN	44318	1

HUGHES XF-11 (Number built: 2)

XF-11	USAAF	44-70155/44-70156	2

McDONNELL F2H (F-2) BANSHEE (Number built: 895)

XF2D-1		USN	99858/99860	3
			XF2D-1 total	3
F2H-1	1st block	USN	122530/122533	4
	2nd block	USN	122534/122539	6
	3rd block	USN	122540/122549	10
	4th block	USN	122550/122559	10
	5th block	USN	122990/122999	10
	6th block	USN	123000/123015	16
			F2H-1 total	56
F2H-2	1st block	USN	123204/123221	18
	2nd block	USN	123222/123245	24
	3rd block	USN	123246/123274	29
	4th block	USN	123275/123299 & 123314	26
	5th block	USN	123315/123340	26
	6th block	USN	123341/123365	25
	7th block	USN	123367/123382	16
	Block 1	USN	124940/124965	26
	Block 2	USN	124966/124991	26
	Block 3	USN	124992/125017	26
	Block 4	USN	125018/125029 & 125032/125038	19
	Block 5	USN	125039/125053, 125055, & 125057	17
	Block 6	USN	125060, 125063, 125065, 125068, 125071, 125501, 125503, & 125649	8
	Block 7	USN	125652, 125655, 125658, & 125663/125666	7
	Block 8	USN	125667/125679	13
			F2H-2 total	306

F2H-2B	Block 4	USN	125030/125031	2
	Block 5	USN	125054, 125056, & 125058/125059	4
	Block 6	USN	125061/125062, 125064, 125066/125067, 125069/125070, 125500, 125502, 125004/125005, & 125650	12
	Block 7	USN	125651, 125653/125654, 125656/125657, & 125659/125662	9
			F2H-2B total	27

F2H-2N	1st block	USN	123300/123301	2
	2nd block	USN	123302	1
	4th block	USN	123303/123305	3
	5th block	USN	123306/123309	4
	6th block	USN	123310/123313	4
			F2H-2N total	14

F2H-2P	6th block	USN	123366	1
	Block 1	USN	125072/125075	4
	Block 2	USN	125076/125079	4
	Block 3	USN	125680/125683	4
	Block 4	USN	125684/125692	9
	Block 5	USN	125693/125701	9
	Block 6	USN	125702/125706 & 126673/126677	10
	Block 7	USN	126678/126686	9
	Block 8	USN	126687/126695	9
	Block 9	USN	128857/128886	30
			F2H-2P total	89

F2H-3	Block 1	USN	126291/126300	10
	Block 2	USN	126301/126320	20
	Block 3	USN	126321/126350	30
	Block 4	USN	126354/126390	37
	Block 5	USN	126391/126430	40
	Block 6	USN	126431/126470	40
	Block 10	USN	126471/126483	13
	Block 11	USN	126484/126489 & 127493/127526	40
	Block 12	USN	127527/127546	20
			F2H-3 total	250

F2H-4	Block 4	USN	126351/126353	3
	Block 7	USN	127547/127586	40
	Block 8	USN	127587/127626	40
	Block 9	USN	127627/127666	40
	Block 10	USN	127667/127693	27
			F2H-4 total	150

McDONNELL XH-20 LITTLE HENRY (Number built: 2)

XH-20		USAAF	46-689/46-690	2

HUGHES HFB-1 (H4) (Number built: 1)

HFB-1		Co owned	NX37602	1

McDONNELL XF-85 GOBLIN (Number built: 2)

XF-85		USAF	46-523/46-524	2

McDONNELL XF-88 VOODOO (Number built: 2)

XF-88		USAF	46-525/46-526	2

McDONNELL F3H (F-3) DEMON (Number built: 521)

XF3H-1		USN	125444/125445	2
			XF3H-1 total	2

F3H-1N	Block 1	USN	133489/133498	10
	Block 2	USN	133499/133518	20
	Block 3	USN	133519, 133521, & 133523/133548	28
			F3H-1N total	58

461

F3H-2N	Block 3	USN	133520 & 133522	2
	Block 4	USN	133549/133568 & 133570/133578	29
	Block 5	USN	133579/133603	25
	Block 6	USN	133604/133622	19
	Block 7	USN	136966/136982	17
	Block 8	USN	136983/137012	30
	Block 9	USN	137013/137020	8
	Block 10	USN	137021/137030	10
	Block 11	USN	137031/137032	2
			F3H-2N total	142
F3H-2M	Block 4	USN	133569	1
	Block 5	USN	133623/133627	5
	Block 6	USN	133628/133638	11
	Block 7	USN	137033/137040	8
	Block 9	USN	137041/137062	22
	Block 10	USN	137063/137082	20
	Block 11	USN	137083/137095	13
			F3H-2M total	80
F3H-2	Block 12	USN	143403/143432	30
	Block 13	USN	143433/143462	30
	Block 14	USN	143463/143492	30
	Block 15	USN	145202/145231	30
	Block 16	USN	145232/145261	30
	Block 17	USN	145262/145291	30
	Block 18	USN	145292/145306 & 145328/145339	27
	Block 19	USN	146709/146740	32
			F3H-2 total	239

McDONNELL 79 BIG HENRY (Number built: 1)

Model 79		Co owned	N12M	1

HUGHES XH-17 (Number built: 1)

XH-17		USAF	50-1842	1

McDONNELL XV-1 (Number built: 2)

XV-1		USA	53-4016/53-4017	2

McDONNELL F-101 VOODOO (Number built: 807)

F-101A:	Block 1	USAF	53-2418/53-2422	5
	Block 5	USAF	53-2423/53-2430	8
	Block 10	USA	F53-2431/53-2436	6
	Block 15	USAF	53-2437/53-2446	10
	Block 20	USAF	54-1438/54-1443	6
	Block 25	USAF	54-1444/54-1452	9
	Block 30	USAF	54-1453/54-1465	13
	Block 35	USAF	54-1466/54-1485	20
			F-101A total	77
YRF-101A	Block 10	USAF	54-149/54-150	2
			YRF-101A total	2
RF-101A	Block 20	USAF	54-1494/54-1496	3
	Block 25	USAF	54-1497/54-1507	11
	Block 30	USAF	54-1508/54-1518	11
	Block 35	USAF	54-1519/54-1521 &	3
			56-155/56-161	7
			RF-101A total	35
F-101B	Block 30	USAF	56-232	1
	Block 40	USAF	56-233/56-237	5
	Block 45	USAF	56-238/56-240	3
	Block 50	USAF	56-241/56-243	3
	Block 55	USAF	56-248/56-250	3
	Block 60	USAF	56-251, 56-252, & 56-254/56-257	6
	Block 65	USAF	56-258, 56-259, 56-261, &	
			56-263/56-268	9
	Block 70	USAF	56-269/56-273 & 56-278/56-280	8

	Block 75	USAF	56-281/56-288, 56-290/56-293, & 56-295/56-298	16
	Block 80	USAF	56-300/56-303, 56-305/56-307, 56-309/56-311, 56-313/56-315, 56-317/56-319, 56-321/56-323, 56-325/56-327, & 57-247/57-262	38
	Block 85	USAF	57-264/57-266, 57-268/57-270, 57-272/57-274, 57-276/57-278, 57-280/57-282, 57-284/57-286, 57-288/57-291, 57-293/57-296, 57-298/57-301, & 57-303/57-306	34
	Block 90	USAF	57-308/57-311, 57-313/57-316, 57-318/57-321, 57-323/57-326, 57-328/57-331, 57-333/57-336, 57-338/57-341, 57-343/57-346, 57-348/57-351, & 57-353/57-356	40
	Block 95	USAF	57-358/57-364, 57-366/57-371, 57-373/57-378, 57-380/57-385, 57-387/57-392, 57-394/57-399, & 57-401/57-406	43
	Block 100	USAF	57-408/57-413, 57-415/57-420, 57-422/57-427, 57-429/57-448, & 57-450/57-452	41
	Block 105	USAF	58-259/58-261, 58-263/58-268, 58-270/58-275, 58-277/58-282, 58-284/58-289, 58-291/58-296, & 58-298/58-303	39
	Block 110	USAF	58-305/58-310, 58-312/58-317, 58-319/58-323, 58-325/58-330, 58-332/58-337, & 58-339/58-342	33
	Block 115	USAF	59-391, 59-392, 59-394/59-399, 59-401/59-406, 59-408/59-412, 59-414/59-418, 59-420/59-424, 59-426/59-436, & 59-438/59-440	43
	Block 120	USAF	59-441, 59-442, 59-444/59-448, 59-450/59-453, 59-455/59-459, 59-461/59-465, 59-467/59-471, 59-473/59-477, & 59-479/59-483	36
			F-101B total	401
F-101C	Block 40	USAF	54-1486/54-1493 & 56-001/56-005	13
	Block 45	USAF	56-006/56-019	14
	Block 50	USAF	56-020/56-032	13
	Block 55	USAF	56-033/56-039	7
			F-101C total	47
RF-101C	Block 40	USAF	56-162/56-173	12
	Block 45	USAF	56-174/56-186	13
	Block 50	USAF	56-187/56-198	12
	Block 55	USAF	56-199/56-221	23
	Block 60	USAF	56-222/56-231 & 56-040/56-057	28
	Block 65	USAF	56-058/56-086	29
	Block 70	USAF	56-087/56-114	28
	Block 75	USAF	56-115/56-135	21
			RF-101C total	166
F-101F	Block 51	USAF	56-244 & 56-245	2
	Block 56	USAF	56-246 & 56-247	2
	Block 61	USAF	56-253	1
	Block 66	USAF	56-260 & 56-262	2
	Block 71	USAF	56-274/56-277	4
	Block 76	USAF	56-289, 56-294, & 56-299	3
	Block 81	USAF	56-304, 56-308, 56-312, 56-316, 56-320, 56-324, & 56-328	7
	Block 86	USAF	57-263, 57-267, 57-271, 57-275, 57-279, 57-283, 57-287, 57-292, 57-297, 57-302, & 57-307	11
	Block 91	USAF	57-312, 57-317, 57-322, 57-327, 57-332, 57-337, 57-342, 57-347, 57-352, & 57-357	10

463

Block 96	USAF	57-365, 57-372, 57-379, 57-386, 57-393, 57-400, & 57-407		7
Block 101	USAF	57-414, 57-421, 57-428, & 57-449		4
Block 106	USAF	58-262, 58-269, 58-276, 58-283, 58-290, & 58-297		6
Block 111	USAF	58-304, 58-311, 58-318, 58-324, 58-331, & 58-338		6
Block 116	USAF	59-393, 59-400, 59-407, 59-413, 59-419, 59-425, & 59-437		7
Block 121	USAF	59-443, 59-449, 59-454, 59-460, 59-466, 59-472, & 59-478		7
		F-101F total		79

HUGHES 269, 200, and 300 (Number built: 3,028 by the end of September 1989; still being produced by Schweizer Aircraft)

Model 269		Co owned	N78P and N79P	2
Model 269A		Various	S/N 0008/0314 & 1107/1109	310
Model 269A	YOH-2	USA	58-1324/58-1328	5
Model 269A	TH-55A	USA	64-18001/64-18020, 64-18025/64-18239, 65-18240/65-18263, 66-18264/66-18355, 67-15371/67-15445, 67-16686/67-17002, & 67-18356/67-18404	792
Model 200		Various	S/N 0001/0041	41
Model 300		Various	S/N 0001/0463	463
Model 300C (Hughes)		Various	S/N 0001/1165	1165
Model 300C (Schweizer)		Various	S/N 1166/1415 (+ others)	250
Model 330 (Schweizer)				

McDONNELL 120 (Number built: 2)

Model 120		Co owned	N6091V and ?	2

McDONNELL F-4 (F4H) PHANTOM II (Number built: 5,195 of which 5,068 by McDonnell and 127 by Mitsubishi)

YF4H-1:	YF4H-1	USN	142259/142260	2
		YF4H-1 total		2
F-4A:	Block 1	USN	143388/143392	5
	Block 2	USN	145307/145317	11
	Block 3	USN	146817/146821	5
	Block 4	USN	148252/148261	10
	Block 5	USN	148262/148-275	14
		F-4A total		45
F-4B:	Block 6	USN	148363/148386	24
	Block 7	USN	148387/148410	24
	Block 8	USN	148411/148434	24
	Block 9	USN	149403/149426	24
	Block 10	USN	149427/149450	24
	Block 11	USN	149451/149474	24
	Block 12	USN	150406/150435	30
	Block 13	USN	150436/150479	44
	Block 14	USN	150480/150493 & 150624/150651	42
	Block 15	USN	150652/150653, 150993/151021, & 151397/151398	33
	Block 16	USN	151399/151426	28
	Block 17	USN	151427/151447	21
	Block 18	USN	151448/151472	25
	Block 19	USN	151473/151497	25
	Block 20	USN	151498/151519 & 152207/152215	31
	Block 21	USN	152216/152243	28
	Block 22	USN	152244/152272	29
	Block 23	USN	152273/152304	32
	Block 24	USN	152305/152331	27
	Block 25	USN	152965/152994	30
	Block 26	USN	152995/153029	35
	Block 27	USN	153030/153056	27
	Block 28	USN	153057/153070 & 153912/153915	18
		F-4B total		649

RF-4B:	Block 20	USMC	151975/151977	3
	Block 21	USMC	151978/151979	2
	Block 22	USMC	151980/151981	2
	Block 23	USMC	151982/151983	2
	Block 24	USMC	153089/153094	6
	Block 25	USMC	153095/153100	6
	Block 26	USMC	153101/153107	7
	Block 27	USMC	153108/153115	8
	Block 41	USMC	157342/157346	5
	Block 43	USMC	157347/157351	5
			RF-4B total	46
F-4C:	Block 15	USAF	62-12199 & 63-7407/63-7420	15
	Block 16	USAF	63-7421/63-7442	22
	Block 17	USAF	63-7443/63-7468	26
	Block 18	USAF	63-7469/63-7526	58
	Block 19	USAF	63-7527/63-7597	71
	Block 20	USAF	63-7598/63-7662	65
	Block 21	USAF	63-7663/63-7713 64-0654/64-0672	70
	Block 22	USAF	64-0673/64-0737	65
	Block 23	USAF	64-0738/64-0817	80
	Block 24	USAF	64-0818/64-0881	64
	Block 25	USAF	64-0882/64-0928	47
			F-4C total	583
RF-4C:	Block 14	USAF	62-12200/62-12201	2
	Block 17	USAF	63-7740/63-7742	3
	Block 18	USAF	63-7743/63-7749	7
	Block 19	USAF	63-7750/63-7763	14
	Block 20	USAF	64-0997/64-1017	21
	Block 21	USAF	64-1018/64-1037	20
	Block 22	USAF	64-1038/64-1061	24
	Block 23	USAF	64-1062/64-1077	16
	Block 24	USAF	64-1078/64-1085 & 65-0818/65-0838	29
	Block 25	USAF	65-0839/65-0864	26
	Block 26	USAF	65-0865/65-0901	37
	Block 27	USAF	65-0902/65-0932	31
	Block 28	USAF	65-0933/65-0945, 66-0383/66-0386, & 66-0388	18
	Block 29	USAF	66-0387 & 66-0389/66-0406	19
	Block 30	USAF	66-0407/66-0428	22
	Block 31	USAF	66-0429/66-0450	22
	Block 32	USAF	66-0451/66-0472	22
	Block 33	USAF	66-0473/66-0478 & 67-0428/67-0442	21
	Block 34	USAF	67-0443/67-0453	11
	Block 35	USAF	67-0454/67-0461	8
	Block 36	USAF	67-0462/67-0469	8
	Block 37	USAF	68-0548/68-0561	14
	Block 38	USAF	68-0562/68-0576	15
	Block 39	USAF	68-0577/68-0593	17
	Block 40	USAF	68-0594/68-0611	18
	Block 41	USAF	69-0349/69-0357	9
	Block 42	USAF	69-0358/69-0366	9
	Block 43	USAF	69-0367/69-0375	9
	Block 44	USAF	69-0376/69-0384	9
	Block 48	USAF	71-0248/71-0252	5
	Block 49	USAF	71-0253/71-0259	7
	Block 51	USAF	72-0145/72-0150	6
	Block 52	USAF	72-0151/72-0153	3
	Block 53	USAF	72-0154/72-0156	3
			RF-4C total	505
F-4D for USAF:	Block 24	USAF	64-0929/64-0937	9
	Block 25	USAF	64-0938/64-0963	26
	Block 26	USAF	64-0964/64-0980 & 65-0580/65-0611	49
	Block 27	USAF	65-0612/65-0665	54
	Block 28	USAF	65-0666/65-0770	105

Block 29	USAF	65-0771/65-0801, 66-0226/66-0283, & 66-7455/66-7504	139
Block 30	USAF	66-7505/66-7650	146
Block 31	USAF	66-7651/66-7774 & 66-8685/66-8698	138
Block 32	USAF	66-8699/66-8786	88
Block 33	USAF	66-8787/66-8825	39
		F-4D total for USAF	793

F-4D for export:

Block 35	Iranian AF	67-14869/67-14876	8
Block 36	Iranian AF	67-14877/67-14884	8
Block 37	Iranian AF	68-6904/68-6911	8
Block 38	Iranian AF	68-6912/68-6919	8
		F-4D total for export	32

F-4E for USAF:

Block 31	USAF	66-0284/66-0297	14
Block 32	USAF	66-0298/66-0338	41
Block 33	USAF	66-0339/66-0382 & 67-0208/67-0219	56
Block 34	USAF	67-0220/67-0282	63
Block 35	USAF	67-0283/67-0341	59
Block 36	USAF	67-0342/67-0398	57
Block 37	USAF	68-0303/68-0365	63
Block 38	USAF	68-0366/68-0395 & 68-0400/68-0409	40
Block 39	USAF	68-0410/68-0413, 68-0418/68-0433, & 68-0438/68-0451	34
Block 40	USAF	68-0452/68-0453, 68-0458/68-0468, 68-0473/68-0483, & 68-0488/68-0494	31
Block 41	USAF	68-0495/68-0498, 68-0503/68-0518, & 68-0526/68-0538	33
Block 42	USAF	69-0236/69-0303	68
Block 43	USAF	69-0304/69-0307 & 69-7201/69-7260	64
Block 44	USAF	69-7261/69-7273, 69-7286/69-7303, & 69-7546/69-7578	64
Block 45	USAF	69-7579/69-7589	11
Block 48	USAF	71-0224/71-0247	24
Block 49	USAF	71-1070/71-1093	24
Block 50	USAF	71-1391/71-1402 & 72-0121/72-0138	30
Block 51	USAF	72-0139/72-0144 & 72-0157/72-0159	9
Block 52	USAF	72-0160/72-0165	6
Block 53	USAF	72-0166/72-0168 & 72-1407	4
Block 54	USAF	72-1476/72-1489	14
Block 55	USAF	72-1490/72-1497	8
Block 56	USAF	72-1498/72-1499	2
Block 57	USAF	73-1157/73-1164	8
Block 58	USAF	73-1165/73-1184	20
Block 59	USAF	73-1185/73-1204	20
Block 60	USAF	74-0643/74-0666 & 74-1038/74-1049	36
Block 61	USAF	74-1050/74-1061 & 74-1620/74-1637	30
Block 62	USAF	74-1638/74-1653	16
Block 63	USAF/Luftwaffe	75-0628/75-0637	10
		F-4E total for USAF	959

F-4E for export:

Block 38	Israeli AF	68-0396/68-0399	4
Block 39	Israeli AF	68-0414/68-0417 & 68-0434/68-0437	8

466

Block 40	Israeli AF	68-0454/68-0457, 68-0469/68-0472, &68-0484/68-0487	12
Block 41	Israeli AF	68-0499/68-0502, 68-0519/68-0525, & 68-0539/68-0547	20
Block 46	Iranian AF	69-7711/69-7726	16
Block 47	Iranian AF	69-7727/69-7742	16
Block 51	Israeli AF	71-1779/71-1786	8
	Iranian AF	71-1094/71-1101	8
Block 52	Iranian AF	71-1102/71-1115	14
	Israeli AF	71-1787/71-1793	7
Block 53	Iranian AF	71-1116/71-1129	14
	Israeli AF	71-1794/71-1796	3
Block 54	Iranian AF	71-1130/71-1142	13
	Greek AF	72-1500/72-1507	8
Block 55	Iranian AF	71-1143/71-1152	10
	Greek AF	72-1508/72-1523	16
Block 56	Turkish AF	73-1016/73-1027	12
	Greek AF	72-1524/72-1535	12
	Iranian AF	71-1153/71-1166	14
Block 57	Turkish AF	73-1028/73-1042	15
	Iranian AF	73-1519/73-1534	16
Block 58	Turkish AF	73-1043/73-1055	13
	Iranian AF	73-1535/73-1549	15
Block 59	Iranian AF	73-1550/73-1554	5
Block 60	Israeli AF	74-1014/74-1015	2
	Greek AF	74-1618/74-1619	2
Block 61	Israeli AF	74-1016/74-102	16
Block 62	Israeli AF	74-1022/74-1037	16
Block 63	Iranian AF	75-0222/75-0257	36
Block 64	ROKAF	76-0493/76-0511	19
Block 65	Turkish AF	77-0277/77-0300	24
	Greek AF	77-1743/77-1750	8
Block 66	Turkish AF	77-0301/77-0308	8
	Greek AF	77-1751/77-1760	10
Block 67	ROKAF	78-0727/78-0744	18
		F-4E total for export	428

F-4EJ: (McDonnell built)	Block 45	JASDF	17-8301/17-8302, 27-8303/27-8306, & 37-8307/37-8310	10
	Block 47	JASDF	37-8311/37-8313	3
			F-4EJ total (McDonnell)	13

F-4EJ: (Mitsub. built)	F-4EJ	JASDF	37-8314/37-8323	10
	F-4EJ	JASDF	47-8324/47-8352	29
	F-4EJ	JASDF	57-8353/57-8376	24
	F-4EJ	JASDF	67-8377/67-8391	15
	F-4EJ	JASDF	77-8392/77-8403	12
	F-4EJ	JASDF	87-8404/87-8415	12
	F-4EJ	JASDF	97-8416/97-8427	12
	F-4EJ	JASDF	07-8428/07-8436	9
	F-4EJ	JASDF	17-8437/17-8440	4
			F-4EJ total (Mitsubishi)	127

RF-4E:	Block 43	Luftwaffe	3501/3508	8
	Block 44	Luftwaffe	3509/3515	7
	Block 45	Luftwaffe	3516/3534	19
		Israeli AF	69-7590/69-7595	6
	Block 46	Luftwaffe	3535/3563	29
	Block 47	Luftwaffe	3564/3588	25
	Block 48	Iranian AF	72-0266/72-0269	4
	Block 61	Iranian AF	74-1725/74-1728	4
	Block 62	Iranian AF	74-1729/74-1736	8
	Block 63	Israeli AF	75-0418/75-0423	6
	Block 66	Turkish AF	77-0309/77-0316	8
		Greek AF	77-0357/77-0358 & 77-1761/77-1766	8
		RF-4E total		132

RF-4EJ:	Block 56	JASDF	47-6901/47-6905	5
	Block 57	JASDF	57-6906/57-6914	9
			RF-4EJ total	14

F-4F:	Block 52	Luftwaffe	3701/3709	9
	Block 53	Luftwaffe	3710/3724	15
	Block 54	Luftwaffe	3725/3748	24
	Block 55	Luftwaffe	3749/3772	24
	Block 56	Luftwaffe	3773/3796	24
	Block 57	Luftwaffe	3797/3820	24
	Block 58	Luftwaffe	3821/3844	24
	Block 59	Luftwaffe	3845/3875	31
			F-4F total	175

F-4J:	Block 26	USN	153071/153075	5
	Block 27	USN	153076/153088	13
	Block 28	USN	153768/153779	12
	Block 29	USN	153780/153799	20
	Block 30	USN	153800/153839	40
	Block 31	USN	153840/153876	37
	Block 32	USN	153877/153911 & 154781/154785	40
	Block 33	USN	154786/154788 & 155504/155569	69
	Block 34	USN	155570/155580 & 155731/155784	65
	Block 35	USN	155785/155843	59
	Block 36	USN	155844/155866	23
	Block 37	USN	155867/155874	8
	Block 38	USN	155875/155889	15
	Block 39	USN	155890/155902	13
	Block 40	USN	157242/157260	19
	Block 41	USN	157261/157273	13
	Block 42	USN	155903 & 157274/157285	13
	Block 43	USN	157286/157297	12
	Block 44	USN	157298/157309	12
	Block 45	USN	158346/158354	9
	Block 46	USN	158355/158365	11
	Block 47	USN	158366/158379	14
			F-4J total	522

F-4K:	Block 26	Royal Navy	XT595/XT596	2
	Block 27	Royal Navy	XT597/XT598	2
	Block 30	Royal Navy	XT857/XT858	2
	Block 31	Royal Navy	XT859/XT862	4
	Block 32	Royal Navy	XT863/XT870	8
	Block 33	Royal Navy	XT871/XT876	6
	Block 34	Royal Navy	XV565/XV571	7
	Block 35	Royal Navy	XV572/XV578	7
	Block 36	Royal Navy	XV579/XV585	7
	Block 37	Royal Navy	XV586/XV592	7
			F-4K total	52

F-4M:	Block 29	RAF	XT852/XT853	2
	Block 31	RAF	XT891/XT895	5
	Block 32	RAF	XT896/XT906	11
	Block 33	RAF	XT907/XT914 XV393/XV398	14
	Block 34	RAF	XV399/XV417	19
	Block 35	RAF	XV418/XV436	19
	Block 36	RAF	XV437/XV442 XV460/XV475	22
	Block 37	RAF	XV476/XV495	20
	Block 38	RAF	XV496/XV501	6
			F-4M total	118

McDONNELL 119 (Number built: 1)

Model 119	Co owned	N119M	1

HUGHES 369 and McDONNELL DOUGLAS 500, 520, and 530 (Number built: Over 4,000; still in production)

YOH-6A	USA	62-4212/62-4216 & 62-2624	6

OH-6A	USA	65-12916/65-13003, 66-7775/66-7942, 66-14376/66-14419, 66-17750/66-17833, 66-17905, 66-17918, 67-16000/67-16686, 68-17140/68-17369, 69-15960/69-16075, & one unidentified	1,420
Model 500	Various	)	
Model 500C	Various	)	
Model 500D	Various	)	
Model 500MD	Various	)	
Model 500E	Various	)	
MD 500E	Various	) Data not released by MDHC	
MD 500MG	Various	)	
MD 520L	Various	)	
MD 520N	Various	)	
MD 530F	Various	)	
MD 530K	Various	)	

HUGHES XV-9 (Number built: 1)

XV-9	USA	64-15107	1

McDONNELL DOUGLAS DC-10 (Number built: 446)

Series 10	46500	American	N10DC (N101AA)	1
	46501	Laker	G-BELO	1
	46502/46525	American	N102AA/N125AA	24
	46600/46636	United	N1801U/N1832U, N1838U/ N1839U, N1841U/N1843U	37
	46645/46646	Western	N912WA & N913WA	2
	46700/46703	National	N60NA/N63NA	4
	46704/46705	THY	TC-JAV & TC-JAU	2
	46706/46710	National	N64NA/N68NA	5
	46727	Laker	G-BBSZ	1
	46900/46904	Continental	N68041/N68045	5
	46905/46906	Laker	G-AZCC & G-AZDD	2
	46907	THY	TC-JAY	1
	46908	Western	N901WA	1
	46928/46930	Western	N902WA/N904WA	3
	46938/46939	Western	N905WA & N906WA	2
	46942/46943	National	N69NA & N70NA	2
	46946	Western	N907WA	1
	46947/46948	American	N126AA & N127AA	2
	46970	Laker	G-GFAL	1
	46973	Laker	G-GSKY	1
	46977	Western	N908WA	1
	46983	Western	N909WA	1
	46984	American	N128AA	1
	46989	American	N130AA	1
	46994	American	N131AA	1
	46996	American	N129AA	1
	47800/47802	Continental	N68046/N68048	3
	47827/47830	American	N132AA/N135AA	4
	47832/47833	Western	N914WA/N915WA	2
	47965/47969	Delta	N601DA/N605DA	5
	48260/48263	United	N1844U/N1847U	4
			Series 10 total	122
Series 10CF	47803/47810	Continental	N68049/N68056	8
	48264	United	N1848U	1
			Series 10CF total	9
Series 15	48258/48259	Mexicana	N1003L, N10045	2
	48275/48276	Aeromexico	N10038, N1003N	2
	48289	Mexicana	N1003W	1
	48294/48295	Mexicana	N1004A, XA-MEX	2
			Series 15 total	7
Series 30	46540/46543	CP Air	C-GCPC/C-GCPF	4

46550/46555	KLM	N1339U (PH-DTA), N1342U (PH-DTB), & PH-DTC/PH-DTF	6
46556/46557	KLM/VIASA	PH-DTG & PH-DTH	2
46575/46584	Swissair	HB-IHA/HB-IHH & HB-IHL/HB-IHM	10
46590/46591	British Cal	G-BFGI & G-BGAT	2
46595/46596	Lufthansa	D-ADPO & D-ADQO	2
46640	Malaysian	9M-MAT	1
46685/46686	Garuda	PK-GIE & PK-GIF	2
46711/46714	National	N80NA/N83NA	4
46850/46854	UTA	F-BTDB/F-BTDC, N54629, F-BTDE, N54649	5
46868/46872	SAS	LN-RKA, SE-DFD, OY-KDA, LN-RKB, SE-DFE	5
46890	Air Afrique	TU-TAL	1
46892	Thai International	HS-TGB	1
46910/46911	Air New Zealand	ZK-NZP & ZK-NZQ	2
46912	KAL	HL7316	1
46914	KLM/PAL	PH-DTK	1
46915	KAL	HL7317	1
46916	VARIG	PP-VMD	1
46917	Lufthansa	D-ADLO	1
46918/46919	Garuda	PK-GIA & PK-GIB	2
46921	British Cal	G-BEBM	1
46922	Iberia	EC-CSJ	1
46925/46927	Iberia	EC-CBN/EC-CBP	3
46931	PIA	AP-AXC	1
46932	Air Zaïre	9Q-CLT	1
46933	KLM/PAL	PH-DTI	1
46934	KAL	HL7315	1
46935	PIA	AP-AXE	1
46936/46937	Aeromexico	XA-DUG & XA-DUH	2
46940	PIA	AP-AXD	1
46941	VARIG	PP-VMQ	1
46944/46945	VARIG	PP-VMA & PP-VMB	2
46949	British Cal	G-BEBL	1
46950	Air New Zealand	ZK-NZT	1
46951	Garuda	PK-GID	1
46952	KLM/Garuda	PH-DTL	1
46953	Iberia	EC-CSK	1
46954	Air New Zealand	ZK-NZS	1
46955	Malaysian	9M-MAS	1
46957	Nigeria	AW5N-ANN	1
46958	PAL	RP-C200	1
46959	Thai International	HS-TMC	1
46963	UTA	F-BTDD	1
46964	Garuda	PK-GIC	1
46965	Lufthansa	D-ADMO	1
46968	Nigeria AW	5N-ANR	1
46969	Swissair	HB-IHI	1
46971/46972	VIASA	YV-135C & YV-136C	2
46976	Wardair	C-GXRB	1
46978	Wardair	C-GXRC	1
46980	Iberia	EC-CEZ	1
46981	JAT	YU-AMA	1
46982	VIASA	YV-137C	1
46988	JAT	YU-AMB	1
46990/46991	Singapore AL	9V-SDA & 9V-SDC	2
46993	Singapore AL	9V-SDB	1
46995	Singapore AL	9V-SDD	1
46997	Air Afrique	TU-TAN	1
46998	Balair	HB-IHK	1
46999	Singapore AL	9V-SDE	1
47811/47815	Laker	G-BGXE/G-BGXI	5
47816	British Cal	G-BHDH	1
47817/47818	Singapore AL	9V-SDF & 9V-SDG	2
47831	British Cal	G-BHDI	1
47834	Iberia	EC-DHZ	1
47837	National	N84NA	1
47838	PAL	RP-C211	1
47840	British Cal	G-BHDJ	1
47843/47845	VARIG	PP-VMV/PP-VMX	3
47846/47849	Air New Zealand	ZK-NZL/ZK-NZN, ZK-NZR	4

47850/47851	Continental	N68060 & N12061	2
47861/47868	Alitalia	I-DYNA, I-DYNE, I-DYNI, I-DYNO,	
		I-DYNU, I-DYNB/I-DYND	8
47886	Air Zaïre	9Q-CLI	1
47887	Air Siam	HS-VGE	1
47888	Afghan AL	YA-LAS	1
47889	PIA	AP-AYM	1
47921/47929	Lufthansa	D-ADAO, D-ADBO, D-ADCO,	
		D-ADDO, D-ADFO, D-ADGO,	
		D-ADHO, D-ADJO, D-ADKO	9
47956/47957	Finnair	OH-LHA & OH-LHB	2
47981/47982	Iberia	EC-CLB & ED-DEA	2
48252	Condor	D-ADSO	1
48265	Finnair	N345HC	1
48266	Zambia AW	N3016Z	1
48267	Thai International	HS-TMA	1
48277	British Cal	G-DCIO	1
48282	VARIG	PP-VMY	1
48283	Malaysian	9M-MAV	1
48285	CP Air	C-GCPG	1
48286	Ghana AW	9G-ANA	1
48288	CP Air	C-GCPH	1
48290	Thai International	HS-TMB	1
48292/48293	Swissair	HB-IHN/HB-IHO	2
48296	CP Air	C-GCPI	1
48315/48316	Japan Air System	JA8550/JA8551	2
48317	Biman	S2-ACR	
	Bangladesh		1
48318	Nigeria AW	N3024W	1
48319	Thai International	HS-TMC	1
		Series 30 total	166

Series 30CF	46800/46802	TIA	N101TV/N103TV	3
	46825/46826	Overseas Nat'l	N1031F & N1032F	2
	46835/46837	World AW	N106WA/N108WA	3
	46891	Martinair	PH-MBG	1
	46924	Martinair	PH-MBN	1
	46956	Martinair	PH-MBP	1
	46960	Overseas Nat'l	N1033F	1
	46961	Thai International	HS-TMD	1
	46962	Overseas Nat'l	N1034F	1
	46975	World AW	N103WA	1
	46985	Martinair	PH-MBT	1
	46986/46987	World AW	N104WA & N105WA	2
	46992	Overseas Nat'l	N1035F	1
	47819/47821	World AW	N109WA & N112WA/N113WA	3
	47835/47836	SABENA	OO-SLD & OO-SLE	2
	47841/47842	VARIG	PP-VMT & PP-VMU	2
	47870	Federal Express	N305FE	1
	47906/47908	SABENA	OO-SLA/OO-SLC	3
			Series 30CF total	30

Series 30F	48287	Federal Express	N306FE	1
	48291	Federal Express	N307FE	1
	48297/48300	Federal Express	N308FE/N310FE & N312FE	4
	48311/48314	Federal Express	N313FE/N316FE	4
			Series 30F total	10

Series 40	46662	JAL	JA8535	1
	46750/46771	Northwest	N141US/N162US	22
	46913	JAL	JA8534	1
	46974	JAL	JA8538	1
	47822	JAL	JA8539	1
	47824/47826	JAL	JA8541/JA8543	3
	47852/47853	JAL	JA8544 & JA8545	2
	47856	JAL	JA8547	1
			Series 40 total	32

Series 40D	46660/46661	JAL	JA8532 & JA8533	2
	46920	JAL	JA8530	1

	46923	JAL	JA8531	1
	46966/46967	JAL	JA8536 & JA8537	2
	47823	JAL	JA8540	1
	47855	JAL	JA8546	1
	47857	JAL	JA8548	1
	48301	JAL	JA8549	1
			Series 40D total	10
KC-10	48200/48251	USAF	79-0433/79-0434,	
			79-1710/79-1713,	
			79-1946/79-1951,	
			82-0190/82-0193,	
			83-0075/83-0082,	
			84-0185/84-0192,	
			85-0027/85-0034, &	
			86-0027/86-0038	52
	48303/48310	USAF	87-0117/87-0124	8
			KC-10 total	60

McDONNELL DOUGLAS F-15 EAGLE (Number built: By the end of 1989, a total of 1,211 F-15s had been built by MCAIR in St Louis and by Mitsubishi in Japan. MCAIR was still producing F-15Es for the USAF and F-15Cs and Ds for foreign customers while Mitsubishi held orders for more F-15DJs and Js.)

F-15A:	Block 1	USAF	71-0280/71-0281	2
	Block 2	USAF	71-0282/71-0284	3
	Block 3	USAF	71-0285/71-0286	2
	Block 4	USAF	71-0287/71-0289	3
	Block 5	USAF	72-0113/72-0116	4
	Block 6	USAF	72-0117/72-0120	4
	Block 7	USAF	73-0085/73-0089	5
	Block 8	USAF	73-0090/73-0097	8
	Block 9	USAF	73-0098/73-0107	10
	Block 10	USAF	74-0081/74-0093	13
	Block 11	USAF	74-0094/74-0111	18
	Block 12	USAF	74-0112/74-0136	25
	Block 13	USAF	75-0018/75-0048	31
	Block 14	USAF	75-0049/75-0079	31
	Block 15	USAF	76-0008/76-0046	39
	Block 16	USAF	76-0047/76-0083	37
	Block 17	USAF	76-0084/76-0113	30
		Israeli AF	76-1505/76-1514	10
	Block 18	USAF	76-0114/76-0120 &	
			77-0061/77-0084	31
		Israeli AF	76-1515/76-1523	9
	Block 19	USAF	77-0085/77-0119	35
	Block 20	USAF	77-0120/77-0153	34
			F-15A total	384
F-15B:	Block 3	USAF	71-0290	1
	Block 4	USAF	71-0291	1
	Block 7	USAF	73-0108/73-0110	3
	Block 8	USAF	73-0111/73-0112	2
	Block 9	USAF	73-0113/73-0114	2
	Block 10	USAF	74-0137/74-0138	2
	Block 11	USAF	74-0139/74-0140	2
	Block 12	USAF	74-0141/74-0142	2
	Block 13	USAF	75-0080/75-0084	5
	Block 14	USAF	75-0085/75-0089	5
	Block 15	USAF	76-0124/76-0129	6
	Block 16	USAF	76-0130/76-0135	6
		Israeli AF	76-1524/76-1525	2
	Block 17	USAF	76-0136/76-0140	5
	Block 18	USAF	76-0141/76-0142 &	
			77-0154/77-0156	5
	Block 19	USAF	77-0157/77-0162	6
	Block 20	USAF	77-0163/77-0168	6
			F-15B total	61
F-15C:	Block 21	USA	F78-0468/78-0495	28
	Block 22	USAF	78-0496/78-0522	27
	Block 23	USAF	78-0523/78-0550	28

	Block 24	USAF	79-0015/79-0037	23
	Block 25	USAF	79-0038/79-0058	21
	Block 26	USAF	79-0059/79-0081	23
	Block 27	USAF	80-0002/80-0023	22
		Israeli AF	80-0122/80-0124	3
	Block 28	USAF	80-0024/80-0038	15
		Israeli AF	80-0125/80-0127	3
		RSAF	80-0062/80-0067	6
	Block 29	USAF	80-0039/80-0053	15
		Israeli AF	80-0128/80-0130	3
		RSAF	80-0068/80-0074	7
	Block 30	USAF	81-0020/81-0031	12
		RSAF	80-0075/80-0085	11
	Block 31	USAF	81-0032/81-0040	9
		RSAF	80-0086/80-0099	14
	Block 32	USAF	81-0041/81-0056	16
		RSAF	80-0100/80-0106 & 81-0002	8
	Block 33	USAF	82-0008/82-0022	15
	Block 34	USAF	82-0023/82-0038	16
	Block 35	USAF	83-0010/83-0034	25
		Israeli AF	83-0054/83-0055	2
	Block 36	USAF	83-0035/83-0043	9
		Israeli AF	83-0056/83-0062	7
	Block 37	USAF	84-0001/84-0015	15
	Block 38	USAF	84-0016/84-0031	16
	Block 39	USAF	85-0093/85-0107	15
	Block 40	USAF	85-0108/85-0128	21
	Block 41	USAF	86-0143/86-0162	20
	Block 42	USAF	86-0163/86-0180	18
			F-15C total	**473**
F-15D:	Block 21	USAF	78-0561/78-0565	5
	Block 22	USAF	78-0566/78-0570	5
	Block 23	USAF	78-0571/78-0574	4
	Block 24	USAF	79-0004/79-0006	3
	Block 25	USAF	79-0007/79-0011	5
	Block 26	USAF	79-0012/79-0014	3
	Block 27	USAF	80-0054/80-0055	2
		Israeli AF	80-0131/80-0132	2
		RSAF	80-0107/80-0110	4
	Block 28	USAF	80-0056/80-0057	2
		Israeli AF	80-0133/80-0136	4
		RSAF	80-0111/80-0112	2
	Block 29	USAF	80-0058/80-0061	4
		RSAF	80-0113/80-0114	2
	Block 30	USAF	81-0061/81-0062	2
		RSAF	80-0115/80-0117	3
	Block 31	USAF	81-0063/81-0065	3
		RSAF	80-0118/80-0119	2
	Block 32	RSAF	80-0120/80-0121 & 81-0003	3
	Block 33	USAF	82-0044/82-0045	2
	Block 34	USAF	82-0046/82-0048	3
	Block 35	USAF	3-0046/83-0048	3
		Israeli AF	83-0063/83-0064	2
	Block 36	USAF	83-0049/83-0050	2
	Block 37	USAF	84-0042/84-0044	3
	Block 38	USAF	84-0045/84-0046	2
	Block 39	USAF	85-0129/85-0131	3
	Block 40	USAF	85-0132/85-0134	3
	Block 41	USAF	86-0181/86-0182	2
			F-15D total	**85**
F-15DJ:	Block 26	JASDF	79-0282/79-0285	4
(MCAIR built)	Block 29	JASDF	79-0286/79-0287	2
	Block 32	JASDF	81-0068/81-0069	2
	Block 33	JASDF	81-0070/81-0071	2
	Block 36	JASDF	83-0052/83-0053	2
(Mitsu built)		JASDF	82-8063/82-8066 + 13 others	17
			F-15DJ total	**29**
F-15E:	Block 41	USAF	86-0183/86-0184	2

	Block 42	USAF	86-0185/86-0190	6
	Block 43	USAF	87-0169/87-0189	21
	Block 44	USAF	87-0190/87-0210	21
	Block 45	USAF	88-1667/88-1687	21
	Block 46	USAF	88-1688/88-1708	21
			F-15E total	92+

F-15J: (MCAIR built)	Block 24	JASDF	79-0280/79-0281	2
(MCAIR built/ Mitsu assembl.)	Block 24	JASDF	12-8803 & 22-8804/22-8806	4
	Block 25	JASDF	22-8807/22-8810	4
(Mitsubishi built)		JASDF	22-8811/22-8815, 32-8816/	
		JASDF	32-8827, 42-8828/42-8844, 52-8845/52-8863, 62-8864/62-8878, 72-8879/72-8895, 82-8896/82-8905	
			+ others	95+
			F-15J total	105+

McDONNELL DOUGLAS YC-15 (Number built: 2)

YC-15		USAF	70-1875/70-1876	2

McDONNELL DOUGLAS (HUGHES) AH-64 APACHE (Number built: By the end of 1989, 540 Apaches had been built by Hughes and MDHC; more were on order.)

YAH-64A (GTV)	AV-01	USA	74-22247	1
YAH-64A	AV-02/AV-03 &		74-22248/74-22249 &	
	AV-04/AV-06	USA	77-23257/77-23259	5
AH-64A	PV-01/PV-526		82-23355/82-23365, 83-23787/83-23834, 84-24200/84-24311, 85-25051/85-25188, 86-8940/86-9055, & 87-0407/87-0507	526+
			YAH-64/AH-64 total	540+

McDONNELL DOUGLAS AV-8B HARRIER II (Number built: By the end of 1989, a total of 271 Harrier IIs had been built by MCAIR in St Louis and BAe in Great Britain; more were on order)

AV-8B:	Block 1	USMC	161396/161399	4
	Block 2	USMC	161573/161578	6
	Block 3	USMC	161579/161584	6
	Block 4	USMC	162068/162076	9
	Block 5	USMC	162077/1620881	2
	Block 6	USMC	162721/1627341	4
	Block 7	USMC	162735/1627461	2
	Block 8	USMC	162942/162962 & 1629642	2
	Block 9	USMC	162965/162970 & 162972/162973	8
	Block 10	USMC	163176/163179, 163181/163185, 163187/163190, & 163192/163195	17
	Block 11	USMC	163197/163201, 163203/163206, 163419/163426, & 163514/163519	23
	Block 12	USMC	163659/163673	15
	Block 13	USMC	163674/163690 & 163852/163855 21	
	Block 14	USMC	163862/163872	11
	Block 15	USMC	163873/163883 & 164115/164116	13
	Block 16	USMC	164117/164121	5
	Block 17	USMC	164123/164135	13
			AV-8B total	211+

EAV-8B:	Block 9	Spanish Navy	163010/163021	12
			EAV-8B total	12

TAV-8B:	Block 7	USMC	162747	1
	Block 9	USMC	162963 & 162971	2
	Block 10	USMC	163180, 163186, & 163191	3
	Block 11	USMC	163196, 163202, 163207	3
	Block 12	USMC	163856/163858	3
	Block 13	USMC	163859/163861	3
	Block 16	USMC	164113/164114 & 164122	3
	Block 17	USMC	164136/164138	3

			TAV-8B total	21+
GR Mk. 5:	Block 4	RAF	ZD318/ZD319	2
(MCAIR kits/	Block 5	RAF	ZD320	1
BAe assembled)	Block 6	RAF	ZD321	1
	Block 7	RAF	ZD322/ZD323	2
	Block 8	RAF	ZD324/ZD328	5
	Block 9	RAF	ZD329/ZD330 & ZD345/ZD348	6
	Block 10	RAF	ZD349/ZD355, ZD375/ZD380, & ZD400/ZD401	15
	Block 11	RAF	ZD402/ZD410	9
	Block 12	RAF	ZD411/ZD412, ZD430/ZD438, & ZD461/ZD464	15
	Block 13	RAF	ZD465/ZD470 & ZG471/ZG473	9
	Block 14	RAF	ZG474/ZG480 & ZG500/ZG505	13
	Block 15	RAF	ZG506/ZG512 & ZG530/ZG533	11
	Block 16	RAF	ZG856/ZG862	7
			GR Mk. 5 total (BAe assembled)	96

McDONNELL DOUGLAS F/A-18 HORNET (Number built: By the end of 1989, a total of 878 Hornets had been built by MCAIR in St Louis and by ASTA in Australia; more were on order.)

F/A-18A:	Block 1	USN	160775/160777	3
	Block 2	USN	160778/160780	3
	Block 3	USN	160782/160783 & 160785	3
	Block 4	USN/USMC	161213/161216, 161248, & 161250/161251	7
	Block 5	USN/USMC	161353 & 161358/161359	3
	Block 6	USN/USMC	161361/161367 & 161519	8
	Block 7	USN/USMC	161520/161528	9
	Block 8	USN/USMC	161702/161703, 161705/161706, 161708/161710, 161712/161713, & 161715	10
	Block 9	USN/USMC	161716/161718, 161720/161722, 161724/161726, 161728/161732, & 161734/161736	17
	Block 10	USN/USMC	161737/161739, 161741/161745, & 161747/161761	23
	Block 11	USN/USMC	161925/161931, 161933/161937, 161939/161942, & 161944	17
	Block 12	USN/USMC	161945/161946 & 161948/161965	20
	Block 13	USN/USMC	161966/161987	22
	Block 14	USN/USMC	162394/162401, 162403/162407, 162409/162412, & 162414	18
	Block 15	USN/USMC	162415/162418, 162420/162426, & 162428/162444	28
	Block 16	USN/USMC	162445/162477	33
	Block 17	USN/USMC	162826/162835, 162837/162841, 162843/162849, & 162851/162852	24
	Block 18	USN/USMC	162853/162856, 162858/162863, 162865/162869, 162871/161875, & 162877/162881	25
	Block 19	USN/USMC	162882/162884 & 162886/162909	27
	Block 20	USN/USMC	163092/163103, 163105/163109, 163111/163114, & 163116/163118	24
	Block 21	USN/USMC	163119/163122 & 163124/163145	26
	Block 22	USN/USMC	163146/163175	30
			F/A-18A total	380
AF/A-18A	Block 14	RAAF	A21-1/A21-3	3
	Block 15	RAAF	A21-4/A21-7	4
	Block 16	RAAF	A21-8/A21-11	4
	Block 17	RAAF	A21-12/A21-18	7
	Block 19	RAAF	A21-19/A21-21	3
	Block 20	RAAF	A21-22/A21-27	6
	Block 21	RAAF	A21-28/A21-32	5
	Block 22	RAAF	A21-33/A21-36	4
	Block 23	RAAF	A21-37/A21-40	4
	Block 24	RAAF	A21-41/A21-44	4
	Block 25	RAAF	A21-45/A21-49	5
	Block 26	RAAFA	21-50/A21-53	4
	Block 27	RAAF	A21-54/A21-56	3

	Block 28	RAAF	A21-57	1
			AF/A-18A total	57
		(Assembled in Australia from MCAIR knock-down kits)		
CF-18A:	Block 9	CAF	188701	1
	Block 10	CAF	188702/188706	5
	Block 11	CAF	188707/188713	7
	Block 12	CAF	188714/188720	7
	Block 13	CAF	188721/188727	7
	Block 14	CAF	188728/188734	7
	Block 15	CAF	188735/188740	6
	Block 16	CAF	188741/188747	7
	Block 17	CAF	188748/188754	7
	Block 18	CAF	188755/188761	7
	Block 19	CAF	188762/188768	7
	Block 20	CAF	188769/188774	6
	Block 21	CAF	188775/188782	8
	Block 22	CAF	188783/188790	8
	Block 23	CAF	188791/188798	8
			CF-18A total	98
EF-18A:	Block 18	Spanish AF	C.15-13	1
	Block 20	Spanish AF	C.15-14/C.15-16	3
	Block 21	Spanish AF	C.15-17/C.15-21	5
	Block 22	Spanish AF	C.15-22/C.15-30	9
	Block 23	Spanish AF	C.15-31/C.15-39	9
	Block 24	Spanish AF	C.15-40/C.15-45	6
	Block 25	Spanish AF	C.15-46/C.15-47	2
	Block 26	Spanish AF	C.15-48/C.15-52	5
	Block 27	Spanish AF	C.15-53/C.15-57	5
	Block 28	Spanish AF	C.15-58/C.15-64	7
	Block 29	Spanish AF	C.15-65/C.15-66	2
	Block 30	Spanish AF	C.15-67/C.15-70	4
	Block 31	Spanish AF	C.15-71/C.15-72	2
			EF-18A total	60
F/A-18B:	Block 2	USN	160781	1
	Block 3	USN	160784	1
	Block 4	USN/USMC	161217 & 161249	2
	Block 5	USN/USMC	161354/161357	4
	Block 6	USN/USMC	161360	1
	Block 8	USN/USMC	161704, 161707, 161711, & 161714	4
	Block 9	USN/USMC	161719, 161723, 161727, & 161733	4
	Block 10	USN/USMC	161740, 161746, & 161924	3
	Block 11	USN/USMC	161932, 161938, & 161943	3
	Block 12	USN/USMC	161947	1
	Block 14	USN/USMC	162402, 162408, & 162413	3
	Block 15	USN/USMC	162419 & 162427	2
	Block 17	USN/USMC	162836, 162842, & 162850	3
	Block 18	USN/USMC	162857, 162864, 162870, & 162876	4
	Block 19	USN/USMC	162885	1
	Block 20	USN/USMC	163104, 163110, & 163115	3
	Block 21	USN/USMC	163123	1
			F/A-18B total	41
AF/A-18B	Block 14	RAAF	A21-101/A21-107	7
	Block 18	RAAF	A21-108/A21-112	5
	Block 19	RAAF	A21-113/A21-114	2
	Block 22	RAAF	A21-115/A21-116	2
	Block 23	RAAF	A21-117/A21-118	2
			AF/A-18B total	18
		(2 by MCAIR & 16 assembled in Australia)		
CF-18B:	Block 8	CAF	188901/188904	4
	Block 9	CAF	188905/188909	5
	Block 10	CAF	188910/188912	3
	Block 12	CAF	188913/188914	2
	Block 13	CAF	188915	1
	Block 14	CAF	188916	1

	Block 15	CAF	188917/188918	2
	Block 16	CAF	188919	1
	Block 17	CAF	188920/188921	2
	Block 18	CAF	188922	1
	Block 19	CAF	188923	1
	Block 20	CAF	188924/188925	2
	Block 24	CAF	188926/188934	9
	Block 25	CAF	188935/188940	6
			CF-18B total	40

EF-18B:	Block 17	Spanish AF	CE.15-1/CE.15-2	2
	Block 18	Spanish AF	CE.15-3/CE.15-4	2
	Block 19	Spanish AF	CE.15-5/CE.15-8	4
	Block 20	Spanish AF	CE.15-9	1
	Block 21	Spanish AF	CE.15-10/CE.15-12	3
			EF-18B total	12

F/A-18C:	Block 23	USN/USMC	163427/163433, 163435, 163437/163440, 163442/163444, 163446, 163448/163451, 163453, & 163455/163456	23
	Block 24	USN/USMC	163458/163459, 163461/163463, 163465/163467, 163469/163471, 163473, 163475/163478, 163480/163481, & 163483/163485	21
	Block 25	USN/USMC	163487, 163489/163491, 163493/163496, 163498/163499, 163502/163506, & 163508/163509	17
	Block 26	USN/USMC	163699, 163701/163706, 163708/163719, & 163721/163726	25
	Block 27	USN/USMC	163727/163733, 163735/163748, & 163750/163754	26
	Block 28	USN/USMC	163755/163762, 163764/163770, 163772/163777, & 163779/163782	25
	Block 29	USN/USMC	163985, 163987/163988, 163990, 163992/163993, 163995/163996, 163998/164000, 164002/164004, 164006/164008, 164010, & 164012/164013	20
	Block 30	USN/USMC	164015/164016, 164018, 164020/164021, 164023, 164025, 164027, 164029/164031, 164033/164034, 164036/164037, & 164039	16
	Block 31	USN/USMC	164041/164042, 164044/164045, 164047/164048, 164050, 164052, 164054/164055, 164057, 164059/164060, 164062/164063, & 164065/164067	18
	Block 32	USN/USMC	164197, 164199/164202, 164204/164206, 164208/164210, 164212/164215, & 164217/164218	17
	Block 33	USN/USMC	164220/164223, 164225/164227, 164229/164232, 164234/164236, 164238/164240, 164242/1642444, & 164246/164248	23
	Block 34	USN/USMC	164250/164253, 164255/164258, 164260/164262, 164264/164266, 164411/164414, & 164416/164421	24
			F/A-18C total	255+

F/A-18D:	Block 23	USN/USMC	163434, 163436, 163441, 163445, 163447, 163452, 163454, & 163457	8
	Block 24	USN/USMC	163460, 163464, 163468, 163472, 163474, 163479, 163482, & 163486	8
	Block 25	USN/USMC	163488, 163492, 163497, 163500/163501, 163507, & 163510	7
	Block 26	USN/USMC	163700, 163707, & 163720	3
	Block 27	USN/USMC	163734 & 163749	2
	Block 28	USN/USMC	163763, 163771, & 163778	3

477

Block 29	USN/USMC	163986, 163989, 163991, 163994, 163997, 164001, 164005, 164009, 164011, & 164014		10
Block 30	USN/USMC	164017, 164019, 164022, 164024, 164026, 164028, 164032, 164035, 164038, & 164040		10
Block 31	USN/USMC	164043, 164046, 164049, 164051, 164053, 164056, 164058, 164061, 164064, & 164068		10
Block 32	USN/USMC	164196, 164198, 164203, 164207, 164211, 164216, & 164219		7
Block 33	USN/USMC	164224, 164228, 164233, 164237, 164241, 164245, & 164249		7
Block 34	USN/USMC	164254, 164259, 164263, 164267, 164415, & 164422		6
		F/A-18D total		81+

McDONNELL DOUGLAS DC-9-80 (MD-80): (Number built: By the end of 1989, 686 DC-9-80s and MD-88s had been built by Douglas; more were on order.)

DC-9-81	48000/48001	Co owned	N980DC & N1002G	2
(MD-81)	48002/48014	Swissair	HB-INC/HB-INI & HB-INK/HB-INP	13
	48015/48021	Austrian	OE-LDP, OE-LDR/OE-LDV, & OE-LDX	7
	48024/48025	Austral	N10022 & N10027	2
	48026	Muse Air	N10028	1
	48027/48028	Air Cal	N475AC & N476AC	2
	48029/48033	Toa/JAS	JA8458/JA8462	5
	48034/48043	PSA	N924PS/N927PS & N930PS/N935PS	10
	48044/48045	Hawaiian	N809HA & N819HA	2
	48046	Inex Adria	YU-AJZ	1
	48049	Muse Air	N10029	1
	48050	Austral	N1003G	1
	48051	Hawaiian	N829HA	1
	48052/48053	PSA	N928PS & N929PS	2
	48058	Hawaiian	N839HA	1
	48059	Austrian	OE-LDW	1
	48070/48072	Toa/JAS	JA8468/JA8470	3
	48073/48074	Hawaiian	N849HA & N859HA	2
	48092/48094	PSA	N936PS/N938PS	3
	48099	PSA	N939PS	1
	49100/49101	Swissair	HB-INA & HB-INB	2
	49115	Austrian	OE-LDY	1
	49120/49122	Muse Air	N932MC/N934MC	3
	49125	Muse Air	N935MC	1
	49164	Austrian	OE-LDZ	1
	49278/49279	Austrian	OE-LMA & OE-LMB	2
	49280/49283	Toa/JAS	JA8496/JA8499	4
	49356/49359	Swissair	HB-INS/HB-INV	4
	149372	Austrian	OE-LMC	1
	49380/49382	Scandinavian	OY-KGT, OY-KGZ, & LN-RLE	3
	49420	Scandinavian	OY-KGY	1
	49422	Scandinavian	SE-DFV	1
	49436	Scandinavian	OY-KHC	1
	49438	Scandinavian	SE-DFY	1
	49461/49463	Toa/JAS	JA8260/JA8262	3
	49554	Scandinavian	LN-RMA	1
	49570/49572	Swissair	HB-INX/HB-INZ	3
	49603	Scandinavian	SE-DIA	1
	49613	Scandinavian	OY-KHG	1
	9820	Toa/JAS	JA8294	1
	49844	Swissair	HB-ISX	1
		DC-9-81 total		98+

DC-9-82	48022	Martinair	PH-MCD	1
(MD-82)	48047/48048	Inex Adria	YU-ANA & YU-ANB	2
	48054/48055	Republic	N301RC & N302RC	2
	48056/48057	Muse Air	N930MC & N931MC	2
	48062/48063	Air Cal	N477AC & N478AC	2
	48066	Air Cal	N479AC	1
	48067/48069	Aeromexico	N1003X, N1003Y, & N1003Z	3

48079/48080	Jet America	N779JA & N778JA	2
48083	Aeromexico	N10033	1
48086	Republic	N307RC	1
48087	Inex Adria	YU-ANC	1
48088/48091	Republic	N309RC, N311RC/N312RC, & N1004G	4
48095/48098	PSA	N940PS/N943PS	4
49102	Frontier	N9805F	1
49103/49104	VIASA	YV158C & YV159C	2
49110	Republic	N1004L	1
49111	Jet America	N781JA	1
49112/49113	Air Cal	N480AC & N481AC	2
49114	Frontier	N9804F	1
49116/49118	Frontier	N9801F/N9803F	3
49119	PSA	N944PS	1
49123/49124	ALM-Antillean	PJ-SEF & PJ-SEG	2
49126	Jet America	N780JA	1
49127	New York Air	N801NY	1
49138/49139	PSA	N945PS & N946PS	2
49140/49141	CAAC	B2101 & B2102	2
49142/49143	PSA	N947PS & N948PS	2
49144	Martinair	PH-MBZ	1
49145	American	N203AA	1
49149	VARIG	N505MD	1
49150/49152	Finnair	OH-LMN/OH-LMP	3
49153/49154	TWA	N902TW & N903TW	2
49155	American	N205AA	1
49156/49157	TWA	N904TW & N905TW	2
49158/49159	American	N207AA & N208AA	2
49160	TWA	N906TW	1
49161/49163	American	N210AA & N214AA/N215AA	3
49165/49166	TWA	N907TW & N901TW	2
49167/49168	American	N216AA & N218AA	2
49169/49170	TWA	N908TW & N909TW	2
49171/49181	American	N219AA, N221AA, N223AA/ N228AA, & N232AA/N234AA	11
49182/49187	TWA	N911TW/N916TW	6
49188/49190	Aeromexico	XA-AMO/XA-AMQ	3
49192/49202	Alitalia	I-DAWA, I-DAWE, I-DAWI, I-DAWO, I-DAWU, I-DAWB/I-DAWD, I-DAWF, & I-DAWG/I-DAWH	11
49203	ATI	I-DAWJ	1
49204/49209	Alitalia	I-DAWL/I-DAWM & I-DAWP/ I-DAWS	6
49210/49215	ATI	I-DAWT & I-DAWV/I-DAWW, I-DAWY/I-DAWZ, & I-DAVA	6
49216	Alitalia	I-DAVB	1
49217/49221	ATI	I-DAVC, I-DAVD, & I-DAVF/I-DAVH	5
49222	Continental	N802NY	1
49229	Continental	N803NY	1
49230	American	N950U	1
49237	PSA	N949PS	1
49245	American	N951U	1
49246	Continental	N804NY	1
49247/49248	Alisarda	HB-IKK & HB-IKL	2
49249	New York Air	N805NY	1
49250	Continental	N812NY	1
49251	American	N236AA	1
49253/49259	American	N237AA, N241AA/N242AA, N244AA/N246AA, & N248AA	7
49260	New York Air	N806NY	1
49261/49263	Continental	N807NY/N809NY	3
49264	New York Air	N810NY	1
49265	Continental	N811NY	1
49266/49267	Ozark	N952U & N953U	2
49269/49273	American	N249AA, N251AA, & N274AA/ N276AA	5
49277	Balair	HB-INR	1

49286/49329	American	N253AA, N255AA, N258AA/ N259AA, N262AA, N266AA, N269AA, N271AA, N278AA/ N279AA, N283AA, N285AA/ N298AA, N400AA, N70401, N402A/ N403A, N70404, N405A/N406A, N407AA/N413AA, N33414, & N415AA/N418AA	44
49331/49343	American	N419AA/N420AA, N77421, N422AA/N424AA, N70425, & N426AA/N431AA	13
49350	American	N432AA	1
49355	CAAC	B2103	1
49366/49369	TWA	N917TW/N920TW	4
49370/49371	Continental	N816NY & N817NY	2
49373/49374	Korean Air	HL7272 & HL7273	2
49379	Inex Adria	YU-ANG	1
49383/49385	Scandinavian	LN-RLF & SE-DFS/SE-DFT	3
49386/49387	Jet America	N784JA & N785JA	2
49391/49394	Frontier	EI-BTA/EI-BTD	4
49415	CAAC	B2106	1
49416/49419	Korean Air	HL7275/HL7276 & HL7282/HL7283	4
49421	Scandinavian	SE-DFU	1
49423/49424	Scandinavian	LN-RLG & SE-DFX	2
49425	CAAC	B2104	1
49426/49427	TWA	N954U & N955U	2
49428	CAAC	B2105	1
49429	PSA	N951PS	1
49430/49432	Alitalia	I-DAVI/I-DAVK	3
49433	ATI	I-DAVL	1
49434	Alitalia	I-DAVM	1
49435	ATI	I-DAVN	1
49437	Scandinavian	LN-RLR	1
49439	Continental	N18835	1
49440	Inex Adria	YU-ANO	1
49441	Continental	N35836	1
49443	PSA	N952PS	1
49444	Muse Air	N936MC	1
49450	Muse Air	N937MC	1
49451/49457	American	N433AA/N439AA	7
49459/49460	American	N440AA & N441AA	2
49468/49477	American	N442AA/N443AA, N73444, & N445AA/N451AA	10
49478/49494	Continental	N818NY/N820NY, N72821/N72825, N69826, N77827, N71828, N72829/ N72830, N14831, N35832, N18833, N10834	17
49501/49502	CAAC	B2107 & B2108	2
49503/49504	China Eastern	B2109 & B2120	2
49505/49506	China Northern	B2121 & B2122	2
49507	China Eastern	B2123	1
49531	Alisarda	I-SMET	1
49549/49552	ATI	I-DAVP & I-DAVR/I-DAVT	4
49553	American	N452AA	1
49555	Scandinavian	OY-KHD	1
49558/49566	American	N453AA/N461AA	9
49569	Balair	HB-INW	1
49580/49582	Continental	N14840, N15841, & N57837	3
49592/49601	American	N462AA/N471AA	10
49604	Scandinavian	OY-KHE	1
49615	Scandinavian	SE-DID	1
49634/49635	Continental	N34838 & N14839	2
49647/49656	American	N472AA/N481AA	10
49660	Unifly	EI-BTX	1
49661	ZASSU-DAK		1
49667	Unifly	EI-BTY	1
49668	Oasis International	EC-EIK	1
49669	Alisarda	I-SMEV	1
49675/49684	American	N482AA/N491AA	10
49701/49704	TWA	N14846/N14847 & N958U/N959U	4
49728	Scandinavian	SE-DIE	1

49730/49732	American	N492AA/N494AA	3
49794	ATI	I-DAVU	1
49877	Finnair	OH-LMT	1
		DC-9-82 total	368+
DC-9-83 (MD-83)	49231/49236	Alaska	N930AS/N935AS	6

49231/49236	Alaska	N930AS/N935AS	6
49252	Finnair	OH-LMS	1
49284	Finnair	OH-LMR	1
49344/49349	American	N562AA/N566AA & N568AA	6
49351/49353	American	N569AA/N571AA	3
49363/49365	Alaska	N936AS/N938AS	3
49390	Trinidad and Tobago	9Y-THN	1
49395	LAV	YV-36C	1
49396/49397	Transwede	SE-DHB & SE-DHC	2
49398	Paramount AW	G-PATA	1
49399	Minerve	F-GGMA	1
49400	Paramount AW	G-PATB	1
49401	Airsur	EC-ECN	1
49402	Aero Lloyd	D-ALLD	1
49442	Airsur	EC-ECO	1
49448	Trinidad and Tobago	9Y-THQ	1
49449	Aero Lloyd	D-ALLE	1
49458	American	N572AA	1
49525/49526	Muse Air	N938MC & N939MC	2
49527/49530	TWA	N931TW, N9302B, N9303K, & N9304C	4
49556/49557	Scandinavian	SE-DFP & LN-RMB	2
49567	LAV	YV-38C	1
49568	Trinidad and Tobago	9Y-THR	1
49574	L. A. Canarias	EC-EFU	1
49575/49576	Spantax	EC-EFJ/EC-EFK	2
49577	Spanair	EC-EHT	1
49578	Transwede	SE-DHD	1
49579	Spanair	EC-EIG	1
49602	Aero Lloyd	D-ALLF	1
49617	Minerve	F-GGMB	1
49619/49620	Unifly	EI-BTU & EI-BTV	2
49621	Spanair	EC-EJU	1
49622	L. A. Canarias	EC-EJZ	1
49623	Transwede	SE-DHN	1
49624	Oasis International	EC-EKM	1
49625	Finnair	OH-LMG	1
49626	L. A. Canarias	EC-EMG	1
49627	Spanair	EC-EOZ	1
49628/49629	Oasis International	EC-EOM & EC-EOY	2
49630	Spanair	EC-216	1
49631	Oasis International	EC-EPM	1
49642	Transwede	SE-DHF	1
49643	British Island AW	G-BNSA	1
49657	Alaska	N939AS	1
49658	British Island AW	G-BNSB	1
49659	LAV	YV-39C	1
49662/49663	Paramount AW	G-PATC/G-PATD	2
49672	Spanair	EC-EJQ	1
49707	Air Liberté	F-GFZB	1
49708	L. A. La Tur	XA-TUR	1
49709	Minerve	F-GGMC	1
49710	L. A. La Tur	XA-TOR	1
49769	Aero Lloyd	D-ALLK	1
49822	Air Liberté	F-GHEB	1
49823	British Island AW	G-BPSC	1
49824	Trinidad and Tobago	9Y-THU	1
49825	Alaska	N940AS	1
49826	British Island AW	G-BPSD	1
49845/49848	German Wings	D-AGWA/D-AGWD	4

	49854	Aero Lloyd	D-ALLL	1
			DC-9-83 total	87+
DC-9-87	49388	Co owned	N87MD	1
(MD-87)	49389	Transwede	SE-DHG	1
	49403/49405	Finnair	OH-LMA/OH-LMC	3
	49411/49412	Austrian	OE-LMK & OE-LML	2
	49464	Toa/JAS	JA8262	1
	49585/49587	CTA	HB-IUA/HB-IUC	3
	49605/49609	Scandinavian	SE-DIB/SE-DIC, SE-DIF, SE-DIH, & OY-KHF	5
	49611	Scandinavian	LN-RMG	1
	49614	Scandinavian	OY-KHI	1
	49670/49671	Aero Lloyd	D-ALLG & D-ALLH	2
	49673	Tradewinds	9V-TRY	1
	49724/49725	Midway	N801ML & N802ML	2
	49767/49768	Aero Lloyd	D-ALLI & D-ALLJ	2
			DC-9-87 total	25+
MD-88	49532/49546	Delta	N901DL/N915DL	15
	49573	Delta	N917DL	1
	49583/49584	Delta	N918DL & N919DL	2
	49591	Delta	N916DL	1
	49644/49646	Delta	N920DL/N922DL	3
	49705	Delta	N923DL	1
	49711/49723	Delta	N924DL/N936DL	13
	49810/49813	Delta	N937DL/N940DL	4
			MD-88 total	40+

McDONNELL DOUGLAS T-45 GOSHAWK (Number built: By the end of 1989, two Goshawks had been delivered by Douglas; more were on order.)

McDONNELL DOUGLAS MD-11 (Number built: One had been completed but not flown by the end of 1989; Douglas then held commitments for 312 MD-11s.)

McDONNELL DOUGLAS C-17 (Number built: None completed before the end of 1989)

NORTHROP/McDONNELL DOUGLAS F-23 (Number built: None completed before the end of 1989)

McDONNELL DOUGLAS/GENERAL DYNAMICS A-12 (Number built: None completed before the end of 1989)